Jim Watson

Jim Spencer

E J Smith & Sons Co
Charlotte, N.C.

Grounds Maintenance Handbook

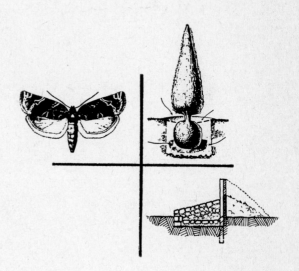

H. S. Conover

Grounds Maintenance Handbook

Second Edition

F. W. Dodge Corporation, New York

First edition published 1953 by Tennessee Valley Authority
Second edition © 1958 by F. W. Dodge Corporation

Printed and bound in U.S.A.

Library of Congress Catalog Card No. 58–6360

FOREWORD

The maintenance of public, industrial, and institutional grounds has become increasingly important during the past ten years. Careless, inadequate maintenance invites misuse and destruction of property in public grounds and a loss of morale and efficiency of employees in industrial plants. Good maintenance means timely repairs and cleanup, constant inspection, and a never-ending endeavor to maintain clean, neat, and orderly grounds in order to minimize misuse and vandalism.

The Tennessee Valley Authority long ago recognized this need for clean and orderly grounds maintenance as a necessary adjunct to inviting the public to their reservations. In experiencing maintenance problems on its reservations TVA found that there was a need for some standardization of accepted maintenance practices. As a result, loose-leaf memoranda and pamphlets, each treating some phase of grounds maintenance, were issued from time to time to the field men responsible for such maintenance. As the information grew in volume, it became apparent that a handbook based solely on grounds maintenance would be a useful document. In such a manner the Grounds Maintenance Handbook originated. TVA first produced a few copies for its own use within the organization. Other agencies responsible for grounds maintenance became aware of the book, and after a large number of requests for copies were received TVA decided to publish the handbook on a limited distribution basis.

The first edition published by TVA was based solely on the particular grounds maintenance problems of TVA reservations. This new edition has been broadened, improved, and brought up to date so that it can be used by all engaged in the maintenance of grounds.

It is obvious, however, that the subject of grounds maintenance is so large that it cannot be treated completely in one volume. I have tried to treat some of the most important phases of grounds maintenance and to provide a guide to the "know-how" needed to perform such tasks. The book is written primarily for use by those responsible for the maintenance of large acreages such as public parks on the national, state, county, and metropolitan scale, large industrial and institutional grounds, semipublic lands such as Boy Scout and YMCA camps, large estates, country clubs, and similar grounds.

Material for the book has come from my own experience in TVA, from many well-known technical works of other authors on individual topics, from manufacturing firms and research personnel, from engineers and architects. To all of these I am sincerely grateful for their cooperation and interest in the development of the handbook. The Tennessee Valley Authority has also graciously permitted me to use the material from the original edition as I see fit, for which I am also grateful. Thanks are also due to the individuals and organizations who have permitted me to use quotations or reproductions of previously published material.

I hope that this volume will contribute in some manner to the better maintenance of grounds, to improved budget requirements, and to the greater enjoyment of public lands by the public through improved maintenance practices.

H. S. Conover

CONTENTS

CHAPTER ONE

PLANNING,

SCHEDULING,

AND PUBLIC RELATIONS

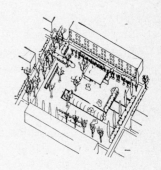

More leisure time, expanding population, increased ownership and use of automobiles, improved highways—all conspire to get more and more people out of doors. These people head for state and national parks, seashore and mountain resorts, hunting and fishing preserves, ski slopes, and historical sites, subjecting these recreational areas to the hardest use they have ever suffered, yet expecting to find everything clean, convenient, and attractive when they arrive. These people can afford to be fussy: if all is not well they can drive on to a spot where the grass is greener.

Not only the pleasure-bent public, but also economy-minded industry is moving out into the countryside. Highways are lined with the lawns of handsome new buildings which might be mistaken for schools were it not for the neat signboards identifying them as factories, offices, or laboratories. Both owners and employees take pride in carefully landscaped grounds, which advertise the firm to passing motorists. For such companies good maintenance has become a necessity. The schools and hospitals they resemble are becoming even more conscious of the need for good maintenance, since they often make practical use of their attractive grounds.

Unfortunately, the cost of maintenance has increased along with its importance, and those responsible must exercise their ingenuity to stretch available dollars as far as possible. This means utilizing mechanized equipment, chemicals, and all sorts of labor-saving devices. For those responsible for public rather than company grounds it also means formulating policies and standards that will demonstrate to the holders of the purse strings the need for adequate budgets.

For grounds which merely form a setting for a building or a group of buildings, the maintenance problems may be fairly simple, although probably not so simple as a layman or a member of the board of directors might picture them. For grounds intended for recreational use, however, the problems become more complex. Besides lawns, flowers, and ornamental shrubbery there are wide scenic drives, overlooks, meadows and forests, and such facilities as visitor reception buildings, picnic areas, playgrounds, boat harbors, swimming pools, beaches, access roads, and parking areas—with attendant traffic problems. Many large tracts require special planning for drainage and waste disposal because of watershed complications. Most reception buildings contain public rest rooms and information displays; some have restaurants or refreshment stands as well.

MAINTENANCE AND DESIGN

Unless maintenance problems are carefully considered in the design of all these structures and grounds, those responsible for their upkeep will have difficulty both in planning for maintenance and in doing the actual work. Maintenance budgets are notoriously inadequate, and poor design can only make them more so. If possible, a competent maintenance engineer should be retained as an advisory member of every design staff, to check maintenance provisions. Otherwise, arrangements should be made for the plans to be reviewed by field personnel, who should give them close scrutiny. This constructive criticism should help to iron out many maintenance problems before construction begins.

It is the landscape architect, however, who is responsible for creating the design. He should be interested in all the ground components of the park, and make careful studies to determine the kinds of planting—trees, shrubbery, turf—that best suit each specific use.

In addition to the maintenance of plantings and special facilities, there is erosion control, the control of insect pests and plant diseases, equipment maintenance, and the never-ending problem of budgeting available funds. Each of these topics can and should be the subject of lengthy study, and each is fully treated in the later chapters of this volume. But in planning for maintenance it is first necessary to formulate (a) objectives; (b) standards; and (c) a maintenance plan.

MAINTENANCE OBJECTIVES

The general objectives of maintenance are to insure the clean and orderly appearance of grounds, structures, and facilities; and to protect the health, safety, and convenience of the people using them.

Specific objectives, however, must be formulated to suit each situation. Type and intensity of use vary widely; some areas require thorough and frequent cleaning, weeding, seeding, fertilizing, spraying, or repair, while others less frequently used or partially left in their natural state can be maintained on a much less exacting schedule. Good judgment must be used in setting up both objectives and standards.

MAINTENANCE STANDARDS

For the purpose of establishing maintenance standards, most lands requiring maintenance can be classified into two major areas:

Area 1 includes all grounds surrounding the major and auxiliary structures considered a part of the operating unit, and those areas in parks and other public lands defined or developed specifically for use by the general public, including picnic areas, observation points, entrance triangles from highways, and major access roads to the general developed area.

Area 2 includes all meadow, pasture, farm, and forest lands within public grounds property lines, and all other areas not covered under Area 1.

Standards for these two areas have been set as follows by the Tennessee Valley Authority, and may be adapted or modified as required:

For Area 1

1. Roads and parking areas shall be maintained in good structural and smooth riding condition, free from all grass, weeds, and other debris. Access roads within public domains shall be maintained according to the standards of state or municipal parkways.

2. Grass areas shall be maintained as lawns.

3. Shrub beds and specimen trees shall be maintained according to the methods described later in this manual. Naturalistic plantings shall receive only such maintenance as needed to insure their continued growth, free of disease and clear of all dead and fallen material.

4. Picnic area maintenance shall conform to exceptionally high standards. Trash and garbage removal shall be as frequent as necessary to maintain the grounds in a clean and sanitary condition. Repairs to equipment and grounds are to be undertaken as required for the use of the area.

Fig. 1.1 A sample of construction devastation

Fig. 1.2 The same area shown in Fig. 1.1, after completion of roadway and landscaping. Note clean lines and adequate maintenance.

5. Footpaths shall be maintained in good and safe condition, free from grass, weeds, and other debris.

6. All other specific items of maintenance, such as signs, rip-rap, structures, guard rails, etc., are to be maintained in accordance with the objective of insuring clean, orderly, and attractive grounds. Structural repairs, paint-

GROUNDS MAINTENANCE HANDBOOK

ings, etc., are to be done as field conditions dictate, so that all structures and facilities are maintained in good structural condition, and present the appearance of being well kept.

For Area 2

1. Prevent and control fires.
2. Prevent and control erosion.
3. Other maintenance of mature forest lands shall be confined to the control and removal of dead, down, and diseased timber, and such timber harvesting as may be carried out under the best forestry practices. Improve and expand seedling plantings where required.
4. Meadows shall be mowed whenever grass is 6 to 12 in. high, depending upon the locality, and shall be fertilized and improved as necessary.
5. Pasture lands shall be limited to areas specifically designated for that purpose by the proper authorities.
6. General farming may be permitted in areas specifically designated for that purpose by the proper authorities.

Maintenance of leased or licensed areas on public parks or lands has always been a problem. A good rule to follow in the administration and maintenance of such areas is to limit the responsibility of any lessee or licensee to the maintenance of the structures and grounds essential to the efficient operation of the concession, not including areas for the general use of the public, such as picnic areas, public comfort stations, etc., except where such facilities are leased to another public agency or where special conditions make such inclusion practicable, and where a good standard of maintenance can be assured and enforced. If local conditions and requirements are such that public use areas are included, adequate safeguards to the public should be written into contracts and enforced in their administration, to insure that maintenance by the concessionaire shall be equal to other maintenance standards in the public domain.

THE MAINTENANCE PLAN

After maintenance objectives and standards have been formulated, and a study has been made of maintenance problems, the program can be put into effect by means of a written maintenance plan. Such a plan will also promote more efficient preparation of budgets.

Organization of the plan

The plan should be readily understood by the men in the field. It should present the maintenance standards in some detail, and also recommend improvements to unfinished areas. Other pertinent data which a field supervisor may find useful may also be included.

The maintenance problems usually encountered can be divided into three major segments: intensive-use areas, scenic areas, and natural areas. These segments provide a convenient organization for the plan.

Intensive use areas are those which contain the major structures and are the focal points for all visitors. Such areas must necessarily be maintained on a very high level, and the plan should therefore describe a pattern of maintenance similar to that followed in large city parks where large expanses of lawn predominate.

Scenic areas include any point from which a view can be seen. In many cases the park is developed around these views, and parking overlooks become a natural adjunct. Maintenance of such areas is often difficult because many of them are on rugged terrain, but nevertheless these scenic spots must be kept open for the full enjoyment of the public.

Natural areas are those which have been left undisturbed. These areas form the immediate foreground from all overlook points, and complete the transition from man-made structures to undisturbed native landscape. Wherever man-made areas have encroached, it may be necessary to do certain cleanup work, such as removing dead, down, and diseased timber, and thinning underbrush.

Form of the plan

Physically, the maintenance plan is an instruction sheet divided into a graphic and a written section, both designed for easy reading and interpretation.

The graphic section shows each area in a different shade or tone, so that those responsible for the maintenance program can tell at a glance where any particular type of maintenance begins and ends. The written section describes in detail the type of maintenance prescribed for each of the shaded areas.

These printed instructions describe methods of maintenance for lawns, meadows, trees and shrubs, structures, roads and parking areas, picnic grounds, and general policing. Soil and grass improvement recommendations; fertilizer and seed quantities; and general notes on the care of lawns, trees, and shrubs; methods of pruning; and other general information on maintenance policies should also be included.

Such a document provides the basic data for all planning and scheduling and the preparation of budgets. The cost of maintenance for each section of the plan can be easily estimated, so that any proposed changes in budgets or allotments may be intelligently interpreted.

MAINTENANCE AND PUBLIC RELATIONS

Putting the plan into practice, however, involves one of the most difficult problems of all. This is the human problem, which is concerned with the public, park employees, and friendly relations between the two.

It is a peculiar characteristic of the American citizen that he feels it beneath him to clean up his own debris on public lands, and he somehow justifies his actions by pointing to what others are doing. It never occurs to him to set an example for others to follow. His behavior does not improve the dispositions of surly, discourteous employees, and such employees tend to drive the citizen to defy correction. Thus are master "litterbugs" created.

Encouraging public neatness

How can the public's careless habits be corrected or counteracted?

1. Provide exemplary housekeeping. Do not let garbage pails overflow, or allow picnic tables to remain littered so that each group must clean up after the one before.

2. Do not let litter accumulate over the grounds until it becomes a major task to clean it up. Daily policing will be more economical.

3. Keep grass mowed, weeds cut, shrub beds and walks neatly edged, so that the grounds look cared for, not abandoned.

Fig. 1.3 A well-designed picnic area, well equipped and well maintained

Fig. 1.4 Visitors building at dam, showing data marker. Good design, clean and attractive surroundings, and good maintenance, plus durable and easily-read signs, are essential to the success of any public area.

4. Try to teach the public to be considerate of others. This is where a courteous employee may be able to make some real progress against vandals and litterbugs. When he sees an infraction of the rules or an act of just plain thoughtlessness, he should try to show the offender, firmly but tactfully, how such behavior hurts others as well as the offender himself. Nine times out of ten an appeal to the pocketbook brings quick results, and the employee can explain how negligence increases the cost of maintenance, which must be borne by the taxpayers. He might also point out that by littering or damaging the place he has chosen for recreation, the citizen is endangering his own future holiday pleasure.

5. Have neat and appropriate signs. Signs that are too big overpower everything in the vicinity, and signs that are poorly maintained obviously do not practice what they preach. There is nothing so damaging to public morale as a sagging, peeling sign with some such notice as "This is your park. Help us keep it clean." This is a sign of a tired, run-down park, and the public will treat the park accordingly.

6. Sponsor talks by personnel in civic clubs, schools, churches, and the like. Provide films of good and proper use of parks. Laws and rigid enforce-

ment are not the answer to carelessness and vandalism; education and example offer much better chances of success.

Employees and public relations

Unlike the public, employees can be selected, at least to the extent that the employment market will permit. They should be chosen not only for their ability to perform the task assigned, but also for neatness, interest, personality, and knowledge of the area in which they are working. It is difficult to find persons with all the necessary attributes, especially during times when higher paid jobs are competing for the same men. It therefore behooves the park superintendent or supervisor to assign work on the basis of the capability of the employee and the degree to which he will be in contact with the public. In addition, it is a wise supervisor who takes the time to train men into these jobs, and to explain not only the immediate job to be done, but also the over-all operations of the park or grounds.

The laborer, who does all the menial tasks, from mixing concrete to collecting garbage, cannot be expected to answer detailed questions on the park operation, but he can be trained to refer the questioner to the proper source for his information. He should be trained to be courteous and to help the public in every way, and to be as neat and clean as his work permits him to be. A good way of counteracting any tendency to sloppiness is to provide regulation work uniforms for all field employees, and special coveralls to be used for really greasy or dirty work.

The second class of employees includes the skilled laborers. These are the power mower operators, tractor operators, skilled mechanics, gardeners, and their supervisors or foremen. These men should be able to answer questions concerning maintenance practices, and to identify trees and shrubs. The standard of personal appearance should be even higher for these employees than for laborers. Uniforms and coveralls should be furnished them, and they should be clean-shaven and cleanly dressed to the extent that their work will permit.

In the third classification are the park attendants or custodians. These are the employees who meet and talk with the public most frequently: the guards, swimming pool attendants, concessionaires, restaurant or refreshment stand employees, guides, and administrative personnel. These people should be well trained in all phases of park or grounds operations. They must be intelligent and tactful as well as neat and courteous. They must be able to say "no" without antagonizing visitors, and to dispense information in a way that can be easily understood and appreciated.

All public park employees should be reminded that parks and recreational areas are nearly all tax-supported, and that people using them consider themselves part owners. Employees should also consider themselves part owners, and should treat visitors as equals rather than as enemies or necessary nuisances.

It is obvious, then, that skillful supervision of both employees and the public, like planning and scheduling, is an important means of reducing maintenance problems and winning financial support for the maintenance program. Details of specific maintenance practices will be treated in the chapters that follow.

CHAPTER TWO

THE GROWING

AND MAINTENANCE

OF TURF

The seeding and care of grass areas is an important feature of well-developed public grounds. It is important that (1) the soil is prepared properly with correct fertilization and liming procedures followed; (2) suitable grasses or grass mixtures are selected; and (3) good maintenance practices are followed after planting.

SOIL PREPARATION

The properties desired in any soil to be seeded to grass include good drainage, good soil texture with sufficient depth for good root development, abundant organic matter, and high fertility. However, many soils, even soils from excavations, can be made to produce good grass if the necessary steps are taken to secure the physical properties mentioned above.

Drainage

It is difficult to establish a good turf without good drainage. It is essential that the water drain rapidly through the soil in order to have a good root system and strong top growth. Under conditions where the soil will not drain properly, and the soil remains soggy and wet after heavy rains, it is essential that a system of underground drains be built.

Soil texture

Sandy soils are generally too light in texture to hold water and fertilizer materials. As a result, grass cannot do its best for lack of water and plant nourishment. A very sandy soil may be improved by working organic material into it. Such materials may consist of an inch or two of heavier soils or a combination of heavier soil and organic matter. The heavier soils should be thoroughly worked into the top 6 in. of the sandy soil.

Clay soils are generally classed as heavy soils. If a soil becomes slippery and sticky when wet and shrinks and cracks open when it dries, the grass cannot survive. A heavy clay soil does not provide enough air in the soil for good root growth. Pedestrians will, by walking or playing, pack a clay soil even tighter. To improve a clay soil, work in organic matter. Sand in a clay soil will not improve it, but is likely to pack it harder than before.

Addition of organic matter

Organic matter may come from several materials. The one that is the most handy and the cheapest will probably be the one selected. The quantity of organic matter to use will vary, but basically for each 1,000 sq ft of area, use 3 bales of peat moss, or from 2 to 3 cu yd of manure or 3 to 4 cu yd of well-rotted sawdust or compost. On large areas, it may be advisable to use cover crops and green-manure crops as an aid in building up the soil. All of these soil conditioners should be thoroughly worked into the top 6 in. of soil. Chemical soil conditioners such as "Krilium" have been introduced in the past few years. These conditioners must be used with great care, but can be beneficial. They are costly, however, and not economical on a large scale.

Analysis and cultivation

After the soil has been conditioned properly, the following steps should be taken before seeding:

1. Make a soil analysis.

2. Cultivate the soil thoroughly, using a heavy disk. This will loosen the soil and work the organic matter into it.

3. Remove all debris and stones turned up because of the heavy disking.

4. Disk or cultipac the area smooth (or rake by hand if the area is small) before application of lime and fertilizers.

Chapter 4 describes mechanical equipment that may be used for cultivation.

LIMING AND FERTILIZATION

To produce the best turf, it is important to provide the necessary food materials in the soil. Such materials are lime, nitrogen, phosphate, and potash. Lime is used as an aid in making the three basic chemicals more readily available to the grass, and to break down other chemicals already present in the soil in trace amounts.

Liming

A slightly acid soil (with pH of 6.0–6.5) is more desirable for grasses and legumes than soils more acid or alkaline. Many grass areas are commonly over-limed, to the detriment of old established lawns, as well as newly seeded areas. For this reason an acidity test should always be made before lime is used.

The presence of moss and certain other plants on a lawn is no true indication of an acid soil. Moss may be an indication of improper soil reaction, but it also may indicate low fertility, particularly a nitrogen deficiency. A soil test is the most reliable guide to determining soil acidity. If no equipment is available to make soil acidity tests, then it is an easy task to have the soil tested by the local county agricultural agent or university. Once the soil reaction has been corrected, lime need not be applied more often than once every five to six years.

Lime should be applied either two to three months before the application of fertilizer, or before the last disking mentioned under "soil preparation." Most soils will not require over 2 tons of ground limestone per acre, and often less is required. Table 2.1 shows the amount of limestone needed for various soil reactions on the basis of 1,000 sq ft and on the acre basis.

TABLE 2.1/QUANTITIES OF LIMESTONE FOR SPECIFIC SOIL REACTIONS

pH	pH desired	Lb per 1,000 sq ft	Tons per acre
6.0	6.5	0–46	0–1
5.5	6.5	46–92	1–2
5.0	6.5	92–138	2–3

If slaked (hydrated) lime is used, apply only two-thirds as much as of ground limestone, since slaked lime is more alkaline than unslaked.

Where excessive liming has been practiced, sulfur is the best material to use to lower the soil reaction from high pH values to the best point suited for turf growth. The amounts needed for reduction of soil reaction of one pH unit are about 25 lb per 1,000 sq ft, or $\frac{1}{2}$ ton per acre.

In the pH scale, a value of 7.0 indicates a neutral soil, neither acid nor alkaline. Values less than 7.0 (as pH 6.5) indicate acidity (the smaller the number, the more acid or "sour" the soil) and pH values more than 7.0 (as pH 7.5) indicate alkalinity (the larger the number, the more alkaline or "sweet" the soil).

Fertilization

The chemical substances most commonly lacking in soils for grass are nitrogen, phosphorus, potash, and calcium. Soil analysis will indicate the approximate amounts needed. The average subsoil from excavations requires, on the acre basis, approximately 60 lb of nitrogen, 240 lb of phosphorus, and 100 lb of potash. This is equivalent to a ton of 3–10–5 fertilizer per acre, or 45 lb per 1,000 sq ft. A ton of 3–9–6 or 4–12–4 or 5–10–5 is close enough to the above formula.

Fertilizers higher in nitrogen content are available, such as 10–10–10 or 12–12–12. Such number designations always are interpreted as follows: the first number indicates the percentage (units) of nitrogen, the second number indicates the number of units of phosphate, and the third number indicates the number of units of potash. Proportionately smaller amounts of fertilizer will be needed if the higher analysis (higher nitrogen content) fertilizers are used.

There are also various high concentrations of chemical fertilizers which are soluble in water and can therefore be sprayed directly on the grass without injuring or browning it. Such soluble chemicals are very high in the basic nutrients—nitrogen, phosphate, and potash—and contain a few of the trace food elements such as calcium, iron, boron, etc. These soluble fertilizers come in various analyses such as 17–26–19 or 20–20–20, and must be dissolved in water before they can be used. The advantages of using a water-soluble fertilizer are safety at any time of the growing season, and compatibility with insecticides and herbicides. Results have been astonishing wherever water-soluble fertilizers can be used economically. It is not economically practical, as yet, to apply all fertilizers as a water spray to very large turf areas, but this type of application can be useful in small lawns, greens, etc.

Under conditions where complete fertilizers are not necessary, nitrogen may be applied in various forms such as nitrate of soda (20 per cent N), ammonium nitrate (33 per cent N), or uramon (42 per cent N). The amount of nitrogen applied will vary with the type; for example, a given amount of ammonium nitrate will produce twice as much N as the same quantity of nitrate of soda. Phosphorus is available as 20 per cent superphosphate or as triple superphosphate (45 per cent P_2O_5).

Potassium is available as muriate of potash (50–60 per cent K_2O).

Manure and compost are often used as physical conditioners of the soil,

14

but weed seeds will in all probability be introduced. These may be eliminated by sterilizing or pretreating the manure with methyl bromide compounds. One ton of manure is equivalent to about 100 lb of 10–5–10 fertilizer.

Sawdust is an excellent soil conditioner, and is being used more and more for this purpose. Well-rotted sawdust is preferred to fresh sawdust. If it is necessary to use fresh sawdust, then an additional 200 lb of ammonium nitrate is required per acre, or 4 lb per 1,000 sq ft. This additional nitrate is required to replace the nitrogen used up in the soil to break down or decompose the fresh sawdust.

In order to maintain a green color through the winter, and especially to give the turf extra vigor for combatting weeds, applications of nitrogen fertilizers are desirable. One autumn application of 150–200 lb of sodium nitrate or its equivalent per acre (4–5 per 1,000 sq ft) is sufficient without producing a mowing problem in the spring. These fall applications should be made in mid-October to November, and should be applied when the grass is dry, to prevent burning. A new high-analysis nitrogen fertilizer which will not burn when applied is "Uramite" (42 per cent N). Applications of this type of nitrogen fertilizer will produce excellent results. Earlier applications will necessitate additional mowing, and later applications will not produce the desired response. Good results in the South have been obtained by applying smaller amounts of nitrogen more frequently during the winter months. Amounts may vary, but usually 50 lb per acre will be adequate.

The quantity of fertilizer to apply at any one time varies greatly with the soil and the job to be done. The best and most practical method is to follow the soil analysis, but lacking that it is possible to apply the phosphate and potash in quantities that will last for several years. This is not possible with nitrogen fertilizer, since it is made available rapidly and any surplus not used by the plants will only leach away. On soils which are of poor quality, such as cherty soils, yellow clay soils, or glacial till subsoils, it is best to apply as much fertilizer as the soils will take, 1 to 2 tons per acre in many instances.

SELECTION OF GRASSES

It is important to select the proper grass or combination of grasses to attain good results. Today the successful turf is not a combination of four or five different grasses, but a concentration of only one, or at most two, predominant grasses. The introduction of new and better strains of the common lawn grasses will probably eventually revolutionize the entire concept of turf building and maintenance.

The Bentgrasses

The genus *Agrostis* includes all the grasses commonly known as bent, and the species known as redtop. These grasses, including redtop, have a more or less creeping habit of growth, and are low to moderately tall annuals or, more usually, perennials. They are adapted to Regions I(a), I(b), and the more northerly portions of IV. See Fig. 2.1.

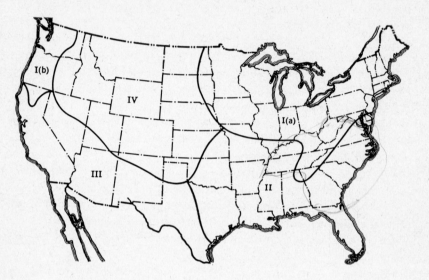

Fig. 2.1   General regions of grass adaptations

Redtop

Redtop is a perennial with a creeping habit that makes a coarse, loose turf. The leaves are about ¼ in. wide, stems are slender, and the panicle is loose, pyramidal, and usually reddish. It grows from Canada to the Gulf of Mexico, and from New York to California. Redtop is used in pasture mixtures under humid conditions, as a soil binder, and as a winter lawn and golf-green grass in the Southeast. Its main value is its quick and vigorous growth, which helps to form a compact turf that protects the soil until the slower-growing grasses become established. Redtop will grow under a variety of conditions. It is one of the best wet-land grasses, but will also resist drought, and it will grow on soils too high in lime content for most other grasses. Because the seeds are small, best results are obtained from planting on a compact, well-prepared seedbed. Usually, it is broadcast 8–15 lb to the acre, when seeded alone, or 2–6 lb in a mixture. Fall is the best time for seeding. Redtop will persist for several years, depending upon the fertility of the soil.

16

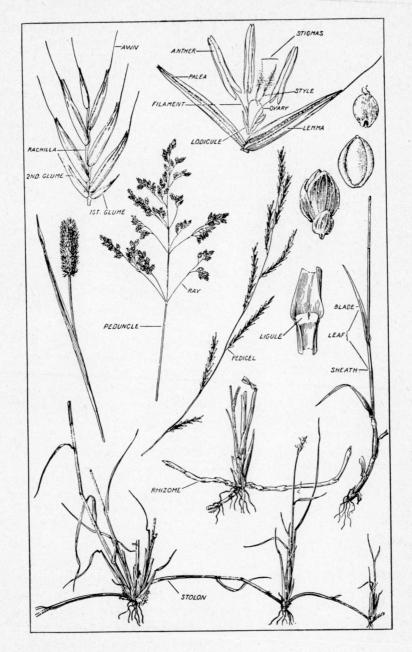

Fig. 2.2   The structure of grasses

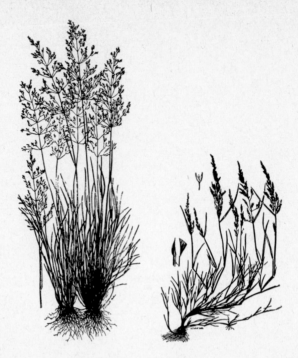

Fig. 2.3   Colonial bentgrass (left); Creeping bentgrass (right)

Three of the bentgrasses: colonial bent (*Agrostis tenuis*), creeping bent (*Agrostis palustris*), and velvet bent (*Agrostis conina*), have been found well adapted for putting greens, and in mixtures with other grasses for lawns, over much of the northern half of the United States.

Most of the creeping bentgrasses must be started by planting pieces of the stolons or runners, although a few, notably seaside bent or velvet bent grasses, can be started from seed now commercially available. All the colonial bents have given good results in lawn mixtures, although they are affected by large brown patch, a fungus disease. Seeds of the bentgrasses run about 8 million to the pound.

The Bluegrasses (*Poa*)

The bluegrasses are generally distinguished by small, awnless spikelets; lemmas with a heavy mid-nerve like the keel of a boat; glumes one- to three-nerved; and flat or folded leaf blades, with boat-shaped tips. They are useful for pasturage, hay, and lawn. Generally, they should be planted in the fall when there is more moisture and temperature conditions are better than in summer. Where bluegrass is used for lawns, nitrogn is required to promote vigorous growth and to maintain a desirable dark green color. For best growth, phosphorus, potassium, and nitrogen are all essential. Lime is not essential unless the soil is deficient in calcium. Bluegrasses are adapted to Regions I (a), IV, I (b), and the more northerly portions of II and III.

Kentucky bluegrass (*Poa pratensis*)

Kentucky bluegrass is grown principally for lawns and turf. It may also be used for pasture grass. It grows 18–24 in. tall, and under very favorable conditions may reach 36 in. It is a long-lived perennial, spreading by underground rhizomes. During periods of hot, dry weather in summer it remains dormant, and will turn brown unless ample water is applied. However, it will stay green all winter in most localities if properly managed and fertilized. Common Kentucky bluegrass is the old stand-by for lawn grass. Al-

Fig. 2.4 Bermuda grass (left); Kentucky bluegrass (center); Canada bluegrass (right).

though it is a very satisfactory grass in most localities, it has not been very successful south of upper Tennessee, since it is dormant during the summer months and is easily crowded out by other grasses or weeds. It has two inherent weaknesses: susceptibility to leaf-spot in spring, and an aversion to close mowing. Bluegrass does best in full sun in the North, in partial shade in the South, and on soils of high fertility and slight acidity (pH of 6.0–6.5). It is slow to germinate, taking about one week under ideal conditions and two to three weeks under more adverse conditions. For this reason, it is advisable to seed in late summer and early fall—Aug. 1 to Oct. 15. Close mowing (less than 2 in.) is very harmful to a good closed bluegrass sod.

Merion bluegrass

Merion is an improved type of Kentucky bluegrass, and is a development of the Merion Country Club at Philadelphia. In appearance, Merion bluegrass is very similar to the Kentucky strain. The Merion strain will out-perform common bluegrass, and can be classed as a superior grass on the following counts:

1. It will thrive under mowing as low as ½ in.
2. It is highly resistant, but not immune, to leafspot disease.
3. It has a much higher drought tolerance than common bluegrass.

A turf of Merion bluegrass will consistently have less crabgrass than the common bluegrass, particularly at the low cut essential to golf turf. Merion bluegrass is not thinned by disease to the same degree as common bluegrass, and therefore will tend to eliminate crabgrass by competition.

There are other factors which work to the disadvantage of Merion bluegrass, namely:

1. The seed of Merion bluegrass is slow to germinate, and therefore it is difficult to establish a turf in a short time.
2. Merion bluegrass responds well to generous fertilization and will suffer from neglect.
3. Merion bluegrass will suffer if it is watered too much, and may even fail if watered constantly at night.
4. Seeding Merion bluegrass into old established turf is a slow process, because of the slow starting seedlings. A fresh, weed-free seedbed is the surest way to establish a good Merion turf. It is also best to seed Merion alone at the rate of ½–1 lb of seed per 1,000 sq ft.

Canada bluegrass (Poa compressa)

Canada bluegrass resembles Kentucky bluegrass, but varies in its blue-green foliage, distinctly flat culms, and short and much contracted panicles. It spreads by underground rootstocks. It grows well in rather poor, dry soils. For lawns and golf links and similar purposes, it can be used to good advantage under conditions too dry, or otherwise unfavorable to Kentucky bluegrass.

Bermuda grass (Cynodon dactylon)

Bermuda grass is a long-lived perennial with a spreading habit of growth. It propagates by runners, underground rootstocks, and seed. The runners vary from a few inches to 3–4 ft in length, and under favorable conditions may grow 15 to 20 ft in a season. The rootstocks, which may become stolons or runners on hard soils, are thick and white. The erect, flowering branches are usually 6–12 in. high, depending on the fertility and moisture of the soil. The leaves are short, flat, bluish-green, and 1–4 in. long. At the base of each leaf is a fringe of white hairs; the leaf sheath is compressed and slightly hairy. The flowers are in slender spikes, three to six in a cluster, and similar in appearance to crabgrass.

Bermuda grass will grow well on almost any soil that is fertile and not too wet, but grows better on heavy soils. Because the seeds are small and light, a well-prepared seedbed is desirable. Spring seedings, 5–7 lb per acre, are usually ample. The seed should be covered by use of a cultipacker or a light harrow.

The most common method of planting stolons is to plow furrows 4–6 ft apart, drop the stolons 2–3 ft apart in the furrow, and cover by plowing or with the foot. If the stolons are not watered when planted, they should be planted deep enough to prevent their drying out. Rolling or cultipacking the soil after planting is desirable. Apply a well-balanced fertilizer just ahead of the planting. A 4–12–4 fertilizer at the rate of 500 lb per acre should be enough. An application of 100–200 lb per acre of ammonium nitrate or nitrate of soda in midsummer will help in rapid establishment of a good Bermuda sod.

Bermuda grass is a common lawn grass throughout the South, but it is generally not considered a good grass to use except for specific purposes such as erosion control, slope treatment, playgrounds, golf courses, and athletic fields. There are several things in favor of Bermuda such as hardiness, drought resistance, and its adaptability to a wide range of soils and soil reactions. Since Bermuda is not hardy as a seedling and does not stay green in winter, it should be seeded between May 1 and July 1, or sprigged between May 1 and Aug. 1. Bermuda is best used in full sun, and it will do well in droughty places, on steep banks, and where heavy traffic is expected. For best results, under normal fertilization programs, it should not be clipped closer than 1½ in.

There are several new strains of Bermuda grass which are much superior to the common Bermuda. Such strains as the U-3 Bermuda grass, the Tifton 57 (Tiflawn), the Tifton 127 (Tiffine) and the Tifton 328 have all proved useful for various activities. These are adapted to Regions II and III.

U-3 Bermuda grass

U-3 is a fine-bladed strain of Bermuda which was selected in Savannah, Ga. It is cold-tolerant to the extent that it has survived the winters in the vicinity of Washington, D.C., for many years. It has been grown at State College, Pa. since 1940 without suffering winter injury. It has been used successfully at Norfolk, Neb., Cleveland, Ohio, and in the St. Louis district.

This grass will find its greatest use in the so-called "crabgrass belt," which is defined, roughly, as a triangle having its points at Richmond, Va., Philadelphia, Pa., and St. Louis, Mo. U-3 Bermuda grass may do well in other areas where crabgrass is a serious pest and where the cool season grasses (bent, blue, and fescue) suffer during midsummer. This grass is adapted to Regions II and III, and southern parts of I (a) and IV.

The best uses for U-3 Bermuda grass are for golf tees in open sun, fairways, athetic fields, playgrounds, park areas, and sunny lawns. Use on lawn areas is probably the least important of these. U-3 Bermuda grass is a fast growing grass, and it produces a wear-resistant turf that will heal rapidly and withstand close mowing, even to putting-green height ($\frac{3}{16}$-in. to $\frac{1}{4}$-in.). It is one of the few grasses that will thrive during hot, dry weather with little or no irrigation. It is highly disease-resistant during hot, muggy weather. It can be mowed without injury to the grass as closely as the mower can be set. When this grass is properly fertilized and mowed, practically no weed can encroach. It makes its best growth during the late spring, summer, and early fall, when turf is used most.

The chief disadvantages of Bermuda grasses, particularly U-3, are as follows:

1. They have poor winter color. U-3, however, retains green color longer than most strains. When frost occurs, Bermuda grass becomes dormant and takes on a light straw color, although the playing quality of golf courses is not affected. The color can be masked by seeding a cool season grass into the Bermuda. Results indicate that Kentucky bluegrass and highland bent may provide color for the cool season and may not require reseeding each year. These grasses should be planted in the fall.

2. U-3 Bermuda grass is not a shade-tolerant grass. It makes its best growth in the open sun. Neither will it tolerate neglect. It must be mowed and fertilized regularly for best results.

3. Seed is not available for U-3, and it is necessary to plant this grass vegetatively. It may be planted any time after the last frost in the spring, and throughout the summer until mid-August.

The U-3 grass may be planted by "spot-sodding" with 2-in. square blocks of sod, by "strip-sodding" with 1-in. strips of sod, or by sprigging. Spot-sods or strip-sods, placed at 1-ft intervals, will form a solid turf in six weeks or less. If sprigs are planted at 8-in. intervals, similar results will be obtained. Sods or sprigs may be planted further apart if material is scarce or if rapid coverage is not essential. The newly planted area should be kept moist until the grass is well established. These planting methods apply whether U-3 Bermuda grass is started on a prepared seedbed or introduced into established turf. Spreading will be less rapid in turf than on a clean seedbed.

To maintain U-3 properly, feed it heavily and mow it frequently. Bermuda grass should be fertilized each year at the rate of approximately 50 lb of a 10–6–4 fertilizer to 1,000 sq ft. This should be applied in three equal treatments—one in early spring, one in early summer, and one in early fall.

U-3 Bermuda grass thrives under a mowing height of $\frac{1}{2}$–$\frac{3}{4}$ in. This has been found to be a desirable height for many turf uses. One mowing a week is the minimum requirement. Two or three mowings a week will pay dividends in a well-groomed appearance.

U-3 Bermuda grass is very resistant to chemicals. Where crabgrass threatens a newly planted area, sodium arsenite or any other proved crabgrass killer may be used with safety, at rates which will kill softer, weaker grasses.

Tifton 57, 127 and 328 Bermuda Grasses

These strains were developed at Georgia Coastal Plain Experiment Station, Tifton, Ga. They have been developed and produced in a breeding program by Dr. G. W. Burton. The differences between the three strains are in the color, texture, and rapidity of growth. The Tifton 57 and 328 strains are dark green color. The 328 strain is a finer-bladed grass than the 57 strain, with slightly better color and much more rapid growth. The 127 strain of Bermuda grass is a very fine-bladed light green grass which grows densely. All three strains produce a very tough turf which will stand considerable wear. The following comparisons can be made between these three relatively new strains of Bermuda grass and the common variety:

1. The new strains spread faster and become established more rapidly after sprigging.

2. They make a denser turf, which means fewer weeds.

3. They will tolerate more punishment and wear, which makes them better for athletic field use.

4. They will stay green longer because of greater resistance to frost and disease.

5. They will be injured less by winter ryegrass and will recover faster when ryegrass goes out in the spring.

6. They require less fertilizer under normal conditions, but if given ample fertilizer they will make an excellent response.

7. They are shorter and look better than common Bermuda with infrequent mowing. For the development of high quality turf, however, they should be mowed regularly.

8. The Tifton strains, like the common Bermuda, will not do well in shade, and should not be planted in shady areas. They can be grown under very light shade if mowed less frequently and cut higher.

9. They are very drought-resistant and will do well on dry soils if properly fertilized.

Establishment of hybrid Bermudas

Since the hybrid Bermudas produce few viable seeds, they must be propagated by planting sprigs. In planting sprigs, the following recommendations should be followed:

1. Prepare the soil as for planting seed or a garden. It is important to begin with a well-prepared and cultivated seedbed.

2. Apply lime if the soil test indicates that lime is needed.

3. Spread 30–40 lb of a complete fertilizer, such as an 8–8–8, per 1,000 sq ft and work both lime and fertilizer into the soil thoroughly. At this time, be sure to establish the final grade, working out all pockets and finally harrowing or cultipacking it smooth.

4. Secure fresh sprigs of the hybrid Bermuda you wish to plant, and when there is ample moisture in the ground, begin planting the sprigs as soon as possible after they have been received. Do not let the sprigs wilt or dry out. If they must be stored, keep them in a shady place, well covered and damp.

5. One of the best planting methods is to drop the sprig on the ground and push the basal end into the soil with a stick with a rounded end until only the tip leaves are left protruding. Then remove the stick and firm the soil around the sprig by stepping on it.

6. Another method is to plow furrows approximately 2 in. deep with a cultivator, and drop the sprigs into the furrow so that only the tips of the leaves are showing. Rake the soil back into the furrow and firm by stepping on the sprig.

7. Whatever planting method is used, the entire area to be sprigged should be rolled with a corrugated roller weighing about 300 lb.

8. Water the sprigs immediately after planting to insure maximum stands. Watering should be a good soaking and not just a light sprinkling.

9. For rapid coverage, plant the sprigs on 12 in. centers. One bushel of sprigs, containing about 2,000 to 4,000 sprigs, should plant 2,000 to 4,000 sq ft on 12-in. centers.

10. Control weeds by hand-weeding or mowing until the grass has covered the soil. To hasten its growth, it is best to mow the grass often, and as short as possible. The trick is to force growth in the early stages into the roots and to keep it out of the tops as much as possible. This method will develop a good tough and thick sod in the shortest possible time.

Maintenance of hybrid Bermudas

In March each year apply approximately 10 lb of complete fertilizer (such as an 8–8–8) per 1,000 sq ft. Follow at intervals of four to six weeks with applications of 3 lb of ammonium nitrate, 6 lb of nitrate of soda, or 15 lb of cottonseed meal or Milorganite per 1,000 sq ft, until the grass has reached the desired thickness and color. Apply the fertilizer evenly with a fertilizer spreader and apply only when the grass is dry. If the fertilizer is applied properly, little or no burning should result. To avoid burning, water the plants immediately after applying the fertilizer, to wash all traces off the leaves. During the summer months, mow at $\frac{1}{2}$–$\frac{3}{4}$ in. at weekly intervals to develop the best turf. In the spring and fall less frequent mowing will be adequate. Do not remove clippings unless they are heavy enough to smother the grass.

Carpet grass (*axonopus affinis*)

This is a perennial creeping grass which makes a dense sod. It is distinguished by its compressed, two-edged, creeping stems, which root at each joint, and by its blunt leaf tips. The slender flower stems grow 1 ft high (rarely 2 ft), if the soil is fertile. It is especially adapted to sandy or sandy-loam soils, particularly where the moisture is near the surface most of the year. It is adapted to Regions II and III.

Carpet grass is most valuable for permanent pastures, but also is valuable for firebreaks in forests, lawns and turf, roadsides, and open areas in pine forests.

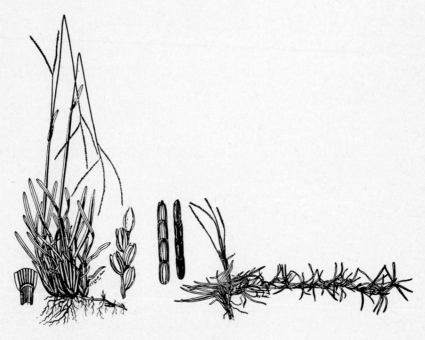

Fig. 2.5   Carpetgrass (left); Centipede grass (right)

Carpet grass is usually sown 5–10 lb to the acre. It can be sown on a well-prepared seedbed, or broadcast on burned-over open areas in timber land. Seeding is best done in spring, early summer, or even in midsummer. One pound contains approximately 1,350,000 seeds, and a bushel weighs 18 to 36 lb.

Centipede grass (*Eremochloa ophiuroides*)

This grass is a low-growing perennial, spreads by stolons, and is perhaps the best all-around lawn grass that can be grown in the deep South. Its appearance is somewhat between carpet grass and Bermuda grass, with shorter nodes than Bermuda. It makes a dense mat of creeping stems and leaves. Like all other grass, centipede grass has its desirable features and its undesirable features. It is adapted to Region III and southern portions of Region II (south of Tennessee).

Some of the desirable features of centipede grass are as follows:

1. It maks a dense, weed-free sod.
2. It grows on poor soils.
3. It requires very little fertilization.
4. It requires less mowing than carpet or Bermuda grass.
5. It tolerates more shade than Bermuda grass, but less than St. Augustine grass.
6. It is more resistant to disease and insect attack than most grasses.

Some of the undesirable features of centipede grass are the following:

1. Like carpet and Bermuda grass, it turns brown with the first freeze and usually stays brown until spring.
2. It makes such a dense sod that it is rather difficult to start over seeded ryegrass.
3. It is not suitable for planting on farm lands, where it soon spreads and rapidly crowds out the other grasses. When centipede grass has replaced the other grass, the pasture will be ruined; cattle can make little gain and often lose weight. Nutritionally, it is about the poorest of all the grasses.

Establishing a new centipede lawn

Prepare the lawn area as for any other seedbed. Apply a complete fertilizer (such as 4–12–4 or 5–10–5) at a rate of 10–15 lb per 1,000 sq ft. Harrow or rake the fertilizer into the soil.

To establish a centipede lawn from seed, follow these steps:

1. Broadcast 2 oz of good seed uniformly over each 1,000 sq ft of lawn. It is a good plan to mix the seed thoroughly with 1 gal of dry sand to facilitate uniform distribution.

2. Rake the seed lightly into the soil. Use the back of the rake for best results.

3. Water the newly planted seed thoroughly and keep the soil moist until the grass is well established. Centipede seedlings have little drought resistance and will die if not watered during dry periods.

4. Mow often to reduce weed competition.

5. About two months after planting, top-dress with 2–4 lb of nitrate of soda, or 5–10 lb of Milorganite per 1,000 sq ft of area. Apply fertilizer only when the grass is dry, and wash in to prevent burning.

To establish a centipede lawn from sprigs:

1. Plant fresh, live sprigs in furrows 2–3 in. deep and spaced 10–18 in. apart. The sprigs are placed about 6 in. apart in the furrows, and covered immediately to prevent drying. Leave 1 in. or more of the plant showing above the surface.

2. To produce a more rapid growth and coverage, plant the sprigs closer together, water well, and top-dress with a nitrogen fertilizer. Spring-planted sprigs spread as much as 8–10 ft in a season.

3. Approximately 15–20 lb of stolons will set 1,000 sq ft of area at the rate of spacing given above.

Establishing centipede grass on an old lawn

Centipede grass may be established on an old lawn without plowing the soil if the area is level and properly graded. Seed directly on top, or dig each sprig into the soil. Plenty of water must be used to keep the seedlings or sprigs from drying out and dying. Use very little fertilizer if there is Bermuda grass in the old lawn, because fertilizer favors the Bermuda at the expense of the centipede grass.

Dallis grass (*Paspalum dilatatum*)

This is an upright growing, bunching grass. It requires a moist but not wet soil; growth is best where organic matter is abundant, and it requires a higher fertility than carpet grass. Since it seldom forms a dense sod, it is an excellent grass to mix with legumes and other grass. Seeded alone, it often fails to make a perfect stand.

Fescues (*Festuca*)

Fescues are adapted to Regions I (a), I (b) and northerly portions of Region IV.

There seem to be few differences among the several named red fescues on the market—Illahee, Trinity, Oregon creeping red, Penn State Chewings,

Fig. 2.6 Dallisgrass (left); Meadow fescue (right)

Olds, and a new strain, Pennlawn. They are all strains of creeping red fescue and have the same general requirements for management. These grasses are drought-resistant, sun- and shade-tolerant, and are adaptable to a wide range of soil types, soil reactions, and fertility levels. They respond to high fertility and pH levels of 6.0–6.5. They are sod formers and do not require so frequent mowing as bluegrass and Bermuda grass. A combination of a creeping red fescue and Kentucky bluegrass in equal quantities will usually produce an excellent lawn in the cooler or more temperate climates.

These newer strains of creeping red fescues have definite advantages over the more common varieties. For one thing, because the seed is usually awnless, it can be thoroughly mixed with other seeds and will flow quite freely in seed equipment. These new strains are definitely creepers by underground roots and stems, and they do not grow in clumps as Chewings fescue has a tendency to do as it gets older. They are not tough like creeping red fescue, can be mowed shorter, and seem to have a much fresher, darker green color than the other fescues.

Fig. 2.7 Sheep fescue (left); Red fescue (right)

Meadow fescue (*Festuca elatior*)

This is a hardy perennial which flourishes in deep, rich soils; when well established it will grow to 15–30 in. The leaves are bright green and rather juicy. The leaf sheaths are smooth and reddish-purple at the base, and the young leaves are rolled inward in the bud. The blade is glossy on the under surface. When the panicles are open they resemble those of Kentucky blue-grass, although they are much larger and coarser. Flowering is in June and July.

Meadow fescue does not propagate itself by rootstocks or form a dense sod. The seed weighs 22–27 lb to the bushel and has 225,000 seeds in a pound. Seed at the rate of 25 or 30 lb per acre.

Sheep fescue (*Festuca ovina*)

This is a bunchgrass that forms dense tufts with numerous rather sharp, bluish-gray leaves. It succeeds better than most grasses on sandy or gravelly

Fig. 2.8   Italian ryegrass (left); Perennial ryegrass (right)

soils; its greatest use is for making a durable turf on sandy soils. Seeds weigh 10–15 lb per bushel. Seed at the rate of 25–30 lb per acre.

The tall fescues

There are two tall fescues, Alta and Kentucky 31, which seem to be preferred. Both are relatively coarse-bladed, deep-rooted, drought-tolerant grasses with good wear-resistance and a high tolerance to chemicals. The fescues will tolerate low fertility, but will respond to good fertilization programs. The tall fescues, especially the Kentucky 31, will tend to be bunchy unless seeded heavily. When thickly seeded they will produce a good tough sod that will withstand the encroachment of weeds and even of Bermuda grass. Recommended rates of seeding if seeded alone are from 2–5 lb of seed to 1,000 sq ft of area.

Ryegrasses (*Lolium*)

Italian ryegrass (*Lolium multiflorum*) is usually an annual, and is generally distinguished from perennial ryegrass by the awned lemma and stem characters and by the arrangement of the leaf in the bud. Awns are present on seed of Italian ryegrass and usually absent on perennial. The culm or stem of Italian is cylindrical, but that of perennial ryegrass is slightly flat-tened. The leaves of Italian are rolled in the bud, but in perennial the leaves are folded in the bud. Italian is yellowish-green at the base, and perennial is commonly reddish. Italian ryegrass is generally used in mixtures, or seeded alone, for quick green effects. Its use in lawn work is extremely doubtful, and it should be used only where a quick grass cover is essential. It is a difficult grass to mow and is a heavy feeder, taking away essential min-eral elements from the permanent grasses. It is often used on Bermuda sod, but this involves reseeding every fall and many mowings, especially in the spring. Bermuda grass tends to run out under it, but this can be prevented by top-dressing with a nitrogen fertilizer in late June or early July, after the ryegrass has mostly disappeared. It is adapted to all regions.

Perennial ryegrass (*Lolium perenne*)

Perennial ryegrass is used principally for permanent pasture seedings. It starts growth early in the spring and affords grazing while the more per-manent or longer-lived grasses are becoming established. It is not considered desirable for lawns, because the toughness of its leaves makes mowing diffi-cult, and it will not give a good turf in the summer months.

Ryegrass can be seeded in the fall or early spring. Seed may be broadcast by hand or seeder and covered with a smoothing harrow or rake, or it may be sown with a grain or seed drill. The seed should be covered with approxi-mately ½ in. of soil. When it is seeded alone, the rate should be 20–25 lb per acre. When it is seeded with small grain or legumes for annual pasture, 8–10 lb per acre is ample. On established lawns for winter green, or when ryegrass is seeded alone in spring or fall for temporary lawn, 3–4 lb per 1,000 sq ft is usually used. It is adapted to all regions.

Orchard grass (*Dactylis glomerata*)

This is a long-lived perennial grass, distinctly of the bunch type, with folded leaf blades and compressed sheaths. It does not produce stolons or underground rhizomes, and therefore never forms a dense sod. It does best on rich soil, but also succeeds on light soil of medium fertility and on moist, heavy land. It does well in shade and is good in orchards, woodland pastures, and other similar areas. It is cold-resistant and continues growth until the first severe frosts. Orchard grass is adapted to all regions.

St. Augustine grass (*Stenotaphrum secundatum*)

This is an extensively creeping, rather coarse, glabrous perennial that produces stolons with long internodes and branches that are short, rather

Fig. 2.9   Orchardgrass (left); St. Augustine grass (right)

leafy, and flat. The sheaths are flat and folded, and both terminal and auxiliary blades are short (4–6 in. long).

St. Augustine grass thrives in shaded areas, and is especially adapted for lawns. It is naturally a seashore plant, withstands salt spray. Because it has no seed available, rooted runners must be used to start a new planting. These are planted in rows or disked into the soil during moist periods and subsequently packed. It should be well watered and fertilized with nitrogen at the rate of 5 lb per 1,000 sq ft, an essential requirement for vigorous growth.

This grass is subject to damage by brown patch fungus and chinch bugs. The former can be controlled by stimulating growth with nitrogen fertilizer or by using calomel and corrosive sublimate. Chinch bugs may be controlled by blowing tobacco dust down between the stems of the grass, or by spraying with nicotine sulfate, using one part nicotine sulfate to 500 parts water. St. Augustine grass is adapted to Regions II and III.

Timothy (*Phleum pratense*)

This grass has stems, or culms, 20–40 in. tall. They emerge from a swollen or bulb-like base and form large clumps. Timothy differs from most other grasses in that one or two of the lower internodes is swollen into an ovoid

Fig. 2.10   Timothy (left); Soybean (right)

body which is referred to as a "bulb" or "corm" although it is really only a thick internode. These "corms" form in early summer and die the next year when seed matures. The leaves are elongate; the panicle is cylindrical and commonly 2–4 in. long. Timothy grows best on clay loams, although it will also grow on light-textured, sandy soils. Fall seedings are best when the grass is planted alone or with winter wheat. Less seed is required for fall than spring seeding; usually fall seeding requires 3–4 lb per acre and spring seeding requires 10 lb per acre. To maintain better soil productivity, timothy is commonly sown with clover—medium red, mammoth, or alsike.

The Zoysia grasses

There are three common species of zoysia and two hybrid zoysias in the United States: Manilagrass (*Zoysia matrella*), Japanese lawngrass (*Zoysia japonica*), Maxcarenegrass (*Zoysia tenuifolia*), and the hybrids, Emerald

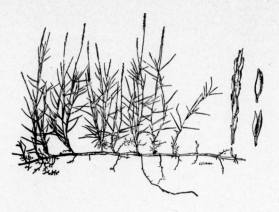

Fig. 2.11 Manilagrass

and Meyer Zoysias. The zoysias are adapted to Regions II and III, and southern portions of I (a) and IV.

Manilagrass (*Zoysia matrella*)

This grass was introduced into the United States many years ago from Korea. It is a low, sod-forming grass native to tropical and eastern Asia, where it is found growing abundantly on the sandy shores and river banks. Importations of both roots and seed have been distributed widely throughout the United States, but it has not been used extensively because it is slow in becoming established and lacks seed. In regions where Bermuda grass can be grown it is usually perferred to Manilagrass.

Manilagrass appears especially valuable for lawns, playgrounds, athletic fields, and other places where a thick turf is desired and speed of establishment is not a factor. It is also useful on road shoulders and embankments, since it requires little or no mowing; the entire season's growth is seldom over 4–6 in. Despite the saving in maintenance this represents, lack of seed and slowness in establishment retards the use of Manilagrass for such purposes.

Since Manilagrass is sensitive to frost, it appear to be most promising in regions having a warm to mild temperate climate (Regions II and III). In its northern limits, it turns brown with the first heavy frost in the fall and does not renew growth until after the last heavy frost in the spring. This brown or straw color makes Manilagrass less desirable than Kentucky bluegrass or other lawn grasses that maintain a partial green color during the winter months and are adapted to the central and northern latitudes. In the latitude of Washington, D.C., Manilagrass will remain green from mid-April to late October, while farther south, as in Alabama, it remains green from nine to ten months of the year. While it has survived as far north as Rhode

Island, when covered with a light mulch, its northern limit is approximately 40 degrees latitude.

Manilagrass will withstand partial shade and still maintain a good sod, if properly managed and fertilized. It is not adapted to dense shade, but is one of the best grasses in the South for shady lawns.

Because this grass sets little or no seed and the seed is difficult to harvest, it is necessary to establish it by vegetative planting. The matted, wiry root system forms a dense sod mass which can be cut up into small plugs about 2 in. square or divided into plant fragments commonly referred to as sprigs. Solid sodding is not recommended, since supplies are limited and costs prohibitive.

Whether done with sprigs or with small sod plugs, planting should be made in rows about one foot apart and set a similar distance apart in the rows. This grass is slow to spread, and if quicker cover is desired, thicker planting will insure earlier establishment. On slopes and terraces it is advisable to plant solid rows across the slope to prevent washing and to insure earlier establishment. In vegetative planting, it is important that the sprigs or sod plugs be firmly set and that the tip ends of the plants extend above the soil surface, since the plants are killed if covered completely.

One square yard of thick sod is sufficient to sprig-plant 750–1,000 sq ft, with rows 8–10 in. apart and the sprigs 3 in. apart in the rows. With wider spacing (planting in rows 12 in. apart and 12 in. in the row), 1 sq yd of sod will set 3,000–4,000 sq ft. Using 2-in. sod plugs, spaced 1 ft apart, 1 sq yd of sod will plant 324 sq ft. It is believed impractical to use wider spacing with a sod that is so slow to establish.

Care of sod before planting

The dense mass of sod, even after the dirt has been removed, can be transported for some distance without injury. The sod for transplanting should be kept moist and in a shady place until planted. The sod is usually transported in blocks 1 ft square. Upon receipt of the sod, (it usually comes in blocks 1 ft square), wet down an area and lay the sod out as though solid-sodding an area. Soak the sod thoroughly at once, and then keep it moist until it is planted.

Use the same methods of soil preparation as for preparing a seedbed for lawn or garden. Be sure the soil is free of all stones and other debris.

Since the grass is for permanent planting, fertilizers should be worked into the soil before the planting is started. Phosphorus and potash should be applied at the rate of 25–30 lb per 1,000 sq ft, and just before planting a complete fertilizer should be applied, at the rate of 15–20 lb per 1,000 sq ft. Do not allow sod or sprigs to come into direct contact with heavy applications of nitrogen fertilizers. If the soil is low in organic matter, well-rotted manure, peat moss, or other available organic matter materials should be worked into the seedbed. Manilagrass, while not too exacting in its soil requirements, does respond to proper soil and fertilizer treatments. It has been shown that lime is not essential, unless the soil is extremely poor and highly acid.

Time of planting

Since this grass is sensitive to cold, it is best established as soon in the spring as the soil is warm. In the extreme South plantings may be made in late summer or early fall. If adequate amounts of water can be given for planting and for subsequent maintenance, Manilagrass may be planted all summer long.

Care of planting

The soil should be rolled after planting, to insure an even turf. It is essential that the soil be kept moist, and it should be watered if rains do not occur to hasten growth. Weeds should be removed by cultivation or hand weeding. It is necessary to encourage as rapid growth and spread as possible, since Manilagrass is slow to establish itself. If sod plugs 2 in. square are used in place of sprig planting, a temporary seeding may be made of such grasses or legumes as redtop, ryegrass, lespedeza, or even Kentucky bluegrass. These seedings should not be heavy, as competition will reduce the rate of spread of the Manilagrass. Grass seedings are not recommended if the Manilagrass has been sprig-planted, as these will not stand so much competition as the sod plugs. After establishment, the usual methods of lawn care and management should be followed.

One of the principal weaknesses of Manilagrass is its slow growth. When sprigs or 2-in. plugs are spaced 12 in. apart, it usually requires two years to obtain a good cover and lawn; under the same conditions, Bermuda grass will have a good cover in two months.

At the present time, Manilagrass has not been seriously injured by insects or diseases common to other turf and lawn grasses, although brown patch, a fungus disease, has been found on it.

Related species

Zoysia japonica, Japanese lawngrass, has a broad coarse leaf similar to redtop. While it does not grow so tall as redtop, it makes a very dense cover. It is extremely hardy and persistent when once established. It is tough, harsh, and unpalatable to cattle, and can be established only from runners or plugs.

Meyer zoysia

Meyer zoysia was the first improved strain of zoysia to be recognized and named. It is a coarser grass than Manilagrass, slow growing compared to

Bermuda, but faster than Manilagrass. Meyer zoysia loses its green color in late fall after the first or second killing frost. It holds its green color a little longer than Manilagrass, however, and regains it a little earlier in spring. It must be planted vegetatively, by plugs or sprigs. The method is the same as for Manilagrass.

Meyer zoysia has the following advantages:

1. It resists crabgrass and other summer weeds, although dormant zoysia turf may be entered by such winter weeds as chickweed, speedwell, henbit, clovers, ground ivy, and broadleaf weeds. They can be controlled with 2,4-D and potassium cyanate.

2. It thrives during the heat of summer.

3. It grows on almost any kind of soil.

4. It is very drought-tolerant.

5. Turf insects apparently do not affect it.

6. It requires less mowing than most turf grasses, and can be mowed at heights from ½ in. to 4 in. without loss of vigor and beauty.

7. It develops a firm, resilient cushion of turf and has a strong resistance to wear.

8. Its color is a dark green similar to Kentucky bluegrass.

Emerald zoysia

This improved hybrid lawn grass is a cross between Japanese lawngrass and Mascarenegrass which was introduced by Ian Forbes at the Plant Industry Station, Beltsville, Md., in 1949. This hybrid combines to varying degrees the greater winter hardiness, nonfluffy growth habit, and faster rate of spread of its japonica parent with the finer leaves, denser turf, greater frost tolerance, and darker green color of its tenuifolia parent. It exhibits hybrid vigor in rate of spread at both Tifton and Beltsville, and in the browning and density ratings at Tifton. All of these characteristics are desirable in a turf grass. The zone of adaptation of emerald zoysia is not fully known. At present, it is not recommended for planting further north than a line from Washington, D.C. west to St. Louis, Mo. Emerald zoysia received its name because of its beautiful, dark green color. Since it is the product of a wide cross, it must be propagated vegetatively to preserve its superior characteristics. Planting methods are the same as specified for the other zoysias.

(The above information is from an abstract from the cooperative investigations at Beltsville, Md., and Tifton, Ga., of the Field Crops Research Branch, Agricultural Research Section, United States Department of Agriculture, the University of Georgia Coastal Plain Experiment Station, Tifton, Ga., and the United States Golf Association Green Section.)

Legumes

Alyceclover (*Alysicarpus vaginalis*) : This is a summer annual, but when left as a cover crop or green manure it will volunteer for several years. In thin stands, it tends to spread and be moderately branched; in thick stands, it tends to be ascending with very few branches. It grows to a height of about 3 ft on moderately fertile soil. The stems are coarse but fairly leafy. The leaves are unifoliate, broadly oval, and are borne the entire length of the stems on short leafstalks. The seed weighs about 60 lb to the bushel, is borne in jointed pods, and 275,000 seeds are counted to the pound. Alyceclover is used principally for hay and soil improvement, and also for pasture. It does not like wet land and grows poorly on soils of low fertility. It should be seeded about the first of May, at the rate of 15–20 lb per acre.

Soybeans (*Glycine max*)

The soybean, an annual summer legume, is an erect, branching plant, resembling in its early growth the ordinary field or navy bean. The pods, stems, and leaves are covered with fine brown or gray hairs. The leaves vary widely in shape, size, color, and degree of persistence. They usually fall before the pods mature. The flowers, either white or purple, are small and inconspicuous and are borne in the axil of the leaf. They are self-fertile. The pod usually contains two or three and occasionally four seeds. The seeds are varicolored—green, brown, black, straw-yellow or greenish-yellow. Soybeans will succeed on nearly all types of soil, but best results are obtained on mellow, fertile loams or sandy loams. Inoculation of the seed is essential for the best results when it is grown for the first time. Soybeans are sown from early spring, after the soil has become warm, until midsummer. For soil improvement purposes, sow 1½ to 2 bushels of seed to the acre.

Lespedeza

There are three species of Lespedeza which are most commonly used: *Lespedeza striata*, common lespedeza; *Lespedeza stipulacea*, Korean lespedeza; *Lespedeza cuneata*, sericea lespedeza. In all species, the leaves are trifoliate but vary in shape from linear to ovate. The lavender flowers are inconspicuous in the three species listed. The common and Korean species are annuals, and the sericea is a perennial. Korean and common lespedezas are especially useful on acid soils of low fertility, and for soil improving purposes on poor soils. Usually they will reseed themselves for several years, if not harvested for seed. Sericea is used for cover crops on poor soils and is excellent for preventing soil erosion on road slopes. Seedings are always made in early spring, either broadcast or in close hills, using 20–25 lb of seed per acre. Fertilizers, especially phosphates, are essential.

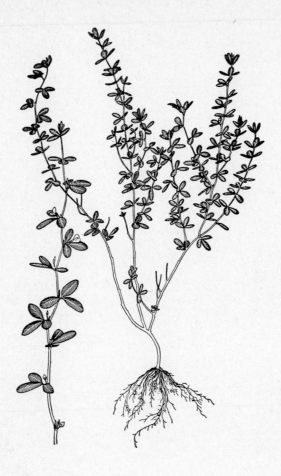

Fig. 2.12 Common lespedeza

Sweetclover (*Melilotus*)

The sweet clovers are upright plants. The leaflets are linear oval, and the flowers are yellow or white. There are three species of clover of agricultural importance: white (*Melilotus alba*), yellow (*Melilotus officinalis*), and sourclover (*Melilotus indica*). The white and yellow species are principally biennial; sourclover is a winter annual. Sweetclover will make good growth in regions where the effective rainfall is 17 in. or more, if the soil reaction is neutral or if limestone and other minerals are applied. After a stand is established, sweetclover is more tolerant of summer drought than other legumes. Sweetclover is valuable for hay crops and grazing, and for maintaining soil productivity.

Fig. 2.13   White sweetclover (left); Red clover (center); Hairy vetch (right).

The true clovers (*Trifolium* genus)

The clovers are perennial or annual, and in general thrive in a cool, moist climate on soils where there is an available supply of phosphorus, potassium, and calcium. There are wide differences in growth habit, flowering, and reproduction. Red clover, alsike clover, and crimson clover form crowns; zigzag and kura clovers produce underground root stocks. White and strawberry clovers spread by creeping stems that root at the nodes. Sub clover is decumbent, with stems lying on the soil, and Hungarian clover produces stiff, woody stems. The flowers of all species are borne on heads, with the number of flowers varying from as low as five in sub clover, to as many as 200 per head in red and white clovers. The number of seeds per pod varies from one to eight, depending upon the species.

There are eight species of clover that are of agricultural importance:

Red clover (*Trifolium pratense*), is an upright perennial and is composed of two forms: medium red (or double) cut, and mammoth (or single) cut.

White clover (*Trifolium repens*), a decumbent perennial, is composed of three general types: large, intermediate, and small. Ladino represents the large type, Louisiana white and New Zealand the intermediate, and English wild white and New York wild white the small type. Common white clover, often called white Dutch clover, is of the intermediate or small type, or a mixture of the two. It is one of the most important pasture plants, and is also used extensively in lawns.

Crimson clover (*Trifolium incarnatum*) is an upright winter annual and is used for hay, pasture, and soil improvement.

Alsike clover (*Trifolium hybridum*) is an upright perennial, suitable for wet soils and used for hay and pasture.

Small hop clover (*Trifolium procumbens*) is a winter annual, tolerant of unfavorable soils and climatic conditions.

Strawberry clover (*Trifolium fragiferum*) is a perennial, adapted to low-lying, wet soils and is tolerant of soil salinity.

Persian clover (*Trifolium resupinatum*) is a winter annual, best suited to the heavy, low-lying soils of the south. It is valuable for pasture and hay.

Sub clover (*Trifolium subterraneum*), used mainly for grazing, is decumbent. It is a winter annual adapted to the Pacific Northwest.

Vetch (*Vicia*)

The vetches are weak-stemmed or semivining plants. The leaves are semivining, terminating in tendrils. The flowers are light to dark lavender, with few or many in a raceme. The pods are linear, never inflated, and burst open readily when ripe.

Hairy vetch has about 18,000 seeds per lb, and common vetch has about 8,000 seeds per lb. Nearly all species weigh 60 lb per bushel. Vetches require a cool climate for the best development. In regions with mild winters, they are planted in the fall; in regions with cold winters, however, they must be planted in the spring. Hairy vetch is the most winter-hardy and is best adapted on sandy or sandy-loam soils.

Lawn mixtures

The common lawn mixtures usually found in the commercial seed houses are not conducive to the establishment of good lawns. Many of these mixtures contain lawn grasses which are not adapted to the region or which are added to cheapen the product. Such species are redtop, timothy, and Italian and perennial ryegrasses. In general, these have a much more vigorous early growth, particularly the ryegrasses, than do the adapted grasses, and thus offer a mowing problem soon after seeding and before the grasses are established. If not mowed regularly, they will smother and shade out the desired grasses and make reseeding necessary. Filler species are not necessary for the establishment of good turf, if proper lawn fertilization is followed.

If a lawn mixture is desired, equal parts of Kentucky bluegrass and creeping red fescue strains are recommended. To improve this mixture, add a small quantity of the Merion bluegrass strain. Any of the three grasses will nearly always make a much more desirable lawn or turf if seeded alone and properly cared for, however. White Dutch clover may also be added, if desired, and it is most compatible with bluegrass. After the desired lawn grass has been established, the white clover may be killed by spraying it with 2,4-D. However, white clover usually disappears in well-drained situations.

Combination turf

Two types of grass are often planted together in the hope of producing a lawn with the best qualities of each. One such combination—Meyer zoysia and Merion bluegrass—is designed to provide a relatively weed-free, disease-resistant turf which will remain green all the year round.

Meyer zoysia is a warm-season grass which makes its maximum growth during the hot summer months, while Merion bluegrass grows during the cool spring and fall. The Merion bluegrass is green during the winter, when the Meyer zoysia has lost its color.

Both grasses are drought-tolerant and resistant to diseases and insects. Compared to Kentucky bluegrass, Merion bluegrass is more resistant to helminthosporium leafspot, and has a better appearance. It resists drought better than common bluegrass.

Under good management, Meyer zoysia will withstand wear and resist weeds, but because it cannot be reproduced from seed, vegetative material must be used for planting, and the grass is slow to spread.

The combination of Meyer zoysia and Merion bluegrass is best adapted to the triangular area defined by Philadelphia, St. Louis, and Norfolk. Climatic conditions limit the growth of Meyer zoysia north of this area, and of Merion bluegrass south of it.

Establishment of combination turf

In a new lawn, the Meyer zoysia should be established before the Merion bluegrass. A well-prepared, weed-free seedbed is desirable. Two-inch plugs of Meyer zoysia planted 1 ft apart will produce a solid turf in approximately two years. Sprigs of Meyer zoysia planted in solid rows, 1 ft between rows, will produce a solid turf in two to three years. Planting of Meyer zoysia should be done between May 1 and Aug. 1.

The Merion bluegrass may be overseeded into the lawn the first fall following spring or summer planting of the Meyer zoysia sprigs or plugs. Merion bluegrass should be seeded at a rate of 2 lb per 1,000 sq ft. Care should be taken to distribute the seed evenly over the entire area.

If it is desirable to plant into an existing turf, the Meyer zoysia may be plugged as described above, without the seedbed preparation. Merion bluegrass may then be seeded into the existing turf during any subsequent fall.

During the first year of establishment of Meyer zoysia, light applications of fertilizer should be made every month from April to October (the active growing season). After the combination turf has been established, it should be fertilized spring and fall with 30 lb of 5–10–5 or similar fertilizer per 1,000 sq ft. In addition, for good maintenance it would be desirable to apply 25 lb of an organic fertilizer per 1,000 sq ft during the summer.

Unless the soil is extremely acid, 75 lb of ground limestone per 1,000 sq ft applied every three years will maintain a desirable reaction.

Meyer zoysia should be watered at three-to-four-day intervals until established. When Merion bluegrass is being overseeded, the area should be kept moist until the seed has germinated and become established. Established combination turf should be watered very infrequently, but sufficient water should be applied each time to wet the soil to a depth of 6 in. Frequent shallow watering should be avoided.

Combination turf should be mowed at a height of approximately ½ in. during the spring and fall and 1 in. during the summer.

Dates and rates of seeding

The best seeding results in Regions II and I (a) are obtained in the mild period beginning in the fall, when night temperatures are ideal—38 to 60 degrees. Day temperatures of 75 to 80 degrees are optimum, but warmer days will not harm germination if night temperatures are low. These mild temperatures should prevail over a period of from three weeks to three months of Mid South winters before the May heat. Winter injury is less harmful to good cover than May and June temperatures are to young seedlings. Seedings made in August and September enjoy the longest periods of correct conditions. It is important that seedings should not be made later than mid-October, since early cold snaps in late November and December may cause the seedlings to be heaved out of the ground. This condition will apply only to temperate climates and not to northern climates. In Regions II and III and southern portions of IV, late seedings, after March 15, invariably run into dry weather in May and June, making excessive watering necessary. In Regions I (a), I (b), and northern parts of IV seedings may be extended as late as June 15, and under good weather conditions could be extended through the summer. February and March seedings afford the desired temperatures, but usually there is not enough time for the seedlings to obtain a sufficient depth of root, or dense enough cover, to meet the drying atmosphere, high temperatures, and poor distribution of rainfall in May and June. Sometimes not even watering will prevent failure.

In seeding with Bermuda, the problem is entirely different. This species requires high temperatures, is normally drought-resistant, and will respond to watering and mulching.

In sowing grass seed either by hand or by machine, the seed should be divided into two equal parts. The second half of the seed should be distributed at right angles to the first sowing. Lightly rake or cultipac, in order to cover the seed no deeper than ¼ in., and then mulch.

TABLE 2.2/RATES AND TIMES OF SEEDING

Grass	Lb of seed per 1,000 sq ft	Fall seeding	Spring seeding
Kentucky bluegrass	2–3 (not over 5)	Aug. 1 – Oct. 1	Feb. 15 – March 15
Creeping red fescue	3–5	Aug. 1 – Oct. 1	Feb. 15 – March 15
Chewings fescue	3–5	Aug. 1 – Oct. 1	Feb. 15 – March 15
Colonial bentgrass	2–4	Aug. 1 – Oct. 1	Feb. 15 – March 15
Creeping bentgrass	1–2	Aug. 1 – Oct. 1	Feb. 15 – March 15
Orchardgrass	1–2	Aug. 1 – Oct. 1	Feb. 15 – March 15
Redtop mixture *	2–4	Aug. 1 – Oct. 1	Feb. 15 – March 15
Alta fescue	1–2	Aug. 1 – Oct. 1	Feb. 15 – March 15
Kentucky 31	1–2	Aug. 1 – Oct. 1	Feb. 15 – March 15
Bermuda (hulled seed)	2	————	May 1 – July 1
Ryegrass	1–2	Aug. 1 – Nov. 15	May 1 – July 1

* Spring seeding can be extended to June 15 in many Northern states. Along the Canadian border successful seedings have been done all summer long.

Hydro seeder

An improvement over the above method is the hydro seeder. This equipment is principally a tank mounted on a truck, in which is mixed a slurry consisting of 100 gal water mixed with 1 ton fertilizer and from 200 to 300 lb seed. The slurry is kept in motion by an agitator. This mixture will cover approximately two acres. Connected to the tank truck, but as a separate unit, is the pumping unit and nozzle tower. The tower permits a 360-degree swing and a 90-degree vertical travel, and the pump will force the slurry a distance of 100 ft. For fast, economical seeding and fertilizing of slopes, ditches, shoulders, and large open areas, this method is unsurpassed. If it is combined with use of the mulch spreader, the entire operation of liming, fertilizing, seeding, mulching, and anchoring the mulch can be done in two operations.

Mulching and rolling

Failures of new seedings are minimized if a good small-grain straw is applied over the seeding. This mulching provides protection from low and high temperatures and slows evaporation. It should be applied at the rate of 2 tons per acre, or about one bale per 1,000 sq ft to give a ¼-in. cover. For the best results the seeded area should be rolled after the mulch has been applied. On large areas, a cultipacker may be used both to roll and to press the straw into the ground. Mulch on steep banks should be held in place with brush or chicken wire. A newly seeded area should be thoroughly watered daily, until the grass is well established. Mulch should not be removed, but allowed to rot in place. If large numbers of leaves fall on the newly seeded area they must be removed if the grass is to survive, but only a bamboo or flexible steel rake should be used, and as much of the straw as possible should be left.

Since mulching of newly seeded areas has become an absolute must in most regions, more economical means of spreading the mulch have had to be found. One such means is the mulch spreader—a machine equipped with a chute into which bales of hay or straw are fed. The straw is forced into a hopper, where it is beaten apart and blown by a powerful fan into a discharge tube. The straw emerging from the end of the discharge tube is distributed evenly over the ground, with a minimum of bunching. To hold the mulch in place on the ground, asphalt can be applied by means of three jets at the end of the discharge tube, which are connected to a drum of asphalt mounted on the side of the machine. The operator can control the amount of asphalt discharged by means of a lever on the discharge tube. As the straw is being discharged, just enough asphalt adheres to it to make the straw form a mat on the ground. Approximately 100 gal of asphalt per acre is required to do an effective holding job on mulch spread at the rate of 2 tons per acre. Normally the mulch can be blown to a distance of 50–75 ft effectively.

Specifications for Asphalt Emulsions

Asphalt emulsions used on vegetative mulch should meet the following specifications:

Viscosity, Saybolt-Furol-60cc, 25°C (77°F) : 20–100
Modified miscibility: 4.5
Mixing: Break not more than 2 per cent
Specific gravity: 25°/25°C (77°/77°F) : Not less than 1.01
Residue at 163°C (325°F) 3 hr 50 gr: 55–60 per cent
Residue from ASTM Distillation Test: 55–60 per cent
Settlement, 7 days: Not more than 3 per cent
Sieve test: Not more than 0.05 per cent
Demulsibility, 50 ml, 0.10N, $CaCl_2$: Not more than 2 per cent

Tests on residue distillation:

Penetration at 25°C (77°F) : 150–200
Solubility in carbon disulfide: Not less than 98 per cent
Ductility at 25°C (77°F) : Not less than 60 cm.
Ash content: Not less than 2 per cent

The asphalt emulsions should be so prepared that their specified characteristics will not change during transportation or normal storage. They should be nontoxic to plants.

The mulch spreader can be adapted to other uses, such as spreading lime, seed, fertilizer, sand, and topsoil. Any combination of seed, fertilizer, and lime can be blown onto the area to be seeded at an even rate by feeding through the jets from the tank of water, fertilizer, and seed. The water shows the operator where he has applied the mixture. From 35–150 lb of mixed seed and fertilizer can be applied per minute.

MAINTENANCE PRACTICES

Renovation becomes necessary when the turf is thin or weedy or the desired species of grass was not used in the beginning. Such areas may be brought back by following these suggestions:

1. Take soil samples for analysis four to five months in advance of the seeding date.

2. Destroy all weed growth. To accomplish this, it is best to mow closely and remove the clippings. The use of strong chemicals such as sodium arsenite to kill weeds is justified in a renovation program, provided its effect on the soil is known and proper precautions are taken to safeguard other materials.

3. Apply lime as recommended by the analysis, preferably during the winter.

4. Late in February or early in March, or during moist periods in early fall or late summer, use an aerifying machine. These machines cut regularly and closely spaced holes in the ground and deposit the cylindrical plugs on the surface. These may be left where they are. Aerifying with a machine is practical only on large areas. For small lawns, a common spading fork or heavy spiked roller may be used. Use the fork by thrusting it into the sod and moving it back and forth. The forking should be done in rows the width of the fork. Aerifying sod permits water, fertilizer, and oxygen to reach the roots, where they will do the most good.

5. Apply the fertilizers recommended by the soil analysis. A nitrogen application should be made whether or not it is recommended by the soil analysis. Sodium nitrate or its equivalent can be applied at the rate of 140 or 200 lb per acre, or about 4–5 lb per 1,000 sq ft.

6. Roll and water.

Shade problems

It is usually impossible to obtain a good stand of grass under dense shade conditions. Magnolias, maples, and oaks, in particular, present conditions under which grass will not thrive unless some remedial measures are taken. Removing the lower branches up to 12–15 ft will increase the light intensity enough to satisfy the needs of shade-loving grasses. Selective thinning of the upper branches will also help. Grasses are very heavy feeders on nitrogen, and they respond in proportion to the amounts available in the soil. Where roots are close to the surface and the soil cover is thin and very deficient in nitrogen, new soil should be applied to a depth of 6 in. After the new soil is fertilized, shade-adapted grasses can be sown.

Ground covers for shade

Whenever it has been determined that grass will not grow under a particular shade condition, the following ground covers may be used:

1. English Ivy (*Hedera helix*) may require some pruning to prevent excessive growth and matting. The Baltic ivy is a lower growing form and may be better suited than the commoner English form.

2. Common periwinkle (*Vinca minor*) is a hardy trailing evergreen plant with blue flowers and dark green foliage.

3. Wintercreeper (*Euonymus fortunei*) is an evergreen plant and thrives in dense shade.

4. Canby pachistima (*Pachistima canbyi*) is a small-leafed evergreen with red berries which makes a matted mass about 6 to 8 inches high.

5. Japanese spurge (*Pachysandra terminalis*) is best adapted to soils of high organic content and dense shade conditions.

Care and maintenance of grass

The following suggestions for efficient watering of grass areas should be followed in order to maintain a green turf:

1. All watering should be done in the afternoon or at night. This enables the soil to absorb a maximum amount of water with a minimum of evaporation.

2. During drought periods, the only way to maintain a desirable greenness is to give the lawn a thorough soaking once or twice a week. Light daily sprinkling does more harm than good. As a general rule, it requires from 500 to 750 gallons of water for every 1,000 sq ft of grass area to give an equivalent of $3/4$ to $1\frac{1}{4}$ in. of rain. This will moisten the soil to a depth of 3 to 5 in.

Irrigation

Many localities have experienced decidely lower rainfall the past few years, especially during the summer months when sufficient water is essential to the proper development of turf, trees, and shrubs. Where an adequate supply of water is available from ponds or rivers, an irrigation system can be installed which will compensate for a lack of rainfall and more than pay for itself in better turf or in the preservation of newly planted trees or shrubs.

There are two general types of irrigation systems: surface and overhead.

The surface irrigation system is usually associated with the flooding of land from irrigation ditches, and the overhead system with the use of various types of sprinklers.

For parks, industrial property, or other lands maintained exclusively for public use, the sprinkler type of irrigation system is practical. Sprinkler irrigation may be as simple as a hose with one sprinkler attachment, or a perforated hose or pipe, or it may be an engineered system of underground pipes with automatic pop-up sprinkler heads at regular intervals, or a portable system using aluminum pipe on the surface of the ground with sprinkler heads spaced to provide adequate coverage. The portable system has become the most popular, principally because of its flexibility, ease of handling and moving, and a lower capital cost for installation. One man can lay and install 800 ft of aluminum pipe, connect the sprinkler heads, and begin watering within 30 minutes. Sprinkler heads are spaced every 20 ft and, depending upon the type of nozzle used and the pressure available, each sprinkler will cover an area from 60 to 100 ft in diameter. A system of this size will irrigate one to two acres at one setting and supply the equivalent of approximately 1 in. of rainfall in three hours' time.

More elaborate and costly systems can be installed which will provide pin-point control in confined areas. These systems are usually installed underground with the sprinkler heads spaced to give complete coverage to one specific area. They are controlled from one valve. Such systems are ideal for turf areas in parking lots, road or highway islands, shrub beds, etc., where it is necessary to cover the grass or planted areas and to avoid pavements, cars or buildings. Although the initial cost of installation is high, such systems usually save enough in cost of labor and water to pay for themselves. Labor is saved because there is no need to move individual sprinklers and hundreds of feet of hose from one location to another. Water is saved because sprinkler heads can be obtained to cover either full circles, half circles or quarter circles, and a properly designed system would therefore cover only the areas to be watered. Thousands of gallons of water can be wasted in a short time on such unplanted areas as pavements and parking lots.

A more recent variation of this same underground, automatic system— one much easier and less expensive to install—has been developed by several of the major rubber companies. This system utilizes the same principle of underground installations and flush sprinkler heads as the more elaborate systems, but uses rubber which has been treated to withstand underground conditions. The system is installed just under the sod, making it a simple procedure to lift established sod, open a trench no deeper than 6 in., lay the hose in the trench, backfill, and tamp the sod into place over the finished system. A layout such as this is ideal for confined areas between curbs, parking area islands, and sections close to buildings, sidewalks or paths where a controlled flow of water is desired.

Topdressing

Every lawn or turf, to be successful, should be topdressed once a year. Topdressing helps to keep the grass level, helps to prevent compaction, and promotes good root growth. Topdressing material may be a very loose, pliable topsoil; sand; or a well-shredded compost of organic materials. Before it is used, all topdressing material should be treated with chemicals to kill insects, diseases, and weeds. See Table 2.3.

Mowing

One of the major reasons for failures in turf is close clipping. It is important that the mower be set not closer than 1½ in., and preferably 2 in. This is the minimum height which supplies enough leaf surface to build the plant foods needed for vigorous root development. Lower clipping will starve the roots, and the turf will thin out, giving poor cover and allowing room for invasion of low-growing weedy species. Such turf is shallow and weak-rooted and is baked by hot daytime temperatures. The only grasses

TABLE 2.3/VOLUME OF TOPDRESSING MATERIAL REQUIRED FOR APPLICATIONS TO VARIOUS DEPTHS*

Depth of topdressing required, in.	Area									
	1,000 sq ft		3,000 sq ft		5,000 sq ft		7,000 sq ft		10,000 sq ft	
	cu ft	cu yd	cu ft	cu yd	cu ft	cu yd	cu ft	cu yd	cu ft	cu yd
⅛	10.4	0.4	31.2	1.2	52.0	1.9	72.8	2.7	104.0	3.9
¼	20.8	0.8	62.4	2.3	104.0	3.9	145.6	5.4	208.0	7.7
⅜	31.2	1.2	93.6	3.5	156.0	5.8	218.4	8.1	312.0	11.6
½	41.7	1.5	125.1	4.6	208.5	7.7	291.9	10.8	417.0	15.4
⅝	52.1	1.9	156.3	5.8	260.5	9.6	364.7	13.5	521.0	19.3
¾	62.5	2.3	187.5	6.9	312.5	11.6	437.5	16.2	625.0	23.1

* From *Turf Management*, by H. Burton Musser. New York: McGraw-Hill Book Co., 1950. Used by permission.

which can withstand close clipping are the bent grasses, the Bermudas and the zoysias. They require a constant good moisture condition and heavy and continuous fertilization.

Rake the leaves or chop them up with a leaf grinder in the fall to prevent matting and consequent smothering of evergreen turf grasses.

Aerifying grass areas

Aerification of turf and grass lands has been standard practice in England for many years. Here in the United States, interest in the aerification principle has increased rapidly since the war. Today it is generally accepted practice for golf course and playfield maintenance.

The principle of aerification is to loosen and aerate the soil under the turf without disturbing the turf surface. Aerification is necessary because rainfall, artificial watering, and traffic by people and maintenance equipment all tend to compact the soil. When the soil is compacted, water, air, and plant foods cannot penetrate, and grass becomes shallow-rooted. The resulting shallow-rooted turf will not stand up during hot, dry weather. Frequent watering, which becomes necessary under such conditions, increases the disease and weed problem.

The frequency of aerification will vary with the type of soil, the turfgrass area, and the amount of use or traffic to which the area is exposed. On golf course greens, thorough aerification is done in spring and fall. The 1/4-in. spoon is now available and should be used during the hot summer months, when slight opening of soil on greens will permit freer movement of cooling air and of water. On athletic fields, and other hard-use areas, aerification once a month is recommended by many of the turfgrass authorities. When aerification is done during hot, dry weather, immediate and thorough watering is recommended.

Soil compaction is not the only condition improved by aerifying. Established turf will form a thatch of dry roots and stems at the surface, preventing water, air, and fertilizer from penetrating into the soil. Aerification will break through this thatch so that air, water, and fertilizer can get into the soil. In time, regular aerification will help to break down thatch and cause it to decay more rapidly. Vertical mowing, combined with aerification, will improve the surface and the soil. With the introduction of the Verti-cut mower by West Point Products Corporation, the combination of Verti-cutting and aerifying has become standard procedure on most golf courses.

Aerifying can also be used successfully for preparing a seedbed in existing turf. The soil brought to the surface forms a light topdressing to cover the seed. When the surface soil and dry plant material are broken through, seed will come in contact with the soil and germinate. Where grass is sprigged the stolons can be planted into the aerifier holes. The aerifier loosens soil by actual removal of soil cores. It is equipped with hollow spoons that are curved at a 15-degree angle so they enter and leave the soil without tearing the turf. Two types of spoons are used on the aerifier: open and thatch spoons. The open spoon scoops out a core of soil and brings it to the surface, leaving a loose-walled cavity in which roots can expand freely. The thatch spoon is used where it is necesary to cut through a thick layer of surface material. Since only the tip of the spoon is closed, the problem of clogging is minimized. Spoon sizes range from 1/4 in. to 1 in. and all spoons are interchangeable on the various aerifier units. For golf course greens, 1/2-in. open or 1/2-in. thatch spoons are used for regular aerification as outlined above, but the 1/4-in. and 3/4-in. thatch spoons are recommended for golf course fairways. Where a thatch condition exists or fairway grasses are shallow-rooted, aerifiers should be equipped with the 3/4-in. thatch spoon. For lawns, athletic fields, and other comparable areas, the 1-in. or 3/4-in. spoon is used.

50

Proper aerification of grass will reduce maintenance cost. Watering can be cut in half and less fertilizer and seed is wasted due to runoff: In addition, the turf will be stronger and better able to stand hard usage, disease, and drought. In the simplest terms, aerification will do four things:

1. Make the soil porous and the turf springy.
2. Allow air, moisture, and fertilizer to get to the roots.
3. Increase growth rapidly, particularly when fertilizer is applied while cavities are still open.
4. Prepare a good seedbed without destroying existing turf.

Use of grass barriers

One method to insure neat and even edges to shrub beds, around specimen trees, and along walks, driveways, and roads is to install a steel barrier. This barrier helps to prevent the occurrence of several maintenance problems:

1. It prevents damaging trees with mowing equipment.
2. It keeps grass from encroaching upon paths and roadways.
3. It maintains an even, smooth edge to grass areas.
4. It retains mulch.
5. It keeps Bermuda and zoysia grasses from encroaching on shrub or floral beds.
6. It reduces the amount of hand trimming to a minimum.

These barriers, or curbs, can be made in the maintenance shop from scrap metal, or they can be purchased ready made. The metal used should be approximately 12 gage galvanized steel, flexible enough so that it can be curved. The curbs should be cut to a minimum width of 10 in. and driven into the ground 8 in.; in hard or rocky ground it may be necessary to dig a trench. A good way to set the proper curve or alignment around a shrub bed is to place a flexible hose on the ground in the line desired, mark the ground with a pick, and begin placing the curb. Along roads or parking areas a heavier metal should be used, approximately $\frac{1}{4}$-in thick. The grass line is always to be flush with the top of the curb. This will prevent a tire from being cut if it should strike the curb. See Fig. 2.14.

Control of pests and diseases

There are several turf pests and diseases which are harmful, in varying degrees, to grass.

Leaf spot: A fungus disease known as leaf spot may appear where there is excess moisture. The spots begin as tiny brown specks scattered over the blades, and as they enlarge they may extend right across the leaf, with the center becoming straw colored. The bordering area varies in color from dark brown to black. The best way to combat the disease is to follow cultural

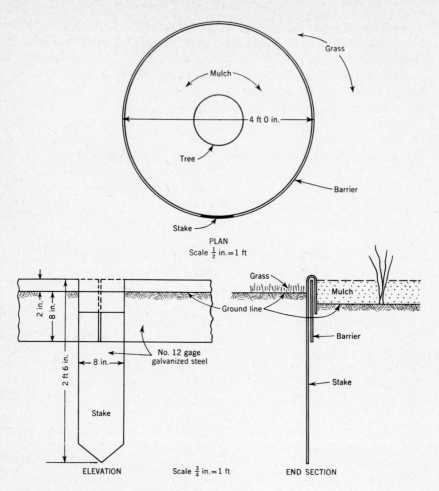

Fig. 2.14 Grass barrier for specimen trees

practices that will encourage a strong growth of grass. Higher clipping is also advisable.

Brown patch: The fungus disease known as brown patch causes much grass to turn brown during the summer months. Attacks of brown patch usually come during periods of hot, humid weather when grass is in a weakened condition. A peculiarity of this disease is that the attack is usually in definite patches which are roughly circular in outline. Part of the grass within the circle usually escapes injury. The disease is worse in turf that is over-fertilized, or where the soil is very acid. It may be controlled by applications of mercurical fungicides. Commercial fungicides include such brand names as Calo-clor, Semesan, Nu-Green, and Curex. A mixture of two parts calomel and one part corrosive sublimate can also be used. This should be applied at the rate of 2 or 3 oz per 1,000 sq ft, as a spray or mixed with soil.

Dollarspot: Another fungus disease is dollarspot. The most noticeable characteristic is the size of the injured spots, usually limited to a diameter of 2 in. The affected turf presents a moth-eaten appearance, and the leaves are more bleached than after an attack of brown patch. Control measures are the same as for brown patch.

Mildew: At times a stand of grass suddenly appears to have been dusted with flour. This is caused by powdery mildew, which resembles the mold that grows on old shoes left in damp places. If the mildew is wiped off the surface, it will usually be found that the grass blade is green and uninjured. Fortunately, mildew causes little real injury and soon disappears.

Damping-off: When seedling turf is spotted with dead patches varying in diameter from one inch to several inches, it is likely that damping-off has occurred. Sometimes this fungus disease kills the sprouts before they emerge from the ground, making it appear that the seed failed to germinate. At other times the disease comes after the grass is well started. The young grass turns black at first, and then withers and turns brown. Damping-off is often responsible for a spotted growth of young grass where parts of the lawn have a good stand and other patches show no grass at all. The growth of damping-off is favored by an ample supply of water near the surface of the ground and an over supply of fertilizer. After an attack, there is nothing to do but let the fungus spend itself, and then repair the damage by reseeding.

Bluegrass leafspot: During periods of wet weather, leafspot may attack bluegrass. The grass blades show purple spots that enlarge and turn straw-colored with purple borders. A spot may girdle the leaf, kill the tip, and destroy the entire blade. In severe attacks the bluegrass turf becomes thin and weak, and therefore open to invasion by summer weeds. High mowing and adequate fertilization decrease the damage from leafspot. Merion bluegrass is less susceptible to injury by leafspot than the Kentucky bluegrass.

Melting-out: In the spring, and until hot weather arrives, bluegrass, fescues, and bents may be attacked by melting-out. The diseased areas are smoky blue in color at first, later become yellow, and finally turn brown when the grass plants are killed. The injured areas are irregular, without any particular pattern.

Curvularia: This fungus produces a disease sometimes called "fading-out" because of its indefinite symptoms. The disease appears in the hot summer months, following the leafspot and melting-out seasons. At first the lawn appears to be drying out, even when there is no lack of moisture. The turf turns pale green, then yellow, and may eventually die. The affected areas are without definite outline, and frequently bright green islands of healthy grass remain in the injured areas.

Leafspot, melting-out, and curvularia can be controlled by means of the phenyl mercury compounds in either liquid or dry form. Another treatment is cychlohexamide, a new antibiotic sold under the trade name of Actidone. Grasses can be protected partially or completely from turf diseases if the grass blades are covered with one of these materials, either before the disease starts or in its very early stages.

Turf pests

Mushrooms: Both edible and inedible mushrooms often develop in turf, due to an excess of decaying organic matter. Regular mowing will give all the control needed, since they do no harm.

White grubs: There are two kinds of white grubs that attack turf. The most common is the larva of the green June beetle, easily distinguished by the fact that it crawls on its back. Other white grubs, usually smaller and shaped more like the letter U, are the larvae of the May beetle. These grubs eat the roots of grass and the sod, sometimes cutting roots so completely that heavily infested sod can be rolled back.

The larvae of the green June beetle damage the sod by boring holes in the ground and mounding the earth adjacent to each hole. They live upon decaying organic matter and their damage is done while searching for food. They may be controlled by applying 5 lb of 10 per cent gamma benzene hexachloride per acre, using fertilizer as a carrier. For example, if 50 lb of fertilizer per acre is desired, add 5 lb of insecticide to the fertilizer and spread. For small areas, use 2 oz of 10 per cent gamma benzene hexachoride per 1,000 sq ft, mixed with 20 oz of fertilizer.

The May beetle grub may be controlled by applying 50 lb of 50 per cent DDT, or 25 lb of 40 per cent chlordane per acre. This application will give control for five or more years. It should be applied as evenly as possible, and then washed into the sod. It will also control the green June beetle grub. For small areas, use 1 lb of 50 per cent DDT, or ½ lb of chlordane solution (emulsion), or dust with 5 per cent chlordane.

Other insects: The Japanese beetle, sod webworm, cutworm, and chinch bug are other insects that injure grass in various parts of the country. These feed on the stem and leaves of the grass and not on the roots as do grubs. Of these pests, only the chinch bugs are truly injurious. They cause yellowing or browning of the grass, usually in patches that gradually enlarge.

Chinch bugs are worst in thick turf, and particularly in bent grasses. To find the tiny bugs, examine the turf closely at ground level. Some are red, but others are dark, and about ⅛ in. long. Flood a small area with water and you will see the bugs struggling to the surface. To control chinch bugs use chlordane or DDT as specified in Table 2.4. A single application of chlordane at the grub-proofing dosage is effective for at least five years.

Ants and earthworms are not actually damaging to turf, but the mounds they form can spoil the appearance of a good turf.

Grub-proofing methods

Grub-proofing may be done by using granulated insecticides in a fertilizer spreader, by wet spraying with a compressed air or a power sprayer, by hose-on sprayers, or by dusting.

Granulated insecticides: To use granulated insecticides in a fertilizer spreader, adjust the spreader by weighing the amount run out over a known area of ground. Put in a weighed amount of granulated insecticide, spread over 100 sq ft, and weigh what is left in the spreader. The difference between the two weighings multiplied by 10 gives the rate per 1,000 sq ft. Most of the more common fertilizer spreaders will require an aperture less than one-fourth open.

Wet spraying: Grub-proofing may also be done by wet spraying. This is the most satisfactory way to control chinch bugs, sod webworms, cutworms, and ants. Mix the insecticide thoroughly with 20 gal of water per 1,000 sq ft and spray the turf thoroughly and evenly.

Dusting: This is a poor way of grub-proofing the turf, but a very good way to treat smaller spots damaged by chinch bugs, sod webworms, cutworms, or ants. Dust the area thoroughly with a 5 per cent chlordane dust. For occasional ant hills, place a teaspoon of 5 per cent chlordane dust in and around each hill.

For large areas, large power sprayer equipment should be used. It is safe to use insecticides recommended for turf-insect control with fertilizers or with 2,4-D weed killers. For dry application it is a good idea to mix fertilizers with the insecticides. Do not use hydrated lime with insecticides; use ground limestone instead.

Precautions: Do not allow children or pets to walk or play on recently treated grass; water in all treatments with a hose or regular sprinkler system.

TABLE 2.4/TURF INSECTS: EFFECTIVE INSECTICIDES AND RATES OF TREATMENT

Pest	Insecticidal materials	Rate of Treatment per 1000 sq ft	per acre	Preferred treatment periods
Japanese beetle	10% DDT dust	6 lb	250 lb	Spring
Oriental beetle	50% DDT wettable	1.25 lb	50 lb	and early
Asiatic	powder			fall
garden	5% Chlordane dust	5 lb	200 lb	
beetle	50% Chlordane	0.5 lb	20 lb	
grubs	wettable powder			
	Lead arsenate	10 lb	430 lb	
May and June	5% Chlordane dust	5 lb	200 lb	Spring
beetle	50% Chlordane wettable	0.5 lb	20 lb	and early
2- to 4-Year	powder			fall
and annual	Lead arsenate	10 lb	430 lb	
grubs				

TABLE 2.4/TURF INSECTS: EFFECTIVE INSECTICIDES AND RATES OF TREATMENT (cont.)

Pest	Insecticidal materials	Rate of Treatment per 1000 sq ft	per acre	Preferred treatment periods
Mound forming beetle grubs (Southern green June bug and Balbocesoma)	5% Chlordane dust	5 lb	200 lb	Spring and early fall
	50% Chlordane wettable powder	0.5 lb	20 lb	
	Lead arsenate	10 lb	430 lb	
Chinch bugs	10% DDT dust	2.5 lb	100 lb	May to August
	5% Chlordane dust	5 lb	200 lb	
Leaf hoppers	50% DDT wettable powder	3 oz	8 lb	June to September
	50% Chlordane wettable powder	2.5 oz	6 lb	
Sod webworms	50% DDT wettable powder	3 oz	8 lb	May, July, August
Cutworms Army worms	5% DDT dust	2.5 lb	100 lb	
	50% Chlordane wettable powder	2.5 oz	6 lb	
	5% Chlordane dust	2 lb	80 lb	
	Lead arsenate	2 lb	80 lb	
Mole cricket	25% DDT oil emulsion	1 pt per 100 gal water 0.25 pt per 100 gal water	Dilutions not determined	Spring to fall
Ants	50% Chlordane wettable powder	4 oz per 20 gal water	10 lb per 500 gal water	May to September
Earthworms	50% Chlordane wettable powder	2 lb	85 lb	Spring to fall
	10% Toxaphene dust	10 lb	430 lb	
	Lead arsenate	10 lb	430 lb	
Flies and mosquitos	5% DDT oil emulsion	1 gal		
	25% DDT oil emulsion	1 pt in 5 gal water		
	50% DDT wettable powder	1 lb in 10 gal water		

The above chart from *Turf Management*, by H. Burton Musser, copyright 1950, McGraw-Hill Book Company, Inc. is used by permission. (Condensed from information in bulletins and published articles by research workers in the State Agricultural Experiment Stations of Connecticut, Florida, Iowa, New Jersey, New York, and Rhode Island and the U.S. Department of Agriculture.)

Moles: To control moles, first roll down or otherwise flatten the tunnels, and for the next day or so determine which of the tunnels are open again. This indicates where the animals are working. Then in the newly opened tunnel apply a poison bait every few feet. A teaspoon of flaked naphthalene or two or three moth balls may also be used. Control can be expected only gradually.

Pastures

Many public grounds have open grass areas which are suitable for development as pastures. Generally speaking, a program of land and grass improvement should be established along the following lines:

1. Remove trees and brush except those needed for shade. Put land in good shape for mowing and keep sprouts cut back to starve out root system.

2. Leave shade trees on high and poorer areas.

3. Provide watering places and plan them so that livestock cannot crowd around and be a source of disease. Do not have shade trees around watering places.

4. On poor soils and old croplands, plant a crop of winter legumes before seeding to pasture.

5. Land preparation: Break land several weeks before time to seed. Harrow and disk to form a good firm seedbed. For August and September seeding, break in June or early July and fallow until seeding time. For spring seeding, break land in November and December.

6. Fertilization and liming: Take a soil analysis to determine the kind and amount of fertilizer to use. Also determine the reading of the soil and add lime accordingly.

7. Disk fertilizer and lime into a soil a week or 10 days before time to seed.

8. Selecting the right grasses to grow is important. Choose the grasses best adapted to your locality. Consult the local extension service or the county agent's office.

9. Rates of seeding for most commonly used pasture grasses: See Table 2.5.

10. Time to seed: Fall seeding should be made after the first good rain in August, and not later than Sept. 15. Spring seeding should be made between March 1 and April 1, weather permitting.

11. How to seed: Freshen the seedbed with a section harrow or weeder. Divide the seed into equal parts and cross-sow to get even distribution.

12. Covering: Cover seeds about $\frac{1}{4}$ in. on heavier soils and about $\frac{1}{2}$ in. on sandy soils. A corrugated roller with seeder attachment will do the job in one operation.

13. Mow at least twice annually, to control weeds and sprouts.

TABLE 2.5/RATES OF SEEDING FOR MOST COMMONLY USED PASTURE GRASSES

Grass	Lb per acre in mixtures	Lb per acre alone
Ladino	3 – 5	—
Kentucky bluegrass	5 – 10	14
Orchard grass	10	25
Kentucky 31	10 – 15	25
Alta fescue	10 – 15	25
Louisiana white clover	1 – 2	—

Management of pastures

1. Do not graze newly seeded pastures until plants are well established and will not be pulled up by grazing animals.

2. Do not overgraze. Manage grazing so the pasture is never grazed closer than 3 in. Seven acres of pasture per head for a five-month grazing period is generally considered desirable.

3. To eradicate weeds, mow two or three times a year before seeds form. Keep top growth cut back to starve out root systems. Sprouts must be kept cut during the growing season. Some sprouts may be controlled by chemicals or burning.

4. Bermuda pasture: Disk or plow it every year or two, and fertilize. If Bermuda sod is not plowed or disked it tends to get "sod-bound" and unproductive. Annual lespedeza may be sown in Bermuda sod for added grazing value. Oats or Italian rye grass may also be sown in the fall for some winter pasture.

5. Do not undergraze. Undergrazing will tend to lower pasture quality, because it allows less desirable plants to mature and seed.

6. Winter pastures may be established on old pastures, wherever desired, by the following methods:

(a) Make soil test and fertilize accordingly. Lightly disk after fertilization; (b) Seed 25 lb crimson clover and 25 lb Italian ryegrass per acre. Make seeding in September or early October; (c) Begin grazing when plants are 3 in. high.

Rehabilitation of borrow areas

Major construction often requires that large areas of land be used for borrow pit and storage yard purposes. Unfortunately, these areas cannot always be hidden from roads or public places. Two methods of soil improvement have been developed which are rather similar, but one requires a longer period of time. For lasting results, Method No. 2 is preferable.

Method No. 1

1. Regrade the area to eliminate all erosion ditches. Provide adequate drainage, terrace (if the slope is steep), and shape the borrow into a smooth rolling terrain devoid of all sharp cuts and frills.

2. Break up subsoil as deeply as possible.

3. Mulch at least 6 in. deep with hay or sawdust. Use straw or hay mulch at rate of 10 tons per acre. If fresh sawdust is used, add 250 lb ammonium nitrate per acre.

4. Disk with a heavy disk, cutting mulch material into the soil and breaking up heavy clods. Remove all large rocks.

5. Make an acidity test and add lime as indicated, if the pH reading is less than 6.5.

6. About one week or ten days before seeding, make another soil test and fertilize as indicated.

7. Disk thoroughly in order to work the fertilizer and lime into the soil. Continue disking until a smooth seedbed is formed, free of all heavy clods and rocks.

8. All the above work should be done during early summer, or early enough to permit the land to lie fallow before seeding time (Aug. 15–Oct. 1).

9. Use a corrugated roller with seed attachment for best seeding results on large areas.

10. Recommended seed mixtures:

Fall seeding	Spring seeding
4 lb Ladino clover or Louisiana white clover	20 lb Korean lespedeza
10 lb Orchard grass	4 lb Ladino clover or Louisiana white clover
15 lb Alta or Kentucky 31 fescue	15 lb Alta or Kentucky 31 fescue

11. Cultipac after seeding and mulch with straw at the rate of two tons per acre.

Method No. 2

Steps 1–7 as for Method No. 1.

7. Disk thoroughly in order to work the fertilizer and lime into the soil. Continue disking until a smooth seedbed is formed, free of all heavy clods and rocks. Cultipac prior to seeding and after seeding.

8. Use a corrugated roller with seed attachment for best seeding results on large areas.

9. Recommended seed mixture:

25 lb Crimson clover per acre
20 lb Italian ryegrass per acre

10. Permit this planting to grow until May, when the crop is to be plowed under while still green.

11. Make a new soil test and fertilize as indicated.

12. Disk fertilizer into the soil and continue disking land into a smooth seedbed.

13. Sow 90 to 100 lb of inoculated soybeans per acre.

14. After the soybeans have matured but are still green, plow under. Make a soil analysis to determine the amount and quantity of fertilizer and lime to be added.

15. Work the fertilizer into the soil by disking into a smooth seedbed.

16. After the soil has been thoroughly worked and is ready (Aug. 15–Oct. 1) seed, using a corrugated roller with seed attachment for best results.

17. Recommended seed mixture (quantities per acre):

    2 lb Louisiana white clover
    8 lb Kentucky bluegrass
   12 lb Alta or Kentucky 31 fescue

18. Mulch with straw at rate of 2 tons per acre.

WEED CONTROL

The control of weeds in turf has received more and more attention during the past few years. The use of chemicals has advanced rapidly, and research into new chemicals continues. The best method of weed control is to combine good management practices with chemical control.

Management practices that favor the desired grasses and tend to reduce weeds are cheaper and easier than chemical treatment, and should be done before or in connection with chemical use.

The following practices will help to reduce weeds:

1. Fertilize regularly and adequately to keep the turf going and to shade out any new weed plants.

2. Mowing at the correct height to keep a dense turf, which will shade out young weed plants.

3. Avoid keeping the soil continuously so wet that weed and crabgrass germination is favored.

4. Avoid damaging or aerating turf at times when weeds are germinating freely.

The best control treatment for general weed infestation on large areas is an over-all treatment with a selective chemical that will kill the weeds and leave the grasses in good condition.

Controlling broad-leaved weeds

The best material to kill broad-leaved weeds without damaging the grass is 2,4-D. Usually one application will eliminate dandelions, plantains, and many other larger weeds. Such weeds as chickweed and other mat-forming weeds may require two or more applications at intervals of about one month. Clover may be somewhat damaged by 2,4-D, especially after spring treatments, but usually recovers rather rapidly.

In most instances 2,4-D works slowly. It works best in warm weather, when a reaction can usually be seen within 24 hours. Within that time the weeds are not generally killed, but the stems and leaves curl and become crisp. In about three or four weeks after treatment the weeds dry up. On new turf it is good practice to wait until the grass is at least one inch high before treating the weeds with 2,4-D. Bent grass may be damaged slightly by 2,4-D applications, but the bluegrasses and fescues are generally unharmed.

The broad-leaved weeds usually killed by a single or double application of 2,4-D are as follows:

Dandelion	Moneywort
Heal-all	Water pennywort
Buckhorn or narrow-leaved plantain	Gosmore
	Winter cress or yellow rocket
Broad-leaved plantain	Purslane
Cinquefoil	Hawkweed or paint brush
Ground ivy	Yarrow
Black medic	Field sorrel or sheep sorrel

A summer annual that thrives on turf that is thin and on compacted soil is knotweed. It is very hard to kill in the summer, but when it is in the seedling stage, in April and May, it can be killed easily with a single 2,4-D treatment.

Other weeds that are hard to kill are wild garlic and onion. They should be treated very early in the spring and the treatment should be repeated a year later; two treatments are needed to kill both the plants of the current season and those that will grow in the autumn from hard bulblets already in the soil.

Common and mouse-ear chickweed cannot be controlled with a single 2,4-D treatment. Usually it requires three treatments at two-week intervals, beginning early in the spring.

Potassium cyanate may also give control.

The greatest weed pest, and the one on which most control effort is expended, is an annual grass known as crab grass. The seeds of crab grass germinate in the late spring and the plants grow rapidly, often crowding out the more desirable grasses. The seed is set in the early fall, and any control program must be based on these facts. Cornell Extension Bulletin 922 lists seven steps to follow in preventing an infestation of crab grass in new turf, or to improve an old turf:

1. Plant your new lawns in early fall; prepare the soil properly and select the right kind of seed for the situation. Crab grass seed is rarely an impurity in even the cheapest and poorest seed mixture. The plants come from the seed already present in the soil.

2. Fertilize the established lawn in early fall. If you fertilize in the spring, use an inorganic fertilizer before the lawn starts to grow, and at about one-half the rate normally used in the fall. Late spring fertilization gives the permanent grasses five or six months of good growing conditions before competition from the crab grass begins again.

3. Cut the grass at least 1¼ in. high. A large leaf area enables the permanent grasses to make strong growth. Crab grass cannot tolerate shade, and many crab grass seedlings die.

4. If the established turf has crab grass troubles, check the sod for grub injury. Beetles damage lawns most seriously in late spring, just when crab grass is ready to fill in the bare spots. If the lawn is infested with grubs, you cannot hope for lasting crab grass control until the soil is grub-proofed.

5. If possible, prevent crab grass from seeding. This is more easily said than done. Raking the seed stalks so that they can be mowed, collected, and discarded is a tiresome and time-consuming job, but it will reduce the next year's seed supply. Several attachments designed to fit on the front of the lawn mower will pull the seed stalks up where they can be cut. These devices merely eliminate hand raking.

6. Hand-weed crab grass when the plants are small. Such weeding is sometimes practical on small areas of particular importance. If the plants are large, pull them out with a "dandelion" rake just before fall reseeding. The "dandelion" rake has a head of sheet metal, with triangular teeth that hook under the crowns of the plants.

7. Water the lawn well or not at all.

Soil treatment for killing crab grass seed

Methods for killing crab grass or other weed seeds in the soil are still in the experimental stage. Calcium cyanamid has been used succesfully for this purpose, however. This fertilizer material should be mixed into the new seedbed thoroughly in mid-August at the rate of 50 lb to 1000 sq ft.

Before planting the grass seed, allow three weeks for the weed-killing action to take place and for the excess chemicals to disappear. It is important to apply the calcium cyanamid when the soil is fairly moist. Do not plant the new grass until after there have been several good rains or irrigations.

Chemical control of crab grass

There are three types of selective crab grass chemicals on the market: They are potassium cyanate, phenyl mercuric acetate, and methyl arsenate.

Potassium cyanate is a foliar burning material which is not toxic to the user. It kills by burning the existing crab grass leaves. If new shoots appear on older plants after the first treatment, a second treatment must be given. It is a chemical which can be used repeatedly to remove crab grass and chickweed without damage to permanent grasses. Apply the potassium cyanate compound in late summer, near the end of July and in August, for best results. Potassium cyanate has been formulated into organic fertilizers. In this way adequate fall fertilizer is added as the weekly doses of p. c. burn out the crab grass. The temporary browning of desired turf, the need for repeat treatments, the possibility of reinfestation are limitations of this chemical.

Phenyl mercuric acetate: These compounds do their best work early in the season, in June and early July, when the crab grass plants are small. They can be obtained in solution or as a dry spreader. The dry formulation can be applied with an ordinary fertilizer spreader. This material is poisonous, and the user must be very cautious in handling it. With repeated applications it has been used successfully to kill young crab grass, reduce disease attacks, and inhibit reinfestations. PMA mixed with other fungicides, particularly tersan, has been successful on putting greens. The two are mixed in solution so that each is applied at three-fourths the usual rate, and treatments are begun in late spring as dollarspot or crabgrass begin to grow.

Methyl arsenate: This compound was developed in 1955. From all indications it appears to offer to definite selectivity, and good cleanup of weedy grasses and crab grass. It may be particularly desirable for removing weeds infesting spring plantings, or emergency plantings made under adverse conditions. For golf course use, methyl arsenate may be used for smooth and hairy crab grass control on tees, aprons, and approaches. It has been used without damage on several selections of bentgrass under putting conditions in cool weather and may be used with caution on putting greens, with treatments repeated until the weedy plant is dead. It is manufactured as Sodar, Weedone L-850, Artox, Di-met, and Crab-E-Rad.

Information on chemical control of crabgrass was obtained from a report by Dr. W. H. Daniel, Turfgrass Specialist, Purdue University.

TABLE 2.6/CHARACTERISTICS, SEEDING RATES, AND PROPAGATION OF TURF GRASSES

Common and Scientific Names	Region	Purity per cent	Germination per cent	Seed per lb	Longevity[1]	Seeding rate per acre for meadows and pastures lb	Seeding Rate per 1000 sq ft for Lawns lb	Best Seeding Time	Vegetative Propagation			Best Planting Season
									Type of Material	Method of Planting	Quantity for 1000 sq ft	
Bermuda grass; Cynodon dactylon	II and III	97	85	1,787,000	1	6-8	1-2	Spring	Sprigs	In rows by hand or machine. Sprigs 6 in. apart in 12-in. rows.	5-10 sq ft of nursery sod	Warm humid spring, summer fall
Bent, Colonial; Agrostis tenuis	1(a), 1(b) IV	95	90	8,723,000	3	-	1-2	Fall, spring	Stolons	Broadcast on prepared seedbed.	80-100 sq ft of nursery sod	Early fall
Bent, Creeping; Agrostis palustris	1(a), 1(b) IV	95	90	7,800,000	3	-	1-2	Fall, spring				
Bent, Velvet; Agrostis canina	1(a), 1(b) IV	95	90	10,800,000	3	-	1-2	Fall, spring				
Bluegrass, Canada; Poa compressa	1(a), 1(b), IV	80	80	2,495,000	2	15-25	2-3	Fall, spring				
Bluegrass, Kentucky; Poa pratensis	1(a), 1(b), IV	85	80	2,177,000	2	15-25	3-5	Fall, spring				
Carpetgrass; Axonopus affinis	II and III	92	90	1,222,000	3	5-12	-	Spring, early summer				
Centipede grass; Eremochloa ophiuroides	III and Southern II	43	70	408,000	1	15-25	2-3	Spring	Sprigs	In rows by hand or machine	5-10 sq ft of nursery sod	Spring summer fall
Dallisgrass; Paspalum dilatatum	All	70	70	220,000	1	8-20	-	Spring				
Fescue, Chewings; Festuca rubra var. commutata	1(a), 1(b) and	97	80	615,000	2	15-40	2-3	Fall, spring				
Fescue, Creeping Red; Festuca rubra	Northern IV	97	80	615,000	2	15-40	2-3	Fall, spring				
Fescue, Meadow; Festuca elatior		97	90	230,000	2	10-25	-	Fall, spring				
Fescue, Sheep; Festuca ovina		96	85	680,000	2	15-25	-	Fall, spring				
Fescue, Tall (Ky. 31 and Alta); Festuca arundinacea		95	90	500,000	2	15-25	3-5	Fall spring				

TABLE 2.6/CHARACTERISTICS OF TURF GRASSES (cont.)

Common and Scientific Names	Region	Purity per cent	Germination per cent	Seed per lb	Longevity[1]	Seeding rate per acre for meadows and pastures lb	Seeding Rate per 1000 sq ft for Lawns lb	Best Seeding Time	Vegetative Propagation			
									Type of Material	Method of Planting	Quantity for 1000 sq ft	Best Planting Season
Manilagrass; Zoysia matrella	II and III	97	50	681,000	2	-	Vegetative	Spring, summer	2-in. sod blocks, sprigs	Sod blocks set 12-in. O.C. Sprigs 6-12-in. apart in 12-in. rows, or broadcast on prepared seedbed.	Sod block 30 sq ft Sprigs 3-6 sq ft of nursery sod.	Early summer
Mascarene grass; Zoysia tenuifolia	Southern	-	-	-	-	-	Vegetative	Spring, summer				
Japanese Lawngrass; Zoysia japonica	1 (a) and IV	-	24	1,300,000	2	-	Vegetative	Spring, summer				
Orchardgrass; Dactylis glomerata	All Regions	85	85	654,000	1	6-15	-	Spring early fall				
Red top; Agrostis alba		92	90	4,990,000	1	5-10	1-2	Fall, spring				
Ryegrass, Italian; Lolium multiflorum	All Regions	98	90	227,000	2	25-35	3-5	Fall.				
Ryegrass, Perennial; Lolium perenne		98	90	227,000	2	25-35	3-5	Fall, spring				
St. Augustine Grass; stenotaphrum secundatum	II and III	-	-	-	-	-	Vegetative	-	2-in. sod blocks, sprigs	Sod blocks set 12-in. O.C. Sprigs 6-12-in. apart in 12-in. rows or broadcast on prepared seedbed.	Sod block 30 sq ft Sprigs 3-6 sq ft of nursery sod.	Early summer
Timothy; Phleum pratense	All	99	90	1,230,000	2	6-12	-	Fall, spring				

TABLE 2.6/CHARACTERISTICS OF TURF GRASSES (cont.)

LEGUMES

Common and Scientific Names	Purity per cent	Viable Seed per cent	Seed per lb	Weight per Bu.—lb	Longevity[1]	Seeding rate per acre for meadows and pastures—lb	Seeding Rate per 1000 sq ft for Lawns—lb	Best Seeding Time
Alyceclover; Alysicarpus vaginalis	98	85	300,000	60	3	10-12	-	Fall, spring
Clover, Alsike; Trifolium hybridum	97	90[2]	700,000	60	3	6-8	-	Fall, spring
Clover, Crimson; Trifolium incarnatum	98	85	140,000	60	2	15-20	-	Fall (early)
Clover, Red; Trifolium pratense	98	90[2]	275,000	60	3	8-12	-	Fall, spring
Clover, White Dutch; Trifolium repens	96	90[2]	800,000	60	3	2-4	¼-½	Fall, spring
Lespedeza, Common; Var. Kobe - Lespedeza striata Var. Tenn. #76 -	97	90	190,000[3]	25[3]	1	10-15[3]	-	Spring
Lespedeza striata	96	90	310,000[3]	25[3]	1	8-10[3]	-	Spring
Lespedeza, Bicolor; Lespedeza bicolor	98	80[2]	82,000	60	2	1-2	-	Spring
Lespedeza, Korean; Lespedeza stipulacea	97	90	225,000[3]	40[3]	1	10-15[3]	-	Spring
Lespedeza, Sericea; Lespedeza cuneata	98	90[2]	250,000	60	2	10-15	-	Spring

NOTES:
1. "1" represents comparatively short-lived seed, "2" represents intermediate, and "3" represents long-lived seed.
2. Medium per cent of hard seed.
3. Unhulled.
4. Planted in rows 3—4 ft apart.

CHAPTER THREE

PLANTING

AND CARE

OF TREES AND SHRUBS

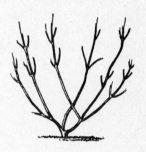

Adequate preparation of the soil before planting trees and shrubs reduces future maintenance problems. Ample depths of topsoil should be provided for shrubbery groups, and holes should be excavated and refilled for specimen trees. Generally the depth of topsoil required varies with the species of plant, but a good rule to follow is to provide a minimum of 12 in. for most deciduous shrubs, 18 in. for evergreen shrubs, and 24 in. for broad-leaved evergreen shrubs. Topsoil for individual trees will vary with the size of the tree and the size of the ball.

Competition for food, water, and sunlight sometimes prevents satisfactory growth of cultivated plants. If the competition is from weeds, the remedy is usually mulching and tillage. Weed control requires much more attention in new plantings than in old ones, because in the top growth of newly set plants there is less foliage to discourage weeds. In new plantings, too, the soil has been recently turned and disturbed and buried weed seeds have come to the surface; in older plantings, weeds generally come from other sources. Complete weed eradication each season for a few years, whether in new or old plantings, greatly reduces the amount of weed growth the following years.

Weed control with chemicals

Chemical control of weeds has improved rapidly the past few years. Most of the chemicals, however, are not adapted for use in and around shrubbery.

One material which has appeared recently and which is safe to use in shrub beds for the control of weeds is known as Crag Herbicide-1. This material eliminates annual broad-leaved and grass weeds by killing the seeds before they germinate. Weeds such as pigweeds, purslane, chickweed, and carpet-weed, and grasses such as crabgrass and foxtail are controlled for periods of from three to six weeks. Late summer applications help prevent fall and winter weeds such as chickweed.

This chemical is inactive until it reaches moist soil, where soil bacteria make it work. It will not harm plants if drift adheres to the leaves during spraying operations. Hard crusted soil should be worked so that this material can penetrate the soil. Also, if the soil is dry the area should be thoroughly watered. Grown weeds will not be killed by this type of herbicide.

TABLE 3.1/APPLICATION RATES FOR HERBICIDE-1

Soil types	Lb per acre of actual area sprayed
Light	2
Medium	3
Heavy	4

Table 3.1 shows application rates for Crag Herbicide-1 for various soil types. Use at least 30 gal of water per acre of ground actually treated. For small areas, use 5 level tablespoons per 1000 sq ft of ground sprayed in 10 gal of water. A good reason for using a material which will kill weeds before they germinate is that the labor formerly needed for hand weeding can now be used for more useful work, and its use saves time and money.

Later culture should not be neglected, but in humid climates plantings will be found to require very little care if the work has been well done the first three years. Plants collected from natural sources are likely to require special attention for a longer time than well-grown nursery plants, if both are handled with the same care.

CULTIVATION

The soil around trees and shrubs is cultivated to control and eliminate weeds, but this work does not seem to have any other value in stimulating plant growth. With small and newly planted trees and shrubs, cultivation may be the most convenient way to insure a good start, especially for the first two or three years. Once the plantings are established, continued tillage is seldom warranted on large public grounds, particularly in remote portions, or along highways.

Cultivated areas are spaded each year, thus bringing to the surface new, mellow soil not occupied by growing roots. Such deep working (to the same depth each year) is usually done in the spring; as the season progresses, cultivation should be gradually shallower. Such culture destroys the feeding roots that formed in the cultivated area the previous year, but does not disturb the carrier roots from which they came. If cultivation is omitted for a few years, however, these feeding roots grow into carrier roots with feeding roots mainly at their ends, so that if deep working of the soil is begun again many of the main roots will be destroyed. If cultivation must be resumed after such an interval, extra care is necessary not to prune the roots too severely. The injurious effects may be partially offset by a correspondingly severe pruning of the top at the same time.

When the need for deep cultivation makes it necessary to root-prune a plant severely, the best method is to divide the operation into two or three parts, spading to the desired depth part way around the plant one year and farther the next. Each section, as root-pruned, should be kept cultivated to the desired depth.

MULCHES

After plantings of trees and shrubs are thoroughly established, a mulch similar to a woodland ground cover is more satisfactory for weed control than cultivation, especially if the plants on the edges of the group have their lower branches close to the ground so that leaves that drop remain and decay. Leaves in sufficient quantity will develop a mulch worth more to the plants than constant clean cultivation. The combination of mulch and shade from the plants will keep down most weed growth; occasionally a few may need pulling. Such a mulch will provide as good a moisture-retaining cover to the soil as the best of culture, and the decaying leaves will supply fertility. It is often desirable to supplement leaves that drop from any tree or shrubbery group with other leaves or other mulching materials. New wood chipping machines made it possible to transform brush and small trees accumulated from cleanup operations into an excellent mulch material for all kinds of trees and shrubs.

Newly planted trees and shrubs are commonly cultivated for two or three years after planting, but frequently it is desirable from the start to control weed growth with mulch rather than by cultivation.

The most widely used materials for mulching are straw, strawy manure, cut cornstalks, leaves, litter, peat moss, wood chips, and cottonseed hulls. Sawdust, if well rotted, makes an excellent mulch for practically all types of planting. Mulching is essential for azaleas, rhododendron, mountain laurel, and other plants of the same family, and it is desirable for nearly all evergreens, both broad-leaved and coniferous, as well as for deciduous plants. These mulches are best maintained continuously from year to year, the leaf drop of each year being permitted to remain under the plants with material added to help maintain a sufficiently deep cover on the soil. Deciduous trees and shrubs should have at least 2 to 4 in. of mulch material; evergreens and broad-leaved evergreens do well with a mulch kept 4 to 6 in. deep.

WATERING

There are great differences in the needs of various plants for water and their tolerance of drought conditions, although all plants require large quantities in their life processes.

Watering is normally done with a hose, and often it is applied too rapidly to be efficient. Water should be applied so slowly that it does not run off, and should be continued long enough so that it penetrates at least 5 to 6 in. into the soil. The ideal way is to supply a small amount per minute, continuously for several hours. Whenever practicable, the ground should be covered with a mulch to keep artificially applied water from evaporating.

Clay soils should not require rewatering for at least a week, possibly three; gravelly soils may need watering twice a week. Water repeatedly applied in limited quantities penetrating only 2 or 3 in. may be injurious, since such watering will stimulate root growth towards the surface where a few days' drying will kill them. Less frequent but heavier watering stimulates deeper root growth where the moisture is likely to fluctuate less. Watering plants in groups, whether trees or shrubs, old plantations or new, is usually easier than watering single specimens, especially newly planted ones.

To make sure that the water penetrates deeply about newly planted specimens, the earth should be ridged about them to form a basin that will prevent the water from running off before it has an opportunity to soak into the soil. By refilling such a basin several times, water can be supplied to the maximum depth of root growth.

Trees growing in lawn areas are especially likely to suffer from lack of water. Where this occurs, both trees and turf reflect the need, the turf showing it first and recovering first. Here again, infrequent drenchings rather than frequent surface waterings give best results.

In areas where long periods of dry weather occur, efficient watering may be done by placing drain tile vertically in the soil, with the top even with the lawn level or slightly below it, so that there is no chance of the lawn mower's striking the top of the tile (See Fig. 3.1). The lower end should be 1 or 2 ft in the ground, depending on the character of the soil and the depth of the tree roots. Tiles 3 or 4 in. in diameter are usually used, although those 2 and 5 in. in diameter are sometimes preferred. No large roots should be cut in digging the holes for the tiles; if necessary the location of the holes may be shifted a little to avoid roots. If the bell end of the tile is placed upward, it

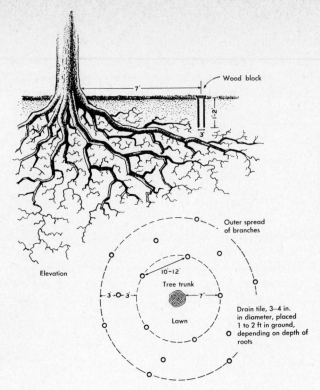

Wood block

7'

1-2'

3'

Outer spread
of branches

10'–12'

Tree trunk

3'–○–3'

7'

Lawn

Drain tile, 3–4 in.
in diameter, placed
1 to 2 ft in ground,
depending on depth of
roots

Elevation

Fig. 3.1 and 3.2
Method of watering
large trees in lawns
during extended peri-
ods of dry weather

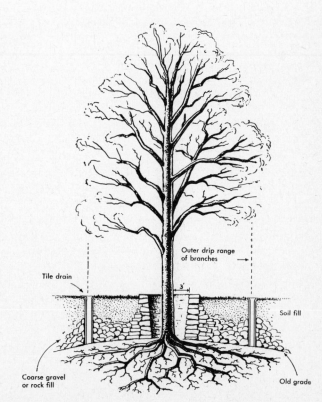

Outer drip range
of branches

Tile drain

3'

Soil fill

Coarse gravel
or rock fill

Old grade

will form a cup which may be closed with a block of wood when not in use. This block will prevent the hole from being filled with leaves and debris, and prevent people and animals from stepping into it. Filling the tile with coarse gravel or stone will serve the same purpose. Tiles should be placed 10 to 12 ft apart, beginning about 7 ft from the trunk of the tree and extending to the end of the branches for flat- or round-headed trees, and one and one-half times to twice the spread of the branches for upright ones.

Water should be run in a slow stream directly into the tiles, one at a time, until all have been filled, and the process repeated until the soil half way between the holes is thoroughly saturated.

The amount and frequency of watering must be determined by local conditions. A soil with a loose gravelly or sandy subsoil will require more frequent light waterings than one with a heavier subsoil. There is no advantage in putting water below the level where roots are growing. A stiff clay subsoil is nearly always the limit of root extension.

FERTILIZATION

Fertilizers should be so applied that growth is steady throughout a long season, but is finished before freezing weather comes. Unripened wood is more likely to be injured by cold than well-ripened wood, and even old wood may be killed by the advent of freezing weather before growth has stopped.

Organic matter

Organic matter is an important part of the soil, and is more likely to be deficient than are any of the other constituents necessary for plant growth. An abundance of such material will facilitate drainage, increase water-holding capacity, improve clay soils, and make sandy soils more retentive of moisture.

Heavy mulching, combined with the action of earthworms and burrowing insects, is the nearest approach to introducing organic matter into the soil after plantings have been established. Fresh manure is suitable for many plants, including the most vigorous deciduous trees and shrubs, such as oaks, maples, lilacs, and crepe myrtles. Cow manure produces the least heat of any of the more common manures, and is especially valuable for roses, lilacs, and plants that do not respond to heating manures or to an abundance of quickly available nitrogen. It produces its results more uniformly over a longer period.

Horse manure probably produces the most heat of the readily available manures; it should not be used about evergreens until it is composted. Sheep, chicken, and rabbit manures are all rich in nitrogen and should be used in moderation, as they may cause extra stimulation and produce soft growth or growth too late in the season. Compost is also good for deciduous shrubs, and it is the only manure that should be used about coniferous evergreens, including pines, spruces, junipers and arborvitae, and broad-leaved evergreens such as evergreen magnolias, camellias, hollies, and rhododendrons. With most of these it should be used only as a mulch and should not be worked into the soil.

Some other organic materials that can be purchased are prepared stockyard sheep and cattle manures, tankage, dried blood, fish scraps, sewage sludge, cottonseed meal, soybean meal, ground bone and steamed bone, and many brands of peat moss and humus. The degree and duration of nuisance should of course be considered in planning use of any natural fertilizer. Applications can be scheduled to avoid subjecting the public unnecessarily to unpleasant odors.

Preparation of composts

Composts are mixtures of manure and other organic matter which have become sufficiently rotted to break up readily and thus be easily worked into the soil. They are made by piling manure and litter together, and keeping the mound moist to prevent too rapid fermentation. The mound should be spaded over at intervals of 6 to 8 weeks during the summer, so that all parts decompose equally. Sods are often added to the pile in layers to add to its bulk and to produce a more friable compost.

A compost pile is made by placing in alternate layers manure, sod and loam, and repeating this process until the pile is as high as can be conveniently handled, usually from 3 to 5 ft. The top layer of the pile should be of soil, to catch any ammonia that might otherwise escape. The layers are thoroughly tamped and each one slightly dipped toward the middle, so that all the water will soak into the pile instead of running off. Add water whenever necessary to stimulate decomposition during hot and dry weather. It is not necessary to carry the composting so far when it is used as a top dressing as when it is worked into the soil. The addition of sulfate of ammonia and lime, superphosphates, and potash salts will benefit the compost and speed up decomposition. Leaves and garden trash and even household garbage can be successfully composted the same way. Diseased plants should not be composted.

To decompose 2000 lb of refuse in a pile $10 \times 10 \times 6$ ft requires one of the following:

60 lb of sulphate of ammonia at rate of 5 lb every 6 in. lift, or
60 lb of lime at rate of of $4\frac{1}{6}$ lb every 6 in. lift, or
30 lb of superphosphate at rate of $2\frac{1}{2}$ lb every 6 in. lift, or
25 lb of potash at rate of 2 lb every 6 in. lift.

Smaller quantities of refuse and a smaller pile will require proportionately less of the above chemicals. Other chemicals such as calcium cyanamid and commercial mixtures are especially prepared to do the job of decomposition in shorter periods of time. Manufacturers' instructions should be implicitly followed.

Prepared Fertilizers

Most of our soils require the addition of complete plant foods to produce good growth. Fertilizers containing nitrogen, phosphate, and potash are usually sufficient, although it is advisable to take periodic soil tests to determine the amount and kind of fertilizers to use. See Table 3.2.

TABLE 3.2/SAFE QUANTITIES OF FERTILIZERS

	Lb per acre	Sq ft covered by 1–2 lb
Phosphate potash ash	200–400	200
Triple superphosphate	200	200
Nitrate of soda	50	800
Sulfate of ammonia	50	800
Superphosphate (16%)	500	80
Sheep manure	4000	10
Dried cattle manure	4000	10
Cottonseed meal	2000	20
Bone meal	2000	20
Soybean meal	2000	20
Dried blood, tankage, and fish scraps	1000	40

For all trees and shrubs, fertilizer should be applied as close as possible to the feeder roots, but away from the trunk to avoid injury to the plant. On small trees, fertilizer should be applied in a circle approximately 1½ ft beyond the spread of the overhead branches and thoroughly worked into the soil to a depth of about 10 in.

After fertilizer is applied, the ground should be watered thoroughly, to soak the fertilizer into the ground. Well established and older trees, particularly those in picnic or other public use areas, should also be fertilized regularly; however, the fertilizer must penetrate deeper into the soil than for small trees, in order to reach the proper roots. This may be accomplished by drilling or digging a staggered arrangement of holes along the outer drip range of the overhead branches, depositing the proper amount of fertilizer, backfilling with soil and/or mulch, and watering if necessary. The holes should be approximately 1½ to 2 ft deep.

Fertilizer should normally be supplied to trees or shrubbery in late winter or early spring, up to June 1 at the latest; however, fall applications are also valuable. Applications during the hot summer months are likely to be harmful to the plant unless the material is used in smaller amounts and thoroughly dissolved by artificial watering. A new high nitrogen fertilizer (Uramite) has been developed which can be applied safely at any time without danger of burning the plant.

TABLE 3.3/COMPOSITION OF FERTILIZER MATERIALS

Materials Supplying:	N (Nitrogen)	P (Phos.)	K (Potassium)	Availability
	Per cent			
Nitrogen				
Ammonium nitrate	30	0	0	Quick
Calcium cyanamide	22	0	0	Medium
Cal-Nitro	16–20.5	0	0	Quick
Cottonseed meal	6.5–7.5	1.5–2	2–3	Slow
Concentrated tankage	11–12.5	1–2	0	Medium
Dried blood, high grade	12–16	0	0	Medium
Dried blood, low grade	10–11	3–5	0	Medium
Dried fish scrap	7–10	6–8	0	Slow
Leuna saltpeter	26	0	0	Quick
Nitrate of soda	16	0	0	Quick
Sulfate of ammonia	20	0	0	Quick
Tankage	5–6	11–14	0	Slow
Uramon	42	0	0	Quick
Phosphoric Acid				
Basic slag	0	13–18	0	Quick
Calcium metaphosphate	0	60–64	0	Quick
Fused rock phosphate	0	28–30	0	Quick
Ground bone (raw)	2.5–4	20–25	0	Very slow
Potassium metaphosphate	0	60	30	Quick
Raw rock phosphate	0	26–35	0	Very slow
Steamed bone meal	1–2.5	22–30	0	Medium
Superphosphate	0	16–20	0	Quick
Triple superphosphate	0	40–50	0	Quick
Potash				
Kainite	0	0	12–20	Quick
Muriate of potash	0	0	50–62.5	Quick
Potassium nitrate	13	0	46	Quick
Sulfate of potash	0	0	48–52	Quick
Sulfate of potash mg	0	0	25	Quick
Tobacco stems	2–4	.5–1.5	4.9–9	Medium
Wood ashes	0	1–2	2–8	Medium

Table 3.4 shows formulae for compounding one ton of fertilizer from materials of known composition. In using this table, look in the first column for the percentage content of the material used and in the first horizontal row for the percentage wanted; the figure at the point where the two lines intersect will represent the amount of the material to use in making a ton of the mixture wanted.

Example: Wanted, a mixture containing 4 per cent nitrogen, 12 per cent phosphoric acid, and 4 per cent potash. The following materials are to be

TABLE 3.4/FORMULAE FOR COMPOUNDING 1 TON OF FERTILIZER FROM MATERIALS OF KNOWN COMPOSITION

Percentage of material used	Desired percentage of chemical in final mixture — Amount of material needed (lb)														
	1	2	3	4	5	6	7	8	9	10	11	12	14	16	20
2	1000	2000													
3	667	1334	2000												
4	500	1000	1500	2000											
5	400	600	1000	1600	2000										
6	333	667	1000	1333	1667	2000									
7	286	572	858	1144	1430	1716	2000								
8	250	500	750	1000	1250	1500	1750	2000							
9	222	444	667	889	1111	1334	1556	1778	2000						
10	200	400	600	800	1000	1200	1400	1600	1800	2000					
11	182	364	546	728	910	1092	1274	1456	1638	1820	2000				
12	166	333	500	667	833	1000	1167	1334	1500	1666	1833	2000			
13	154	308	462	616	769	924	1077	1232	1384	1538	1692	1845			
14	143	286	430	570	715	860	1000	1143	1286	1430	1570	1715	2000		
15	133	267	400	533	667	800	933	1067	1200	1333	1467	1600	1867		
16	125	250	376	500	625	750	875	1000	1125	1250	1375	1500	1750	2000	
17	118	235	353	470	588	706	824	940	1059	1176	1294	1410	1647	1882	
18	111	222	333	444	556	667	778	889	1000	1111	1222	1333	1556	1778	
19	105	210	316	421	526	631	737	842	947	1053	1158	1263	1474	1684	
20	100	200	300	400	500	600	700	800	900	1000	1100	1200	1400	1600	2000
21	95	190	285	381	476	571	667	762	857	952	1047	1142	1333	1524	1905
22	91	182	273	364	455	546	636	727	818	909	1000	1091	1273	1455	1818
23	87	174	261	348	435	522	609	696	783	870	957	1044	1217	1391	1739
24	83	166	249	332	422	500	583	666	749	835	917	1000	1167	1333	1667
25	80	160	240	320	400	480	560	640	720	800	880	960	1120	1280	1600
47	43	86	127	170	212	253	298	340	383	425	468	511	596	681	851
48	42	84	125	168	208	250	294	336	375	417	458	500	583	667	833
50	40	80	120	160	200	240	280	320	360	400	440	480	560	640	800

76

TABLE 3.5/QUANTITIES OF CHEMICALS TO USE FOR COMPOSTING

Straw or other refuse	Dimensions (ft) of pile 6 ft high	Quantities for pile				Quantities for 6-in. layers			
		Sulfate of ammonia (lb)	Lime (lb)	Super-phosphate (lb)	Potash (lb)	Sulfate of ammonia (lb)	Lime (lb)	Super-phosphate (lb)	Potash (lb)
First formula:									
1 ton	10 × 10	60	60	30	25	5	4–1/6	2–1/2	2
1/2 ton	7 × 7	30	25	15	12–1/2	2–1/2	2	1–1/4	1
1/6 ton	4 × 4	10	8–1/2	5	4–1/6	5/6	2/3	5/12	1/3
Second formula:									
1 ton	10 × 10	80	60	30	–	6–2/3	5	–	2–1/2
1/2 ton	7 × 7	40	30	15	–	3–1/3	2–1/2	–	1–1/4
1/6 ton	4 × 4	13–1/3	10	5	–	1–1/9	5/6	–	1/2

used: 16 per cent nitrate of soda, 20 per cent superphosphate, and 50 per cent muriate of potash. Proceed thus: As the nitrate contains 16 per cent, find 16 in the first column and follow across to column headed 4; the number 500 at the intersection is the weight in pounds of 16 per cent nitrate of soda required. In like manner for phosphoric acid, follow row 20 to column 12, and 1200 is the weight of 20 per cent superphosphate required. For potash, follow row 50 to column 4, and 160 is the weight in pounds of 50 per cent muriate of potash required. We have thus—nitrate of soda, 500 lb, 20 per cent superphosphate, 1200 lb, and 50 per cent muriate of potash, 160 lb, making a total of 1,860 lb. By adding 140 lb of limestone or sand (filler) we have 2,000 lb of 4–12–4 fertilizer.

Time to plant

The time to plant varies with the section of the country. In the South the best time to do most planting is in the fall, from November 1 to January 1. Broad-leaved evergreens are best transplanted in the spring. In the North, planting has been done successfully in both fall and spring. Planting with a ball of earth can be done all summer if the leaves and stem are treated with a plastic spray. The essential point to remember is to provide the plant with adequate amounts of water after planting so that the root system can survive without drying out.

SOIL ACIDITY

Besides differing in fertility and water-holding capacity, soils differ in acidity. Some are neutral, some acid, and still others are alkaline. The acidity of soil may be changed for the benefit of plants requiring it. Lime is the standard material for making acid soils alkaline. Hydrated lime, finely ground limestone, and wood ashes are used in quantities less than sufficient to neutralize soil acidity. Where soil tests indicate that 8 tons or more of lime per acre would be required to neutralize the soil, often only one ton, or even one-half ton per acre (or 1 lb to 20 or 40 sq ft) is used, and seems to produce satisfactory results.

To make soil more acid in as short a time as possible, as required for rhododendrons, azaleas, and laurel, it is possible to use aluminum sulfate at a rate up to 1 lb for 20 sq ft. It is not advisable to use this treatment over an extended period of time. For most acid soil plants, however, it is better to provide acidity with a mulch. In order to produce the desired effect the mulch must remain about the plants and rot; acidity is not produced until the material is partially decayed, about the second year. Soil acidity can also be maintained by addition of powdered sulfur, as shown in Table 3.6.

TABLE 3.6/USE OF POWDERED SULFUR TO MAINTAIN SOIL ACIDITY

Condition of soil	Lb powdered sulfur per 100 sq ft
Medium acid (pH 5.5 to 6.0)	2
Slightly acid (pH 6.0 to 7.0)	4
Slightly alkaline (pH 7.0 to 7.5)	7
Strongly alkaline (pH 7.5 to 8.0)	unsuitable

PRUNING

Prune trees at the time of planting to insure well-developed framework and to reduce top growth to compensate for roots lost in moving. Do not cut back vigorous trees that were thoroughly thinned out at the time of planting. Cutting back the branches removes a year or more of growth and gives trees a formal shape until the condition is outgrown.

Prune new trees before setting them in the hole, to save time and trouble. The chance to use hand tools, which cut closer than the pole pruners needed for trees in an upright position, is one of the advantages. Start at the top of the tree and work down; remove closely parallel branches, crossing and broken limbs, and superfluous growth at the base of the main branches.

Fig. 3.3   Removal of limbs and stubs

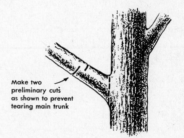

Make two preliminary cuts as shown to prevent tearing main trunk

Method of removing large limb. Final cut is made along dotted line to allow tree to heal over wound.

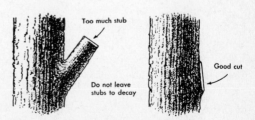

Too much stub

Do not leave stubs to decay

Good cut

Correct and incorrect method of removing branch stubs.

Cutting branches: When removing a branch, make the cut flush with the branch. Any remaining stub may decay and permanently injure the tree, since the healing callus cannot close over it. For the same reason, cut close to a bud when cutting back a branch, so as not to leave a stub. All pruning wounds over 1 in. in diameter should be painted with a tree-wound compound to retard checking and decay of the exposed wood.

Cutting leaders: When pruning, do not cut back central leaders (main stalks or trunks). When the terminal bud is removed, the one nearest the cut becomes the terminal bud, and on trees with opposite buds, each bud produces a shoot that competes with the other, and a structurally weak double-leader tree results. Cutting back the leader always flattens the top and stunts the tree.

Pruning existing trees

Large trees should be pruned only by experienced climbers. Each should be equipped with 125 ft of ½-in. rope having a bowline knot in one end. The climber passes the bowline through a stout crotch and around his thighs, using the loose end, or tail, of the bowline to tie a taut-line hitch in the rope leading to the ground (see Fig. 3.19). The climber is free to work with both hands, and can swing back to the trunk without injury if a limb should snap. A ground man should always work with a climber to tie needed tools to the rope and to keep it free of brush. When pruning is done on street trees, the ground man must keep the climber's rope out of the road where it might cause a serious accident.

Pruning large trees from extension ladders is hazardous. Satisfactory work cannot be done because pole saws and pole pruners must be used instead of hand tools. New and more satisfactory methods have been devised using hydraulic lift platforms (Fig. 4.27) from which the treeman can prune high off the ground with perfect safety. These platforms are equipped with pneumatic power tools for easier pruning.

Procedure

Prune large trees by working from the top down. Prune each large branch individually. Remove crossing limbs, broken branches, and superfluous growth next to the tree to admit sunlight and air circulation; this helps to control insects and diseases. Paint all pruning cuts with a good tree-wound compound immediately.

To remove large, dead, or broken branches, make three saw cuts to prevent ripping the bark of the tree trunk (Fig. 3.3). Start the first cut on the under side of the limb about one foot from the trunk, and saw through one-third of the branch. Start the second cut on top of the branch, about 3 in. behind the bottom cut, sawing until the branch splits off at the parallel point of the two cuts. Saw off the stub flush with the trunk to allow the wound to heal, and paint with tree-wound compound.

Bark tracings

Treat bark abrasions on tree trunks promptly to permit rapid healing of the wound and to prevent decay. See Fig. 3.4 and 3.5.

Tools and material

A sharp curved-blade pruning knife and a half-inch paint brush are needed. If the bark is thick, a sharp wood chisel and light mallet are used to cut it. Small quantities of shellac and tree wound paint are also required.

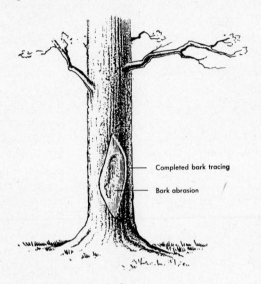

Completed bark tracing

Bark abrasion

Fig. 3.4   Bark tracing of abrasion on trunk of tree

FOR TWO INJURIES
CLOSE TOGETHER
MAKE ONE TRACING

Fig. 3.5   Bark tracing

PLANTING AND CARE OF TREES AND SHRUBS

Procedure

Determine the extent of injury and carefully remove all loose bark. Start the bark tracing in sound bark above the injury, and work knife or chisel down on a slight curve to one side of it, removing all sprung bark. Hold chisel at a slight angle away from the injury, with beveled edge toward the sound bark. Shellac the exposed edge of bark as tracing progresses, to prevent drying. Continue tracing downward until distances above and below the center of the injury are equal, and then repeat the procedure on the opposite side of the injury. Apply a second coat of shellac to exposed bark edge, and paint the exposed wood with a tree-wound compound.

The top and bottom points of the tracing must be established on the center line of the injury to permit uniform healing. The healing callus does not develop on the lower side of a bark tracing made on an angle.

When two small injuries are close together (Fig. 3.5), make one bark tracing, because the thin strip of bark between two abrasions dries out and tracing must be repeated.

Pruning shrubs

When transplanting deciduous shrubs, remove part of the woody growth in order to compensate for partial loss of the root system. Shrubs pruned when planted recover and regain natural shape more quickly than unpruned plants. In general, prune away about one-third of the top growth. Shrubs produce new growth near the base of the plant while trees grow from the ends of the branches. Tree trunks do not grow upward; a nail driven 3 ft above the ground always remains at that height. Vigorous, established shrubs do not have to be pruned unless they have outgrown their location to block sunlight from buildings, or interfere with walks.

Pruning new shrubs

Prune all newly planted deciduous shrubs according to their natural habit of growth. Do not shear them uniformly, because varieties are usually chosen for their contrasting growth habits. Shearing produces a formal shape, destroys the plant's identity, and is monotonous and unsightly. Cut heavy canes at a greater height from the ground than smaller canes.

Pruning established shrubs

Prune old, oversized shrubs by cutting the heavy canes back to the ground so that new shoots grow from the base of the plant. Unsightly shrubs can be reclaimed by this method. When a shrub consists entirely of old, heavy canes, remove only half of the canes the first year to avoid the undesirable brush-like effect of a mass of stiff stalks.

Prune such shrubs as forsythia immediately after flowering, to prevent the following year's bloom from being destroyed. Prune fruiting types before and after they bloom in early spring or in the fall. Shrubs pruned severely in the late fall have a dehorned appearance all winter.

Hedges

There is a right and wrong method to trim a formal hedge. The usual tendency is to prune the sides, gradually sloping inward until the top is considerably broader than the base. Such pruning will cut off all sunlight from the lower branches, thereby causing the plant to become thin at the base with a heavy leaf crown supported by a few open stems. See Fig. 3.6.

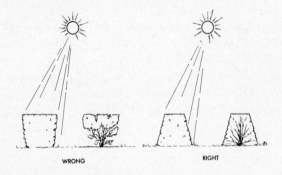

WRONG   RIGHT

Fig. 3.6   Right and wrong methods of hedge pruning

The proper method of pruning is to keep the top narrower than the base, with the sides sloping outward. This method takes advantage of full sunlight from top to bottom, thereby maintaining the whole hedge compact and dense.

Following are suggestions for pruning the most common shrubs. The number following the common name of the plant refers to its botanical name found in the master list on pages 152–158.

Abelia (1) Remove old flower-heads and thin the plant out occasionally. The shrub needs no regular pruning.

Azalea; see Rhododendron.

Barberry (25–29) Most of the common species do not require regular pruning. It may be necessary to remove dead wood in old stock.

Bayberry (175) No formal pruning necessary.

Beautyberry (34–36) These shrubs should be thinned out when necessary, retaining as much young wood as possible through shortening the points or tips.

Boxwood (33) No regular pruning is necessary. Hedge effects may be cut during the summer.

Buckthorn (219–220) No special pruning required.

Cotoneaster (68–76) No special pruning required.

Dogwood (52–63) Can be successfully grown without specific pruning. Overgrown plants may be cut back severely without injury, and the many kinds grown for the colored bark may be cut to the ground in the spring.

Daphne (81) No special pruning required.

Deutzia (82–85) Should be thinned out well once in three years by removing as much of the old wood as possible. The best time for pruning is in early summer, after flowering period is over.

Eleagnus (87–89) Does not require regular pruning except to curb straggling habits of growth by shortening the longest shoots during the summer. Green-leaved shoots that often appear among the variegated varieties should be removed as soon as they are observed.

Euonymus (90–100) Most of the species need no pruning. The evergreen burningbush (*Euonymus japonica*) requires a little shaping when grown as a shrub, but treated as a hedge it should be clipped once or twice during the summer. The wintercreeper (*Euonymus radicans*), grown normally as ground cover under trees or as a border for shrub beds, should be trimmed or cut over either in spring or summer.

Forsythia (103) Special pruning is not necessary except for thinning out every third year, or the shrubs may be clipped moderately each year as soon as the flowering period is over. When Forsythia is grown as a bush, the main branches should be cut back to the same height each year. This method stimulates the formation during the summer of long shoots which will be in full bloom from end to end the following spring.

Hawthorn (77–80) No special pruning required.

Holly (122–129) Do not clip back the shoots, since they are naturally stiff and erect; instead, clean out some of the laterals of the shoots to accentuate them. Holly hedges may be clipped back at the middle or end of summer.

Honeysuckle, bush (161–164) The true shrub species should be thinned out every three to four years. If overgrown, the longer shoots should be cut back, in summer, if possible and not every year. The climbing species requires very little formal pruning if the plants have room to develop, but if they are growing under restricted conditions they may be cut after the flowering period.

Ivy (112) Grown in the form of a bush, ivy may require a little shaping each year, merely removal of a branch here and there. Old plants may be invigorated by cutting back in spring. Where it is grown against walls, ivy should be cut back as close as possible to the walls in February or March. On the sides of buildings, cut back the upper shoots well below the roof or gutters. Also examine and cut the plants toward the beginning of July, removing long shoots that are protruding away from the wall.

Jasmine (131–132) The bushy species requires occasional thinning, but no other formal treatment. The winter jasmine (*Jasminum nudiflorum*) and the primrose jasmine (*Jasminum primulinum*) should have the flowering shoots cut back to within two buds of the base as soon as the flowers fade, but no further pruning should follow.

Laurel (143) This species has no need of formal pruning.

Leucothoe (150) Plants treated as shrubs should have their older stems removed and the younger shoots shortened in late February before the spring season starts. Shrubs grown for the color effect of their bright green barks should be cut close to the ground in March.

Locust (108–109 and 233) The shrubby locusts should be cut back a little in summer to prevent branches from becoming too long and rank.

Lilac (269–276) If the plants are flowering freely, no regular pruning is needed. If flowers are sparse, and growth is weak, thin out the branches in April, removing some of the inside wood and weak shoots. Inspect shrubs again early in June, and remove weaker shoots. All new growth should be removed from the base of the plant at least once a year.

Magnolia (165) The shrubby species does not require regular pruning.

Mock orange (183–184) This shrub needs no formal pruning, and in fact does best if left untouched; it may be thinned out a little at intervals of a few years.

Privet (151–157) Shrubs need no special pruning; hedges should be clipped several times during the summer.

Periwinkle (326) Formal pruning is not necessary, though the bigleaf periwinkle may be cut back occasionally.

Quince (45) When grown as a bush, quince requires no pruning. If grown as a hedge, it may be cut back when the flowering period is over.

Redbud (43–44) Shape the plants when young, but prune as little as possible when plant is mature. Remove only dead wood as plant matures.

Rhododendron (221–222) Needs no regular pruning except for the removal of the flower heads as soon as the flower fades. However, young plants should be clipped occasionally to induce sturdy growth. Overgrown plants that are old may be cut back severely without serious injury. Such cutting should be done in March or April.

Rose (234–243) Ramblers and climbers should have all the old flowering canes removed as soon as the flowers fade. Bush roses should have all weak wood removed, and vigorous young canes from the root should be encouraged. This general pruning is best done in March.

Shadblow (15) No specific pruning is necessary.

Sweetshrub (37) No specific pruning is necessary.

Spurge, Japanese (180) No specific pruning is necessary.

Sumac (225–231) When sumac is grown for the large compound leaves and autumn coloration, the young shoots must be cut down to within a few inches of the ground in February or early March. If the plants are grown for shrubbery or mass effects no special pruning is required.

Spirea (253–259) Needs very little pruning. The Thunberg spirea (*Spiraea thunbergi*) and some others may be slightly "winter killed" on the tips; such injured shoots should be removed.

Snowball (318) No special pruning is necessary.

Witch-hazel (111) Prune only to shape the plants, particularly when they are young; older plants have no need for further formal pruning.

Willows (244) If they are grown for colored bark effects, cut willows back in February; otherwise no regular pruning is required.

PLANTING METHODS

Dig the pits for trees and shrubs before the plants arrive, so that the plants are out of the ground no longer than necessary. Large sized balled and bur-lapped plants should be placed in the holes directly from the truck.

If the plants are left out of the ground for a few days, cover the balls of earth with soil to prevent the roots near the surface from drying out. Cover the roots of all bare-root trees and shrubs with wet burlap or similar material as soon as they are unloaded, if planting is to take place within a few hours.

Heel in all other bare-root trees and shrubs at once in a trench deep enough to accommodate the roots of the plants. Place them at a 45 degree angle, and cover the roots with soil or sawdust to prevent drying. When shrubs or trees are delivered in bundles, keep the bundles intact to facilitate future handling. Avoid injury to plants by rough treatment. When removing plants from the heeling-in trench, uncover roots carefully. Do not grasp the top of the plants and pull them out of the trench without removing the covering soil. Locate the heeling-in ground as near the final planting site as possible, preferably where water is available. Water heeled-in stock periodically, if the plants are to stay in the trench longer than normal. Do not wash the soil away from the roots when watering.

Planting Pits

In digging planting pits for trees, separate the soil into three piles: sod, topsoil, and subsoil. Use the salvaged sod elsewhere to repair grassed areas. Arrange the piles to keep open the side of the pit from which the tree will be placed.

The planting pits should be dug wide enough to accommodate all roots without crowding or twisting. Dig tree pits at least 1 ft wider than the spread of roots or ball of earth. Prepare all planting pits with straight sides. Dig tree pits just deep enough to allow for a 6 in. cushion of topsoil in the bottom and to permit the top of the ball to be flush with the existing grade. Deeper planting hinders air from reaching the roots and may kill the tree. Shape the pit bottom with the center slightly raised for proper drainage. Place about 6 in. of compacted topsoil in the bottom of the pit.

Setting plants

If the tree is delivered on a platform, tip the ball on its side by pushing against the ball after it is set in the hole. Do not crack or damage the earth ball. Cut the ropes holding the platform and remove the platform from the pit. Carefully right the tree by lifting against the ball. Cut the rope lacing, and cut away as much burlap wrapping as possible. Leave the burlap in place under the ball, because it helps to hold the ball together and will soon disintegrate in the soil. To prevent crumbling, do not cut rope lacing while the tree is tipped. Placing trees and shrubs without a platform follows the same general procedure. The plant is set directly into the pit, with a minimum of movement after it reaches its final level.

Set all plants plumb before backfilling. Avoid straightening trees or shrubs after the backfill has been placed. Damage to plants may result from air pockets formed under the roots when the tree or shrub is moved. See Fig. 3.7.

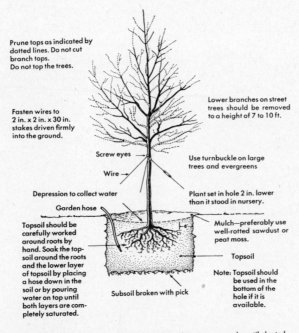

Prune tops as indicated by dotted lines. Do not cut branch tops. Do not top the trees.

Fasten wires to 2 in. x 2 in. x 30 in. stakes driven firmly into the ground.

Lower branches on street trees should be removed to a height of 7 to 10 ft.

Screw eyes

Use turnbuckle on large trees and evergreens

Wire →

Depression to collect water

Plant set in hole 2 in. lower than it stood in nursery.

Garden hose

Topsoil should be carefully worked around roots by hand. Soak the topsoil around the roots and the lower layer of topsoil by placing a hose down in the soil or by pouring water on top until both layers are completely saturated.

Mulch—preferably use well-rotted sawdust or peat moss.

Topsoil

Note: Topsoil should be used in the bottom of the hole if it is available.

Subsoil broken with pick

Note: Keep roots covered with moist soil, wet packing, or wet sacks until planted.

The same general principles as are indicated in the above drawing will apply to transplanted shrubs that are not balled and burlapped.

Fig. 3.7   Method of planting bare root trees and shrubs

Backfill the space between the ball and the side of the planting pit with good loam topsoil. Work soil under the ball to eliminate air pockets. Place backfill in 6-in layers, using the salvaged topsoil. Firm each layer by tamping until the pit is half filled. If the soil is wet, use a light wood tamper to avoid heavy compaction, which reduces air spaces too much. It is always best to avoid using wet soil. If the soil is reasonably dry, fill the top-half of the pit with water to settle the backfilled soil. Allow the water to be absorbed and fill the remainder of the planting pit with topsoil, tamping lightly as it is filled. Settle the soil with water to prevent tight compaction. See Fig. 3.8.

Bare-root plants

Before setting bare-root trees and shrubs, shape the bottom of the pit so that the center of the pit is slightly higher than the sides, forming an inverted

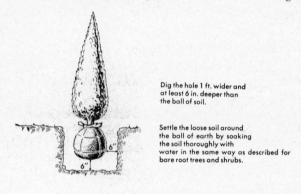

Dig the hole 1 ft. wider and at least 6 in. deeper than the ball of soil.

Settle the loose soil around the ball of earth by soaking the soil thoroughly with water in the same way as described for bare root trees and shrubs.

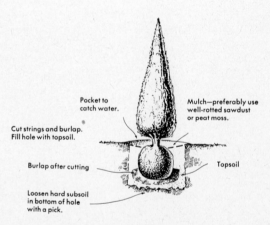

Pocket to catch water.

Mulch—preferably use well-rotted sawdust or peat moss.

Cut strings and burlap. Fill hole with topsoil.

Burlap after cutting

Topsoil

Loosen hard subsoil in bottom of hole with a pick.

Fig. 3.8 Method of planting balled and burlapped trees and shrubs

GROUNDS MAINTENANCE HANDBOOK

cone. The plant should then be set on this cone so that the center of the plant is resting on the highest portion, and the roots are carefully spread out along the sides. Prune all broken roots before backfilling. Plumb the plant so that it is standing straight, and hold it in place by backfilling enough topsoil to cover the roots. Add water until the soil becomes a thick liquid. Gently raise and lower the plant to allow the soil to fill between the fibrous roots. Continue adding soil and water until the planting pit is filled to grade. It is not a good idea to do too much tamping on bare-root plants for fear of damaging the roots.

Settlement: After the water has drained away, check all planting pits for settlement and add enough soil to bring them up to grade, keeping the surface sloped slightly toward the tree.

Earth ring: If planting is done in the spring, make an earth ring about 3 in. high around the plant. This ring should vary in size with the size of the plant. A good rule of thumb to follow in determining the diameter of the ring is to make the ring extend to the outer edge of the spread of the branches. Omit earth rings around trees and shrubs planted in the late fall; level all existing rings in the fall, because water collecting inside the rings may freeze the plants.

Dry planting: If water is not available at planting time, carefully work the loose soil around the roots by raising and lowering the tree or shrub slightly. Cover the roots with soil, backfill, and tamp the topsoil in 6-in. layers.

Vines

Plant field-grown vines by digging individual soil pockets wide enough to hold the roots without crowding. Place about 2 in. of topsoil under the plant. Firm the soil around the roots until the planting pocket is filled.

Remove pot-grown vines from the containers carefully to avoid breaking the soil around the roots. Set 2- to 3-in. pot-grown vines in planting pockets about 6-in. wide; proceed as in planting field-grown vines.

Planting broad-leaved evergreens in limestone regions

Normally it is not a good practice to plant acid-loving plants such as the azaleas, rhododendrons, laurel, andromedas, etc. in soils which are high in lime or have pH readings above 5.0. However, it has been done successfully by following these rules:

a. Do not set plants in individual holes, but first excavate the entire bed to a depth of 2 ft.

b. Fill excavation with water to test for drainage. If the water drains away within 2 to 3 hours no further measures need be taken. If, however, the water continues to stand in the hole for periods up to 12 to 24 hours, a

French drain should be dug. Broad-leaved evergreens will not stand poor drainage situations.

c. Place 4 lb. powdered sulfur per 1000 sq ft of area in the bottom of this excavation.

d. Backfill with composted oak leaves or acid peat moss. Bring backfill to top of excavation and settle thoroughly by watering.

e. Place the plant on top of the backfill and fill around it with acid peat moss or composted oak leaves. Do not hesitate to bring the backfill well up into the plant a foot or more. This type of plant thrives in deep mulches and likes to keep its roots cool.

f. Replenish the mulch each year. It is essential to maintain this mulch at least a foot deep at all times.

g. It usually is not necessary to anchor the plants when they are planted in groups. Single plants can be staked with one stake.

Staking and guying

Stake or guy all trees and treelike shrubs immediately after planting. Unless they are staked or guyed at once, newly planted balled and burlapped trees are loosened from the ball by the wind; both bare-root and balled and burlapped plants may be pushed out of alignment, and need to be pulled back to a vertical position. If a tree is straightened after planting, not only may air pockets be formed around the roots, but all the strain will be placed on one stake or guy wire. Keep tension on all stakes or guy wires equal. Do not use guy wires where pedestrians may trip over them.

Staking street trees

Stake street trees up to 3-in. caliper with two stakes on opposite sides of the tree, about 18 in. from the trunk and parallel to the curb. Use cedar stakes with the bark attached, if available. Select stakes 8 ft long with a diameter of about 2 in. at the top and about 3 in. at the butt. Stakes must be this long in order to provide the proper stiffening to the tree at least one quarter of the way up the trunk. Drive the stakes 3 ft deep at a slight angle away from the tree.

Stake street trees of 4- to 5-in. caliper with four stakes 10 ft long, driven 4 ft into the ground. Place the stakes in box formation at equal distances 18 in. from the tree.

Place scrap rubber hose, 1 to 2 in. in diameter, around the tree trunk near the top of the stakes to prevent damage to bark by supporting wires. If scrap rubber hose is not available, use fairly thick cloth wrappings, or laths cut 6 in. long, where the wire makes contact with the tree.

Use 12-gage wire between the stakes and the tree. Cut the wire in proper lengths and draw it through the rubber hose or around the protective collar until the cut ends meet. Pull the ends of the wire around the stake near the top until taut. Wrap the cut ends around the stake and twist them together on the inside of the stake. Secure tree to the second stake in the same way. To give added tension, insert a stick between the strands of double wire and twist until the wire is tight.

Staking shrubs and small trees

Stake treelike shrubs and small trees with single stakes placed on the side toward the prevailing winds. Set the stake about 1 ft from the trunk and about 2 ft deep. When planting bare-root stock, drive the stake before setting the plant to prevent injury to the roots. Use scrap rubber hose and 12-gage wire as described above. If half-inch rope is used instead of wire and hose, cross the rope between stake and tree, wrap loose ends around the stake, and tie in place with a square knot.

Guying

In nontraffic areas, guy trees up to 4-in. caliper from three directions (Fig. 3.9). Drive three equally spaced 4-ft stakes of cedar or scrap lumber around

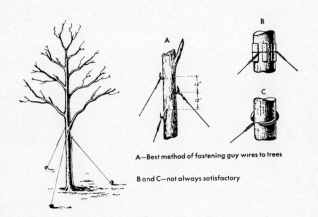

A—Best method of fastening guy wires to trees

B and C—not always satisfactory

Fig. 3.9 Method of bracing trees

the tree outside the planting pit. Place the stakes so that guy wires will not interfere with the lower limbs. Notch the stakes near the top on the side away from the tree and drive them to within 6 in. of the top at a slight angle away from the tree. Place scrap rubber hose or protective collar around the trunk, about 6 ft from the ground. Another method is to screw small but heavy lag screws with a hook into the trunk of the tree. The guy wires can be fastened to these hooks without damage to the tree. After the tree has become firmly anchored and fully established, remove guy wires and lag screw hooks from the tree. The holes left by the screws should be treated with a good tree wound paint and filled with wood putty.

If the protective collar method is used, put the wrapping slightly above the lower limbs for street trees. Run a single strand of wire through or around the protective collar and back to the stake. Cut the wire free from the coil, allowing enough slack to fasten the wires securely and to permit driving the stake below the ground level. Repeat for the other two stakes. Get the same tension on all guys to give proper alignment. If the tree settles, tighten the guys by driving the stakes deeper or inserting a stick between the two strands of wire and twisting until the wire is tight.

Guy 5-in. caliper trees with two double strands of 12-gage wire attached to three 2- by 4-in. stakes, 4 ft long, in the method shown (Fig 3.9) for 2- to 3-in. caliper trees.

Remove identification tags and labels from trees to prevent wire or cord from constricting the limb or trunk as the tree grows.

Remove guy wires and stakes the second year after planting. The root growth by that time is anchored firmly, and failure to remove the wires may cause total or partial girdling as the tree grows against constricting wire.

Wrapping

Newly planted trees of 2 in. caliper and over should always have the trunk and the lower parts of the first limbs wrapped with burlap or kraft crepe paper 6 in. wide to reduce the amount of water given off by the tree through the bark while the roots are becoming established.

Start at the lower part of the bottom branches and wrap spirally to the ground. Overlap half of each spiral to form a double wrapping. Secure the last wrapping with twine, winding the twine in wide spirals up the trunk and tying above the lower branches. Do not wrap species subject to borers, because the larvae may work undetected beneath the wrappings.

Waxing

Another way to reduce the amount of water given off through the bark pores is to spray newly planted trees with a paraffin-base preparation. This spray takes the place of burlap or crepe paper wrappings.

Prepare the material according to the manufacturer's directions, and apply as a fine spray. Limit the spray to heavy limbs and trunk; do not cover entire tree. Do not use these sprays for trees with thin bark, such as dogwood and sugar maple, unless the ingredients are known to be harmless.

Watering after planting

The water needs of newly planted trees, shrubs, and vines depend on temperature, water-holding capacity of the soil, drainage, and normal rainfall. Generally, plants do not need watering in cold weather. During the first few years after planting, artificial watering is necessary in hot, dry periods.

Too much watering in clay soils may reduce soil temperatures and retard plant growth. It also may drown the plant by preventing air from reaching the roots.

To determine the need for watering, dip up a shovelful of earth and test the soil below the first few inches. Squeeze it in the hand, and if it keeps the shape of a ball watering is not necessary.

Quantity

When watering is required, soak the soil thoroughly. About 27,000 gal of water per acre equals 1 in. of rainfall, or a little over $\frac{1}{2}$ gal per sq ft. Clay soils generally require $\frac{1}{2}$ gal per sq ft, while sandy soils require 2 gal; soils between these two extremes require about 1 gal.

Wilt-Pruf

A product known as Wilt-Pruf, manufactured by Rosedale Nurseries, Eastview, N.Y., gives promise of reducing transplanting losses to a minimum by coating the leaves to prevent escape of moisture. It may also be useful in preserving new plantings or during periods of extreme drought. This product is a plastic-latex suspension that can be sprayed on as a milky-white liquid and dries to a colorless, slightly glossy film. It is harmless, does not stain, and wears away completely in about three months.

There are three major uses for this plastic coating:

1. As an antitranspirant to prevent moisture loss in hot weather planting. By applying the coating before digging, one can transplant practically all types of nursery material at any time of the year, with very little wilt or setback.

2. As a fall spray to prevent winter-burn and sun scorch.

3. As a sticker for insecticides and fungicides. The combination of a plastic spray with insecticides and fungicides prolongs the life of such materials. It lessens the necessary number of applications.

Transplanting shrubs and trees from native stands

The safest procedure in transplanting or collecting deciduous shrubs from native stands is to dig them with a ball of earth on the roots. In clay or clay loam soils this is a simple process, because the soil is heavy enough to stay around the roots. The ball of earth for an average size shrub should be about one-half the spread of the branches.

Shrubs growing in sandy or gravelly soils are more difficult to move, because it is difficult to keep the soil from falling away from the roots. Use a pick to dig the plants, and comb the soil away from the roots, without damaging or destroying them. Prepare a soupy mixture of soil and water, and dip the roots into the mixture to puddle the mud around the roots and keep them from drying out. Cover the roots with wet burlap or some other suitable material for further protection from the sun and wind.

Deciduous trees

In collecting deciduous trees from native stands it is wise to select trees of 3-in. caliper or less. Such trees are easier to move and will frequently catch up to trees of a larger size transplanted at the same time. Transplant only with a ball of earth, allowing 1 ft in its diameter for each inch of tree trunk diameter taken 1 ft above the ground surface.

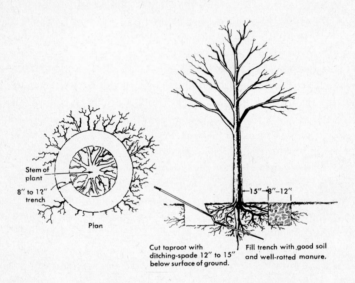

Fig. 3.10   Root pruning before transplanting

A large tree should be root pruned at least one growing season before it is moved from its natural site. To do this, dig a trench during the dormant season, about 3 ft in diameter for a 3-in. caliper tree, deep enough to sever all roots extending into the trench. A trench 2 ft deep will usually suffice. This trench should then be backfilled with good soil, preferably mixed with peat moss or well-rotted sawdust. This mixture should be about 75 per cent soil and 25 per cent humus. Prune the tree back about one-fourth, by pruning only its side branches.

The tree will produce new fine roots during the following year within this trench. To dig for transplanting, dig a trench outside the trench previously dug, being careful not to damage the new roots (Fig. 3.10). Protect the ball by wrapping with burlap. This method will reduce the size of the ball considerably, making it easier to handle.

GROUNDS MAINTENANCE HANDBOOK

Evergreens are transplanted in much the same manner, except that they must always be moved with a ball of earth.

Preserving existing trees when grades are changed

When the grade is raised around existing good trees, a dry well should be constructed. Increasing the depth of soil over tree roots makes it difficult for air to reach the roots and may smother the tree. There are three general methods of protecting the tree:

1. Construct a dry well 1 to 3 ft from the trunk of the tree, using flat field-stone or brick, with open (uncemented) joints. If the fill is over 1 ft deep, place a layer of crushed stone from the outer drip of the branches to the dry well. Place vertical tile at intervals at the outer drip range of the tree, to admit air to the root system.

2. Use the same method described above, but bring the crushed stone up to finished grade to form a ring around the tree under the outer drip of the branches. See Fig. 3.11

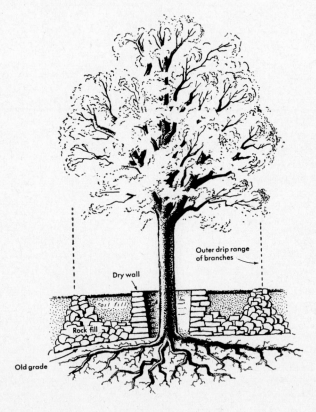

Fig. 3.11   Method of preserving trees when grades are changed

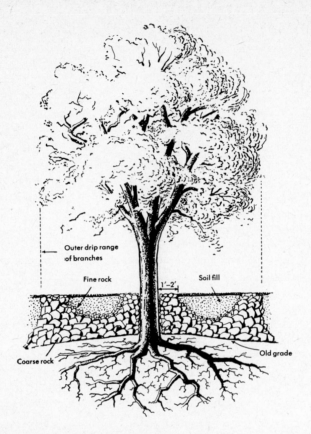

Outer drip range of branches

Fine rock

Soil fill

1'–2'

Coarse rock

Old grade

Fig. 3.12 Method of preserving trees when grades are changed

3. Place a coarse rock fill up to the trunk of the tree. This rock fill should cover an area 10 ft in circumference around the tree. See Fig. 3.12.

Reforestation

Many parks or publicly owned lands have areas which cannot be developed for recreational use. Such areas are usually well removed from the major area of activity and would serve little purpose as grass or meadow areas. Such areas may include slopes on which the erosion problem is acute. Land of this kind can be reforested to native trees at a very nominal cost and will serve to reduce maintenance costs, control erosion, supply cover for wildlife, and provide a future crop of timber and pulpwood.

Because the kind of tree to plant for this purpose will vary from one locality to another, it is best to consult your local state forester before making a selection. He will also be able to add detailed advice on your particular problem to the planting information given below.

Season to plant

In most locations the time to plant seedlings is in the spring, beginning as soon as the frost is out of the ground. The length of the planting season will vary with the year and the locality, but seedlings must always be started early enough to become established before hot weather.

Care of trees

Seedling trees usually arrive from the nursery in bundles, cartons, or crates, with the roots packed in sphagnum moss. They should be taken out of the container immediately after arrival and "heeled in." The heeling-in trench (about 8 in. deep and as wide as the ordinary shovel blade) should be prepared beforehand in a moist, shaded area, or in an area where brush can be cut to shade the seedlings. The trees should be placed in the trench and the roots covered with loose soil. Do not let the roots dry out; water if the trees remain in the trench for any length of time.

Planting

Planting may be done either by hand or by machine. In planting by hand use a mattock or grub hoe. Strike the hoe into the ground, press downward and to one side to open a slit in the ground or sod, whip the tree roots into this slot, remove the blade, and press the soil or sod firmly about the roots with the heel of your boot. Carry the trees in a pail with enough water in it to keep the roots moist. A two-man team, one planting and one carrying and tamping, should be able to plant from 800 to 1500 trees per day, depending on the weather, ground conditions, and the physical stamina of the men.

Machine planting is being done more and more, especially on large areas where the land contour allows a farm tractor to be used with safety. Tree planting machines come in various forms and operate on one of three principles: (a) the scooping out of a clump of sod by lugs mounted on a tractor or on a pair of wheels pulled as a trailer; (b) the cutting of a continuous slit by a tractor-mounted, hydraulically-operated, single-bottom plow, and (c) the same operation by a unit manufactured specifically for tree planting, mounted either on small wheels or on runners, and towed behind a tractor with the man who is planting the trees riding the unit. Machine operators have claimed that they can plant up to 10,000 seedlings per day with two men.

Spacing

Spacing of seedling plantings will vary with the type of tree used. Table 3.9 shows the number of trees per acre at various spacings.

TABLE 3.7/AVERAGE TIME FOR DIGGING AND PLANTING

Height of shrub in feet	Time to dig (min.)	Time to handle (min.)	Time to plant, prune, water and clean up	Total time, (min.)	No. one man can move per day
Shrubs with bare roots					
2 to 3	5	5	20	30	18
3 to 4	6	5	25	36	15
4 to 5	8	6	31	45	12
5 to 6	10	8	42	60	9
6 to 8	20	10	60	90	6
Shrubs with soil, burlapped but not laced					
2 to 3	8	6	31	45	12
3 to 4	10	8	42	60	9
4 to 5	20	10	60	90	6
5 to 6	30	15	90	135	4
6 to 8	60	30	180	270	2

Tables 3.6, 3.7, and 3.8 compiled by and reproduced here by permission of Owen B. Schmidt, Superintendent, F. D. Moore & Sons, Landscape Contractors and Nurserymen.

TABLE 3.8/AVERAGE TIME FOR PLANTING 1,000 SQ FT WITH GROUND COVERS

Number and kind of plants	Labor to dig bed 10 in. Deep	Labor (spread manure and peat and prepare bed*)	Time to plant	Total labor (time)
500 Ivy	9 hr.	9 hr.	5 hr.	23 hr.
4000 Pachysandra	9	9	18	36
750 Sarococca	9	9	7½	25½
4000 Ajuga	9	9	18	36
334 Roses	9	9	18	36
334 Honeysuckle	9	9	9	27
1000 Vinca minor	9	9	10	28

* On each bed was spread four bales of peat moss 1 in. deep and 1 ton of rotted manure, also 1 in. deep.

TABLE 3.9/AVERAGE TIME FOR DIGGING, HANDLING, PLANTING, WATERING, PRUNING, GUYING, AND WRAPPING TREES

Ball size diam. depth (in.)	Cu ft of soil in ball	Weight of ball (lb.)	Time to dig & lace (min.)	Time to handle ball (min.)	Size hole required (in.)	Cu ft soil hole, to excavate	Time to dig hole, (min.)	Cu ft soil dis- place- ment	Time to plant & prune (min.)	Time to water, wrap, guy & clean up (min.)	Cu ft topsoil handled in moving	Total time in moving
12x12	7/10	56	15	10	24	3-3/4	20	3	15	4	10-1/2	64 min.
18x16	2	160	30	20	30	7-1/2	28	5-1/2	21	5	21	1-2/3 hr.
24x18	4	320	60	40	36	13	65	9	49	12	38	3-2/3 hr.
30x21	7-1/2	600	114	76	48	26-1/2	133	19	100	25	76	7-1/3 hr.
36x24	12-1/2	980	189	126	54	38	190	25-1/2	143	36	114	11-1/3 hr.
42x27	19	1520	285	190	66	64	320	45	240	60	185	18-1/2 hr.
48x30	28	2040	420	280	72	85	360	57	270	68	254	23-1/3 hr.
54x33	38-1/2	3060	579	386	84	127	635	88-1/2	476	119	370	36-1/2 hr.
60x36	52	4160	780	520	90	159	795	107	596	149	474	47-1/3 hr.
66x39	68	5440	1020	680	96	196	905	128	679	168	596	57-1/2 hr.
72x42	87	7160	1305	870	108	267	1240	180	930	233	795	76 hr.

TABLE 3.10/TREES PER ACRE AT VARIOUS SPACINGS

Spacing (ft)	No. trees per acre
5	1,740
6	1,210
7	890
8	680
9	538
10	436
12	303

Care of plantings

The most serious hazard to forest plantings is fire. Fire breaks should be provided around all plantings less than 10 acres in size, and for larger areas there should be a system of fire lines as breaks. Protection from grazing animals is also necessary. A thinning program should be instituted when the plantings are 15 to 20 years old. Consult the local state forester for detailed plans for forest control and management.

White pine plantations must be protected from the spread of the white pine blister rust. This disease must spread from the *Ribes* plants (currant and gooseberry), and therefore a program of intensive eradication of these plants must be carried forward.

Protection and control of street trees

The installation and care of street trees is complicated by the interests of a variety of departments of town and city government. The safety of the public, space requirements, traffic, utilities, and many other factors must be considered. The hazards and inconveniences that result when these factors are ignored can be seen today in many cities where the older trees were planted before controlling ordinances were enacted.

It is important, first of all, to select the right tree for the spot available. A tree that requires a space of 40 to 50 ft within which to mature should not be forced to crowd itself into a 20-ft space. Trees with surface roots and trees that require a great deal of moisture should not be placed where the roots will be cramped or can interfere with sewer lines. Large trees should not be planted where there are overhead power lines, as anyone will appreciate who has seen an avenue of trees with branches on only one side, or the tops cut out, or even with holes cut out among the branches. Smaller flowering trees are suitable for planting under power lines: dogwood, crabs, mountain ash, redbud, fringetree, hawthorns, flowering cherry, and other similar species. Any of these may be spaced 20 ft apart, and will grow successfully in a strip of lawn 4 ft wide. Larger shade trees should be planted a minimum distance of 40 ft apart, and only where the lawn between sidewalk and curb is at least 8 ft wide.

Below is a list of the more common regulations governing the planting and care of street trees. These regulations should become a part of the city or town ordinances:

1. Posting of signs on trees should not be allowed.
2. The hitching of animals to trees should not be allowed.
3. The anchoring of ropes and chains to trees should not be allowed.
4. Adequate guards should be provided around trees in construction areas.
5. No chemicals, including salt, should be placed in contact with trees.
6. No cement or stone paving should be placed around the trunks of trees.
7. No excavations should be permitted within 20 ft of a tree.
8. Heavy equipment should not be permitted to operate within 20 ft.
9. Gas leaks should be repaired immediately.
10. Electric lines and poles should be safeguarded during trimming operations.
11. Branches should be trimmed to allow a minimum clearance of 8 ft if they overhang sidewalks or streets.
12. Branches of trees should not be permitted lower than 5 ft at street corners in order to allow motorists a full view of the intersection.
13. Trees should be planted or spaced 20 to 40 ft apart, depending upon the individual species.
14. No trees should be planted closer than 20 ft to a sewer line.
15. All diseased trees, including elms with the Dutch elm disease, should be removed immediately. No diseased trees should be planted.
16. There are several species of trees that should never be used for street or city use because their habits of growth create problems of maintenance repair to streets and sidewalks. Some have excessively large leaves and seed pods difficult to clean up; with others thorns and brittleness of branches create a safety problem; others are too spreading in growth, and some have shallow root systems which get into sewer lines and break up sidewalks. The most common of these undesirable trees are poplar, boxelder, willow, catalpa, tree of heaven, soft maple, chestnut, black locust, Chinese elm, ash, basswood or linden, and cottonwood.

In order to make the proper selection of plant materials for various conditions, uses and requirements, the following list has been prepared. The number following the common name refers to the scientific name found in the master list on pages 152–158.

TABLE 3.11/PLANT MATERIALS FOR SPECIFIC CONDITIONS

Screens—quick-growing

Trees
Arborvitae, pyramidal (290)
Douglas fir (208)
Hemlock, Canada (300)
Maple, silver (10)
Pine, scotch (193)
Pine, white (192)
Poplar (197)
Retinospora, Sawara (46)
Spruce, Norway (187)
Willow (244)

Shrubs
Buckthorn, glossy (220)
Honeysuckle, bush (161)
Nannyberry (313)
Ninebark (186)
Olive, Russian (87)
Privet, ibota (153)
Privet, California (155)
Photinia, oriental (185)
Wayfaring tree (312)

Hedge—formal clipped

Trees
Arborvitae, American (289)
Hawthorn, cockspur (79)
Hawthorn, English (80)
Hawthorn, Washington (78)
Hemlock, Canadian (300)
Hornbeam, American (40)
Maple, Amur (5)
Maple, hedge (4)
Pine, white (192)
Spruce, Norway (187)
Yews (280)

Shrubs
Barberry, Japanese (27)
Boxwood (33)
Buckthorn, common (219)
Buckthorn, glossy (220)
Euonymus, dwarf (91)
Euonymus, winged (90)
Firethorn, Laland (210)
Holly, convex leaved (124)
Holly, littleleaf Japanese (125)
Privet, California (155)
Privet, Ibolium (152)
Wintercreeper, bigleaf (97)

Hedge—Informal

Shrubs, flowering, fruiting or evergreen
Althea, shrub (114)
Arrowwood (310)
Barberry (26)
Deutzia, lemoine (84)
Deutzia, slender (82)
Euonymus, spreading (96)
Forsythia, showy border (103)
Honeysuckle, bush (161)
Hollygrape, Oregon (166)
Juniper, pfitzer (138)
Kerria, white (144)
Lilac, common (275)

Lilac, common white (276)
Quince, Japanese flowering (45)
Rose, hugonis (235)
Spirea, Anthony Waterer (254)
Spirea, Kashmire False (249)
Spirea, thunberg (257)
Spirea, vanhoutte (259)
Sweetbrier (240)
Viburum, doublefile (323)
Wayfaring tree (312)
Yew, Brown's (286)
Yew, Hatfield (287)

Wet locations

Trees
Arborvitae, American (289)
Cedar, white (47)
Elm, American (302)
Hemlock, Canadian (300)

Shrubs
Arrowwood (310)
Buttonbush (42)
Chokeberry, red (18)
Cranberrybush, American (208)

Hornbeam, American (294)
Linden, American (294)
Maple, red (9)
Maple, silver (10)
Oak, pin (216)
Poplar (197)
Shadblow, downy (15)
Sourgum (177)
Sweetbay (165)
Sweetgum (160)
Sycamore, American (195)
Willow (244)

Cranberrybush, European (316)
Dogwood, Tatarian (52)
Dogwood, red osier (63)
Dogwood, silky (54)
Fringetree, white (48)
Hardhack (258)
Inkberry (126)
Nannyberry (313)
Rose, swamp (239)
Rose, Virginia (242)
Summersweet (50)
Willow (244)
Winterberry (129)
Withe rod (209)

Dry locations

Trees

Ash, green (105)
Birch, gray (32)
Elm, dwarf asiatic (303)
Hackberry (41)
Locust (109)
Maple, amur (5)
Maple, hedge
Oak, mossycup (215)
Oak, scarlet (214)
Pine, scotch (193)
Pine, white (192)
Scholartree, Chinese (248)
Tree of Heaven (13)
Goldenrain-tree (145)

Shrubs

Aralia, five leaved (3)
Bladder-senna, common (51)
Blackhaw (319)
Buckthorn, glossy (220)
Cinquefoil, shrubby (201)
Dogwood, gray (59)
Eleagnus, cherry (88)
Honeysuckle, Tatarian (164)
Indigobush (16)
Juniper, Douglas (138)
Juniper, Sargent's (134)
Locust, black (233)
Olive, Russian (87)
Pea tree, Siberian (38)
Plum, beach (206)
Privet (151–157)
Sumac (225)
Tamarix, Algerian (278)
Tamarix, five-stamen (279)

Berry-bearing

Red berries

Ash, European mountain (252)
Barberry, Japanese (27)
Cherry, cornelian (58)
Chokeberry, red (18)
Coralberry (268)
Cotoneaster, Diels, (69)
Cotoneaster, ground (73)
Cotoneaster, Franchet (71)
Cotoneaster, rock (72)
Cotoneaster, Simons (76)
Cotoneaster, spreading (70)

Cotoneaster, willowleaf (75)
Crab, Sargent's (173)
Cranberrybush, American (308)
Cranberrybush, European (316)
Dogwood, flowering (55)
Dogwood, kousa (57)
Eleagnus, cherry (88)
Euonymus, winged (90)
Euonymus, dwarf winged (91)
Firethorn, Laland (210)
Hawthorn, cockspur (79)

Hawthorn, thicket (77)
Hawthorn, Washington (78)
Holly, American (128)
Honeysuckle, Morrow (163)
Honeysuckle, Tatarian (164)
Photinia, Oriental (185)
Rose, meadow (234)
Rose, swamp (239)

Sweetbrier (240)
Snowberry, Chenault (215)
Sweetbay (165)
Viburnum, linden (311)
Viburnum, tea (322)
Viburnum, Wright (324)
Winterberry, common (129)
Wintercreeper, bigleaf (97)

Black berries

Barberry, warty (29)
Blackhaw (319)
Buckthorn, common (219)
Buckthorn, glossy (220)
Chokeberry, black (19)
Cotoneaster, Peking (68)
Holly, convex-leaved (124)
Holly, Japanese littleleaf (125)
Inkberry (126)

Kerria, white (223)
Nannyberry (313)
Privet, ibota (153)
Privet, regal (156)
Shadblow, downy (15)
Viburnum, Siebold (321)
Viburnum, mapleleaf (307)
Wayfaring-tree (312)

White berries

Bayberry, northern (175)
Coralberry (268)
Dogwood, gray (59)
Dogwood, Tatarian (52)
Dogwood, red osier (63)
Spurge, Japanese (180)

Blue-black berries

Arrowwood (310)
Barberry, wintergreen (25)
Barberry, three-spined (28)
Beautyberry, American (35)
Beautyberry, Chinese (36)
Dogwood, silky (54)
Viburnum, Kentucky (314)
Withe rod (309)
Withe rod, smooth (315)

Small or dwarf plants

Abelia, glossy (1)
Almond, flowering (205)
Andromeda, mountain (189)
Arborvitae, globe and dwarf (288)
Azalea, amoena (20)
Azalea, Hinodegiri (21)
Barberry, three-spined (28)
Barberry, warty (29)
Boxwood, common (33)
Cinquefoil (202)
Cotoneaster, ground (73)
Cotoneaster, rockspray (74)
Deutzia, Lemoin (84)
Deutzia, slender (82)
Goldflower (121)
Hollygrape, Oregon (166)

Holly, convex leaved (124)
Holly, Japanese littleleaf (125)
Honeysuckle, Southern bush (86)
Juniper, Sargent's (134)
Leucothoe, drooping (150)
Rose, bristly (238)
Snowball, Japanese (318)
Snowberry (264–267)
Spirea, Anthony Waterer (254)
Spirea, thunberg (257)
Spurge, Japanese (180)
Stephanandra, cutleaf (260)
Wintercreeper (98)
Yellowroot (328)
Yew, dwarf Japanese (284)

Smoky, dusty, city situations

Trees

Corktree (182)
Hackberry (41)
Hornbeam, European (39)
Locust, honey (108)
Maidenhair tree (107)
Maple, Norway (6)
Pine, Austrian (191)
Pine, Scotch (193)
Plane tree, European (196)
Poplar, Carolina (199)
Poplar, Japanese (200)
Scholar tree, Chinese (248)
Thorn, cockspur (79)

Shrubs

Aralia, five-leaved (3)
Barberry, Japanese (27)
Bladder-Senna, common (51)
Forsythia (103)
Holly, Japanese (122)
Holly, Japanese littleleaf (125)
Honeysuckle, winter (162)
Kerria, white (223)
Lilac, common (275)
Nineback, common (186)
Privet (151–157)
Snowberry (264–267)
Spirea, Vanhout (259)
Thorn, Washington (78)
Withe rod (309)

Street Trees

Tall, formal and heavy

Linden, American (294)
Maple, Norway (6)
Maple, sugar (11)
Oak, red (217)
Sycamore, American (195)
Tulip tree (159)

Oak, pin (216)
Oak, scarlet (214)

Medium height for narrow residential streets

Ash, European mountain (252)
Birch, European white (30)
Corktree, Chinese (181)
Golden rain-tree (145)
Hackberry (41)
Linden, European littleleaf (295)
Maple, columnar Norway (7)
Maple, hedge (4)
Scholar tree, Chinese (248)
Sweetgum (160)

Tall, medium to light textured

Ash, green (105)
Ash, white (104)
Elm, American (302)
Honeylocust, thornless (108)
Maidenhair tree (107)
Maple, red (9)
Maple, silver (10)

Seashore locations

Trees

Holly, American (128)
Maple, sycamore (8)
Plane tree, London (194)
Poplar, Bolleana (198)
Poplar, Carolina (199)
Shadblow, downy (15)
Sourgum (177)

Eleagnus, autumn (89)
Hydrangea, Otsaka (116)
Inkberry (126)
Juniper, Andorra (139)
Juniper, Bar Harbor (137)
Lilac, common (275)
Olive, Russian (87)
Plum, beach (206)
Privet, California (155)
Rose, meadow (234)
Rose, wichurian (243)
Sumac (225)
Summersweet (50)
Tamarix (277)

Shrubs

Althea, shrub (114)
Arrowwood (310)
Bayberry (176)
Chokeberry, red (18)

Partial shade

Trees

Dogwood, red flowering (56)
Dogwood, white flowering (55)
Fringetree, white (48)
Hemlock, Canadian (300)
Holly, American (128)

Maple, Amur (4)
Sweetbay (165)
Shadblow, downy (15)
Silverbell, great (110)
Sourwood (179)

Shrubs

Abelia, glossy (1)
Aralia, five-leaved (3)
Barberry, wintergreen (25)
Blackhaw, (319)
Buttonbush (42)
Cherry, cornelian (58)
Chokeberry (17)
Cinquefoil, shrubby (201)
Cranberrybush, European (316)
Euonymus (90–99)
Firethorn, Laland (210)
*Hollygrape, Oregon (166)
Holly, Japanese littleleaf (125)
Honeysuckle, Morrow (163)
Honeysuckle, Southern bush (86)
Honeysuckle, winter (162)
Hydrangea, oak leaf (118)
Hydrangea, snowhill (115)
Inkberry (126)
*Ivy, English (112)

Kerria, white (223)
*Laurel (143)
*Leucothoe, drooping (150)
Nannyberry (313)
*Periwinkle (326)
Privet, California (155)
Privet, regal (156)
Redbud, American (43)
Redbud, Chinese (44)
*Rhododendron, rosebay (222)
*Snowberry (264–267)
Spurge, Japanese (180)
Stephanandra, cutleaf (260)
Summersweet (50)
Sweet shrub (37)
Viburnum, mapleleaf (307)
Winterberry, common (127)
*Witchhazel (111)
Yellowroot (328)
Yew, spreading Japanese (282)

* Tolerates dense shade.

PARK WOODLAND CLEANUP AND CLEARING

In most areas there are many woodlands that require a certain amount of cleanup or clearing before they can be made useful and available to the public for general use. This cleanup can be classified into four general types: general cleanup, clear cutting, selective cutting, and pruning.

Cleanup

Areas usually requiring cleanup are those which are in general park use, such as picnic areas, overlooks, areas adjacent to structures, and (if time and funds permit) all other areas serviced by foot or horse trails or otherwise made accessible to the public.

(a) All areas designated as requiring cleanup should be cleared of dead, dying, or structurally dangerous standing trees, all flammable material on the ground, and all undesirable underbrush.

(b) Dying trees should include all trees that will not survive if left in their present condition, and cannot be saved by normal maintenance pruning and care. Any tree with a 25 per cent dead crown, unless otherwise marked for saving, should be considered a dying tree and removed.

(c) All trees to be removed should be cut as close as possible to the ground —no higher than 5 in.—and felled in such a manner as not to damage adjacent material. In order to control regrowth of undesirable material, remaining stumps 3 in. or more in diameter should be painted or sprayed within two weeks after cutting with a mixture of one part herbicide (such as 2, 4D or 2–4–5T) and 19 parts fuel oil. Do not use kerosene because of its toxicity to desirable plants and its flammability.

(d) All undesirable underbrush, including vines and all scrubby growth such as blackberry and locust, should be removed.

(e) Debris, including fences, wire, cans, junk, rubbish, or other types of refuse should be removed or disposed of.

Clear cutting

Areas usually requiring clear cutting are those designated for opening views or vistas, to provide open lawns or playfields, or to vary the tree line along roads or highways by cutting bays at appropriate intervals.

(a) All trees and underbrush, except those specifically marked as specimen plants, should be completely removed.

(b) In areas where it is desirable to maintain a lawn or grass cover, the stumps should be removed and disposed of. In all other areas the trees should be cut flush with the ground and the stump treated with herbicide to prevent resprouting.

(c) All ruts, holes, and scars caused by the removal of logs, trees, or stumps should be filled in and the grade restored.

(d) No heavy equipment which would in normal operation injure desirable material should be used. Any equipment in operation should stay far enough away from permanent trees to avoid damage to large roots close to the trunks.

Selective cutting

Areas to be cut selectively include picnic areas, the borders of access roads or highways, and other areas where an open woods effect is desired close to buildings.

(a) Specifications applicable to cleanup also apply to the areas to be cut selectively. In addition, trees should be removed in such a manner as to provide adequate room for more desirable material to grow. Enough trees should be left to allow their crowns to touch after normal growth. For instance, elm should be thinned to approximately 30-ft spacing; maple to 25 ft; ash to 40 ft; oak to 35 ft; linden or basswood to 20 ft. Other species of trees should be spaced proportionally. Such cutting of trees should apply only to trees up to 6 in. in caliper.

(b) Avoid an even spacing of trees in any wooded area. Small clumps of the better trees scattered throughout the cutting area will produce a more attractive appearance.

(c) Clear away all growth from mature specimen trees for a distance of approximately 35 ft.

Pruning

Areas to be pruned should be limited to the areas designated for selective cutting. If funds permit, some pruning can be done on the better specimen trees in the cleanup areas, if such pruning will prolong the life of the tree. Specimen trees are those which stand out above all others, full grown and healthy.

(a) All dead wood and rubbing branches 1 in. or more in diameter, measured 6 in. out from the base, should be removed, as well as all borer-infested and structurally weak branches, stubs from broken branches, and old rotted stubs. The cuts should be made flush with the trunk or branch and painted with an acceptable tree wound paint.

Disposal of materials

(a) All waste materials should be removed from the site of the work or burned completely. The burning of such waste should never be allowed to harm or damage material in any way.

(b) All materials to be burned should be piled, and burned when in a suitable condition. Burning should be so thorough that the materials are reduced to ashes. Piling for the burning should be done where it will cause the least fire risk and with all possible fire precautions. Ashes should be scattered and the burned sites obliterated.

(c) Every precaution should be taken to prevent fires from spreading. A supply of axes, saws, mattocks, shovels, rakes, and other fire fighting equipment should be available at all times for use in preventing and suppressing fires.

(d) Material which cannot be burned should be buried in pits and covered with a minimum of 3 ft of earth.

(e) An approved type of brush shredder is useful in disposing of brush and tree limbs up to 10 in. in diameter. Stumps of all sizes can also be disposed of easily with a new stump chipper which removes the stump cleanly 10 in. below the ground surface. The chips thus produced from both types of machines are useful for mulching trees and shrubs.

SAFETY FOR TREE WORKERS

The best information available today on rules for safe practice for tree workers is Tree Preservation Bulletin No. 2 written by A. Robert Thompson, Forester, National Park Service. These rules, slightly adapted, are reproduced on the following pages by permission of the Government Printing Office.

Rules of safe practice

The purpose of these rules is to bring out the following facts: (a) the man who is to avoid accidents and reduce loss of life and human suffering must exert every personal effort; (b) all tree workers, especially those who are inexperienced, should be informed of the dangers incident to tree preservation work, so far as it is possible to do so in a set of rules; (c) precautions must be taken by all tree workers, experienced or inexperienced, to reduce the hazards of their work to a minimum; and (d) experience with causes and prevention should be applied to future work.

The rules have been established not from one person's ideas of safety, but from the accumulated experience and observations of many individuals and organizations over a period of many years. Each rule, without exception, has evolved directly from one or more accidents caused by failure to observe proper safety principles. These safe practice rules apply generally wherever tree preservation work is done.

General

1. Every tree worker should know these safety rules. It is his duty to observe them at all times. He should have a good working knowledge of first aid and resuscitation.

2. No man should engage in any phase of tree work until he is able to tie the following knots readily and until he knows when to use them: bowline, bowline-on-a-bight, running bowline, square knot, clove hitch, timber hitch, taut-line, and figure-of-eight knot. See Fig. 3.13–3.20.

3. Before any man attempts to do actual work in a tree he must be trained in the use of rope and knots and must spend sufficient time in practice climbing and knot tying to become proficient.

4. Before any tree operation is started, all necessary time should be taken to find out if any local danger exists. Haste causes accidents; it pays to take time to be careful.

5. Except under exceptional circumstances, trees should not be climbed or worked in when wet. It is impossible to get a good foothold on slippery bark, and knots are likely to slip if the rope is wet.

6. Men should stay out of trees in high winds, except in emergencies.

7. Only men who are physically fit should be allowed in trees. Men suffering temporary ill health should be sent home.

8. There is no place for intoxicating liquors on a tree preservation operation. Men suffering from after effects of alcohol must not be allowed on the job.

9. A tree is not the place for a person with an exhibitionist complex. Men who persist in taking unnecessary risks or in showing off should be released from the job.

10. As a general rule, only one man should work in a tree at a time, especially during pruning operations.

11. Workmen should request assistance only from men working directly on the job, never from passers-by or casual observers, regardless how simple the assistance temporarily required.

12. Danger signs or red flags or both should be placed on sidewalks, roadways, or streets where any tree work is to be done. Dangerous areas should be roped off and ground men used to divert traffic when necessary.

13. The foreman should exercise close supervision over his men at all times. He should satisfy himself that the men working under him are competent to perform their work with safety. He should outline safe methods and see that his instructions are obeyed implicitly.

14. The foreman must make a daily inspection of all tools, rope, and other equipment before use, and condemn or destroy all tools, etc., which in his opinion are unsafe. Each tree worker must also inspect all tools, rope, etc., before using them.

15. Foremen are held responsible for all safety rules.

Clothing

Men who are engaged in tree climbing will find that ordinary street or work clothes are unsuitable for tree work.

For tree workers a cap is preferable to a hat because it offers less obstruction when passing between limbs and thick foliage. For ground workers a hard hat is better protection than a cap.

High-topped leather shoes with composition or rubber soles are preferable to ordinary shoes with leather soles. Hobnailed shoes should never be used for climbing, and nailed soles should be avoided. Special tree climber's boots with instep flaps and steel stays are sometimes preferred.

Breeches of strong, dark-colored material are preferable to long trousers which are easily caught and torn. They should be fairly loose in the leg and knee to give freedom in cramped positions.

A long overcoat is unsuitable for tree work. Long underwear and snug-fitting wool or leather jackets or extra shirts are preferable when cold weather requires extra warmth.

An athletic strap with a wide abdominal band should be worn by all men engaged in tree work.

For protection of the hands and wrists, gloves of the gauntlet type are generally considered satisfactory for tree work. Sleeves should be kept rolled down to protect forearms and wrists.

Rope

The standard safety rope for tree work is a first-grade, 3-strand, rot treated, one-half inch diameter manila rope not less than 120 ft and preferably 150 ft in length. The half-inch nylon rope is coming into wider use and is acceptable as a standard rope where preferred. Standard power rope consists of first grade, three-strand, rot-treated, ¾-in. diameter manila rope in lengths of not less than 150 ft. It is often desirable to have a number of longer lengths as well. A 1-in. diameter manila rope is recommended for pulling trees over. Cheap substitute ropes should be avoided.

The following table gives the breaking strength and safe loads of different sizes of manila rope. This table may be used in estimating stresses for manila rope used for tree work.

TABLE 3.12/FEDERAL STANDARDS FOR MANILA ROPE (3-STRAND)

Diameter (approx.) in.	Length of coil (approx.) ft	Gross weight of coil (approx.) lb	Weight per ft (max.) lb	Length per lb ft	Breaking strength (min.) lb	Safe load (⅛ max.) lb
¼	2,750	55	0.020	50.0	600	75
½	1,200	90	.075	13.3	2,650	331
¾	1,200	200	.167	6.0	5,400	675
1	1,200	324	.270	3.71	9,000	1,125

Under average conditions the working load on a rope should not exceed one-sixth of the breaking load, but under the best conditions, if the rope is new, the working load may be one-fourth the breaking load.

Under unfavorable conditions where rope is used frequently and for in-

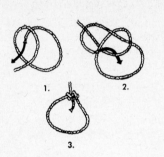

Fig. 3.13 Bowline

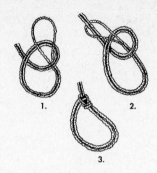

Fig. 3.14 Bowline on a bight

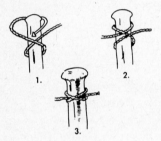

Fig. 3.15 Clove hitch

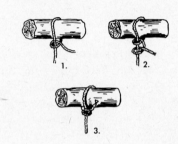

Fig. 3.16 Timber hitch

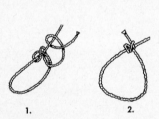

Fig. 3.17 Tautline hitch

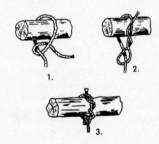

Fig. 3.18 Double half hitch

definite periods, as with a climbing rope, the working load should not exceed one-eighth of the breaking load.

Every rope must be thoroughly inspected for cuts or abrasions before each use. Occasionally the strands should be separated and the inside of the rope examined to see that the yarns are bright and unbroken. There is no positive way of testing a rope by subjecting it to an overload; this may weaken it so that it will soon break under normal use.

GROUNDS MAINTENANCE HANDBOOK

If the rope end becomes worn at the knot or at the saddle, it should be cut off immediately. Don't try to make the rope last too long. A man's life is worth more than the price of a new rope.

Kinking is one of the main causes of injury to manila rope and should be avoided, especially when the rope is wet. To avoid kinks in new rope, uncoil from the inside of the coil, never from the outside.

A rope should not be "burned" by being allowed to run through a crotch too rapidly. Great care should be used to avoid dropping cigarettes on rope. Rope should be kept away from fire, excessive heat, acids, and such sources of acid fumes as storage batteries.

Rope deteriorates rapidly when it is saturated with water and improperly dried, so unnecessary wetting must be avoided and wet ropes must be dried properly before storing. Rope should not be allowed to freeze after wetting, as frozen rope breaks easily. Rope should not be left in a tree overnight when there is reason to expect a heavy dew or rain, or where it might be stolen or injured.

All rope should be kept coiled when not in use. It should never be stored or transported where it may be cut by sharp tools. Rope should not be dragged in the dirt, over rough surfaces, or across itself. Avoid sharp bends over unyielding surfaces.

Climbing

All limbs should be inspected before the weight of the body is allowed to rest on them. Do not trust your weight to a dead limb. If possible, all dead limbs should be broken off as the climber comes in contact with them.

Trees are of varying strengths, but it is necessary to remember that no matter how tough the wood of the tree or how large the diameter of a limb, a rotten or decayed limb is never safe. The limbs of old cherry and apple trees are likely to be weak because of heart rot, and black locusts are likely to be weakened by borer attack. All old or diseased trees may have invisible decay which makes them more hazardous than young trees.

Tree Trimming Practices publication No. 110 of the Edison Electric Institute, 1937, lists the following groups of trees according to strength:

1. Very easily broken: willow, poplar, aspen, box elder, catalpa, ailanthus, soft maple, white pine, and sassafras.
2. Split easily: linden, ash, red elm, persimmon, magnolia, and tulip tree.
3. Rather hard to break: apple, pear, plum, most conifers, hackberry, birch, oak, walnut, hickory, sycamore, hard maple, American elm, black locust, and osage orange.

Trees with thorns which cut and scratch and may also set up infection are: honey locust, osage orange, black locust, and hawthorn.

When climbing without a rope, the climber should rarely entrust his full weight to one limb. A better practice is to keep one arm around the trunk or to keep the hands on separate limbs, so that if one limb breaks the body can be supported by the trunk or the other limb. A rope should not be climbed hand-over-hand unless a footlock is used or the legs are gripping the tree. Shinning a tree over 15 ft is an unsafe practice. Climbs over 30 ft should be made by using a safety sling. Fatigue and cramps should be avoided. Feet, hands, and rope should be kept out of tight crotches.

A bowline-on-a-bight tied into a safety line, a standard tree worker's belt, or a saddle with or without separate leg straps, in combination with a taut-line hitch, constitutes the safety sling (Fig. 3.19). The saddle is preferred

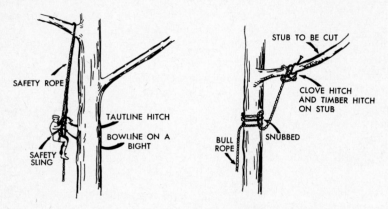

Fig. 3.19 The safe way to climb a large tree   Fig. 3.20 Method for tying stubs to be cut to main trunk

by many because it is more comfortable, and permits free action of the legs. The ordinary lineman's belt and strap are neither safe nor practical for tree work.

The safety sling must always be used for tree work, even if a ladder or scaffold is also used. Many men have been injured or killed by failing to observe this cardinal rule. The safety sling should be tied immediately after the climber has crotched his rope. The crotch should be as high and as close to the trunk as possible. Tight crotches which will bind the rope should be avoided. When practicable, the rope should be crotched on the side of the tree opposite that to be worked, so as to avoid accidentally slipping the rope out along the limb to a point where the limb cannot support the climber's weight. The climber should check the location of the entire length of the safety sling and the taut-line hitch before swinging free.

A figure-eight knot should always be tied in the ground end of a safety rope to prevent accidental pulling of the end through the taut-line hitch when the climber is coming down the rope. If someone else ties the knots, the climber should check them himself before trusting his weight to them.

The ground end of a safety rope must not be left dangling over roadways or walks, and it must be kept free from obstructions, tight crotches, and fallen brush. All slack must be kept out of the safety rope.

The safety rope may be recrotched whenever this will make the work safer or quicker. To be absolutely safe, the climber should tie himself to a convenient limb while making the change.

The climber should stay in the safety sling until he is again on the ground. He should never release the taut-line hitch before coming out of a tree. A climber should not slide down a limb or tree trunk without carefully inspecting it for projecting stubs, nails, or loose bark. Severe gland injuries have occurred through failure to observe this rule. At the end of a working day all knots should be removed from the rope. To leave knots tied for a prolonged period, or to tie knots repeatedly in the same point in a rope, will cause kinking and undue wear. Remember: A good safety rope is the tree worker's most important accident insurance policy.

Ladders

Ladders are used in tree work primarily for climbing into trees. If any trimming or other work is done from a ladder, a safety sling should also be used.

Ladders used in connection with tree work should comply with all of the provisions contained in the *American Standard Safety Code for Construction, Care, and Use of Ladders,* New York, 1935.

Ladders should not be used in tree work unless the base can be set on a firm foundation. They should never be used in trees with the bottom rung or rail bases resting in a crotch. A ladder should never be set on a truck or other object which can be moved while a man is working on it. If it is absolutely necessary to place a ladder in a street or on a walk, and no other footing can be obtained, it should be guarded by a ground man and lashed in place with hand lines. The foot of the ladder should be moved out of the perpendicular by one-fourth the length of the ladder; i.e., if the ladder is 12 ft long, the foot of the ladder should be 3 ft from the base of the trunk of the tree, provided the top of the ladder rests against the trunk and the trunk is perpendicular.

Ladders should be inspected frequently to make sure they are sound. Ladders with broken or cracked rungs or rails should be discarded or immediately repaired, and protruding slivers should be removed. Ladders used against trees where the limbs will not support the weight of the climber should be secured with hand lines. Lashings should pass over the rails and the ends of the rungs, not the center of the rungs. When a ladder is leaned against a tree, the weight should be distributed equally on both rails and not against the top rung unless this has been especially braced. The ladder should be lashed in place if there is any danger of slipping.

Ladders should be placed in proper racks or on the ground after use, and not left leaning against trees or buildings. They should not be left on the job at the end of a working day unless they are secure from tampering or use by unauthorized persons.

Pruning

Tree pruning or other work in the crowns of trees should be performed only when weather conditions are favorable. Branches are more apt to snap off on a cold day than on a warm one. Branches wet by rain or snow or covered with ice are dangerous to the climber.

Before any tree job is started, the program should be worked out carefully with the foreman if at all possible. This planning may eliminate extra climbing and additional hazards.

Automobiles that are found under trees where overhead work is being done should be pushed clear, or the owners should be asked to move them to a safe place. When possible, "No Parking" signs should be placed the day before the work is to begin.

Warning should always be given when a limb is about to be dropped from a tree. The shouts "Timber!" "Heads up!" or "Look out below!" are common signals for this purpose. The dropping of limbs or stubs should be permitted only when there is no danger to men or objects beneath. Ground men should wear hard hats painted with bright colors, which can readily be seen by men in the trees.

A limb which cannot be controlled by hand while being severed from the tree should have a line or lines attached before it is cut off, to permit controlled lowering. The end of the safety sling should never be used for this purpose. Lowering ropes should be snubbed to prevent injury to the holder. It is well to remember that a snubbed rope does not hold so well on wet limbs or trunks as on dry wood. A man should hold only one rope at a time. Never allow ground men to wrap a bull line around their hands or bodies.

The trimmer should never cut a large limb above him except as a last resort. When large limbs or parts of the trunk of a tree are to be sawed off and no suitable crotch is available for passing the support rope, the limb should be snubbed to the lower portion of the trunk and lowered when completely severed (Fig. 3.20). The climber should be sure that he is in a safe position or on the ground before the stub or branch is finally swung clear. Be sure the bull line being used is large enough to handle the weight of the limb being lowered. A sudden jerk may break the line if it is too light.

Care should be used in pulling branches out of trees by hand or by means of pole pruners; the limbs may fall and cause injury. The worker should stand in a place to the side, or if possible above the limb, in order to allow it to fall without striking him.

Never leave "hangers" or anything not securely fastened in the tree. If a tree is not completely pruned at the end of a working day, all "hangers," tools, and ladders should be removed, since they might become dislodged during the night and fall on someone. If a climbing rope must be left in a tree overnight, it should be tied up out of reach.

Electrical hazards

Special care must be exercised when work is being done close to charged wires or electrical apparatus. Only men who are thoroughly familiar with the dangers involved should be allowed to do this work, and only insulated tools should be used under such conditions. In manipulating aerial lifts close to limbs and wires, the trimmer must be very careful not to bring himself or the equipment in contact with the wires.

Before work is undertaken in trees that are close to or touching live wires, the power company concerned should be notified so that if possible they may de-energize and ground the lines locally. In any event, lines should be declared safe by a qualified power company employee before men are allowed to work in trees touching wires.

Wet materials are conductors of electricity—even materials which are nonconductors when they are dry. If clothing, rope, equipment, or the trees are wet or even damp, no work should be done in trees near or touching wires. The use of weatherproof rope and periodic shellacking of poles and wooden handles are worthwhile practices.

The climber should never pass between wires unless authorized by the foreman, and never until rubber guards such as hoods, snakes, or blankets are placed on the wires by a thoroughly experienced man. No one should ever stand on either conductor or guy wires.

Special care must be used to avoid dropping limbs or branches on wires, but if they accidentally fall or are resting on wires, they should be removed by means of either a dry rope slung over the branch or a long-handled pruner equipped with a rope pull. Rope or pruner should be handled with rubber gloves. Fallen wires should not be touched. The power company should be called at once and the wires guarded from passers-by until the company responds to the call. Even if the wires are known to be dead, they should be brushed lightly with the back of the hand before they are touched. If a person does come in contact with live wires, do not allow the victim to be touched. The wire may be lifted from him, or he may be lifted off the wire by using dry, nonconductive materials such as clothing, rope, boards, or rubber materials. After rescue, the back pressure-armlift method of artificial respiration should be applied if the patient has stopped breathing, and a doctor or the emergency squad should be called.

During thunderstorms, trees, especially those standing alone, should be avoided.

Tools

Tools should be raised or lowered by means of a hand line or the free end of the safety rope. They must never be thrown into or dropped from a tree.

Tools should not be left where they may be tripped over or stepped upon, nor in a leaning position from which they may fall. Rope and rope ends should be kept free.

Handsaws with teeth on only one edge should be used for general tree work. They should be kept sharpened and properly set so that they will not jump out of the cut and cause injury. Each handsaw and bullsaw and other small-handled tool should be provided with a leather or wire loop through the handle.

Handsaws should not be carried on the belt or in the hand when a worker is climbing. A saw may be attached to the end of the safety line or hand line before the tree is climbed and then pulled up. When temporarily out of use, a saw should not be laid on a limb or in a crotch, but it should be securely hooked on the belt or over a branch of sufficient size to hold it securely. There are scabbards or sheaths which are hooked to the belt in which saws are safely carried when not in use. Pole saws should be as light in weight as possible and of sufficient length to allow the trimmer to reach his work readily. They should be made with a one-piece wooden handle, angular in cross-section, and be provided with a hook just below the blade.

Pole saws should be raised or lowered by means of a rope tied below the blade. When temporarily out of use in a tree, they may be hooked over limbs of sufficient size to hold the weight. They should never be laid on limbs or in crotches or hung on wires.

Pole pruners should be as light in weight as possible, and of sufficient length to allow the trimmer to reach his work readily. They should be made with a one-piece wooden handle, and be provided with a rope pull leading from the lever arm to the end of the handle. Poles which are hexagonal or square in cross-section are easier and safer to handle than round ones.

Pole pruners should never be raised or lowered by placing a finger in the hook, but by means of a rope tied under the head of the tool, never over the jaw, as the cutting edge may close on the rope and cut it. They should never be thrown by a ground man to a trimmer in the tree. A pole pruner temporarily out of use in a tree may be hooked over a limb of sufficient size to hold the weight securely. They should never be hooked over wires, laid on limbs or in crotches, or used for lifting other equipment.

Chisels, gouges, and other sharp-edged tools should never be carried in the boot. A leather kit with a wooden bottom is a convenient way to carry such tools. Chisel kits should be made so as to prevent the tools' falling out if the kits are accidentally tilted. When working in awkward or confined places, the operator should use long chisel handles to prevent bruising his hands. When using a chisel or gouge he should keep his head out of the line of swing to prevent possible injury of the face from the rebound of the mallet. Chisel handles should be provided with iron ferrules to prevent splitting. Operators should remember that chisels and gouges are cutting tools and should not be used as levers or wedges. They should be kept sharp.

Axes are, of course, necessary on tree operations for felling and bucking, but they should never be used as wedges or for pruning or trimming shade trees. They should not be used for driving wedges. They should be kept sharp.

Steel wedges should be provided on each felling operation. They should be kept free from burred edges, and should be driven only with a sledge hammer.

Spurs or climbing irons should never be used on live trees except possibly during tree-removal operations. Use of spurs at any time is a questionable practice and should be discouraged, since the gaffs are apt to tear out of the bark and cause the climber to slip, fall, or spur himself. The tree climber has so little occasion to use spurs that he rarely becomes expert and consequently should avoid them.

Toolboxes should provide special places for saws, chisels, and other sharp-edged tools so that they will not come in contact with other tools and rope. After use, saws, rope, small tools, picks, shovels, etc. should be placed inside the toolbox in their designated places. When not in use, tools should be kept covered with light machine oil or easily-removed metal protector to prevent rust.

Pneumatic pruners and saws are coming into wider use, particularly with aerial lifts. They should be handled with care. The pruner or saw should not be handed from one trimmer to another unless it is disconnected from the air hose. The trimmer should not try to catch the pruner or saw if it falls and is still connected to the air hose. The pruner should not be laid down with air hose attached; it may be tripped with the foot.

The use of electric or gasoline chain saws in trees is common, but is also hazardous. The trimmer must place himself in the tree so that the saw cannot fall against him. The saw should be suspended from a line crotched at a point other than where the climber's safety line is crotched, and if possible so that if the saw should be released by the trimmer for any reason, it would swing away from him. A special carrier is available for use with a chain saw in a tree.

Tree felling

Before any tree is felled, the crew should be properly instructed by competent authority in the proper manner of notching and wedging, so that the tree may fall where desired. Space immediately around the tree should be cleared of all brush.

Before each tree is felled it should be carefully studied by a competent man in order that the following factors may be taken into consideration: (a) height of tree, (b) soundness, (c) direction of lean, (d) slope of ground, (e) species of tree, (f) top-heaviness, (g) direction of wind, (h) proximity to other trees, structures, and wires, and (j) dead limbs or stubs which may break off and fall, endangering workmen.

If there is danger that the trees being felled may damage property, block and tackle should be used. In most cases in shade tree felling guide lines will be necessary to avoid damage. Guide lines should be tied and snubbed around other trees before any cutting is done at the base of the tree. Winch line, block and tackle, or pull lines assist in controlling the direction of the fall. It may sometimes be necessary to fell a tree by lowering it in sections instead of simply cutting it off at the ground. If this is done, careful study must be given to the size and position of limbs, location and order of making cuts, and methods of snubbing and guiding. Great care must be exercised to avoid severing any guide ropes or power lines. Special precautions in roping rotten or split trees are important because they may fall in an unexpected direction even though the cut is made on the proper side.

Not more than two men at a time should be allowed to work on the base of a tree being felled. Both should know where the tree is to fall and where they are to go when the tree starts to fall. All persons should keep away from the butt of a tree starting to fall. It may kick back or take an unexpected roll. Just before the tree is ready to fall, the shout "Timber!" should be given, and all who are working in the vicinity should immediately take cover in a place safely out of range.

Felling operations, once started, should be finished before the crew leaves the job for lunch or at the end of the working day. It is especially important to complete such operations when roots have been excavated or cut, or when the base cut has been started.

Additional precautions are necessary in felling trees with a chain saw. If there is loose bark on the trunk where the cut is to be made, it is best to remove it with an ax; othewise the saw may throw it into the face of the operator. An undercut should be made to the proper depth on the side of the desired direction of fall and notched out with an ax. All but small trees should be undercut. When trees must be cut flush to the ground, it is safer to make the first cut at a stump height above the swell of the roots and a second cut flush with the ground after the tree is down.

As the cut proceeds, the saw operator should check to see that the cut on the tailstock end is even with the depth of cut on the saw end. If any binding occurs, wedges may be used, but care must be taken not to drive them in against the chain. Sometimes the pull rope may be sufficient to prevent binding. When the final cut is to the proper depth for felling, the tree should be pulled or wedged over. If there is danger of driving the wedge into the saw, a wooden wedge should be used. Extreme care must be exercised not to make the final cut too deep and beyond the wood controlling the direction of fall. Because of the speed with which the saw cuts, there have been incidents when trees have been cut clear off so that there was no control over direction of fall.

Small brush should not be cut with a power chain saw, as the saw may either throw the operator or throw the butt of the brush back at the operator. Special power brush saws are made for the cutting of brush. On very steep slopes a one-man saw is much the safest, because one operator can abandon the saw quickly if the tree should fall in the wrong direction. Where the tree leans in the opposite direction to that of its intended fall, and where there is not enough room to drive a wedge back of the saw, it is safest and best to go back to the old cross-cut saw. With most two-man and one-man saws, the operators should be very careful that the hand does not slip over the edge of the outboard handle. Especially when gloves are worn, the hand can be very easily pulled into the chain. On one-man saws, this is true when the saw is used in a horizontal position and the guard, where the hand is placed, is on the underside of the saw.

Brush and wood removal

Brush and logs should not be allowed to accumulate at the site of the operation, but should be cleared away as rapidly as possible. Pending removal, debris should be piled so it will not interfere with the operation or where men might stumble over it.

Ground men handling brush should not attempt to pick up the brush or limbwood from under that side of a tree where the climber is working. A ground man having his attention called by workmen in a tree should first step out from under the tree before looking up, in order to avoid falling brush.

Men should not try to lift logs or other loads that are too heavy. A large number of tree accidents result from strains. The loads should be reduced by the use of skids, by cutting logs into shorter lengths, by use of winch equipment, etc.

The man on the truck who is loading the brush should stand between the brush and the cab—never on or straddling a load of brush. Brush should be kept within the bed of the truck and held down tightly by rope lattice. This gives a better vision to cars passing around the truck and prevents the brush from scraping cars or striking pedestrians. Whenever brush extends beyond the confines of the truck, red flags should be placed on the ends.

When disposing of brush by burning, the truck driver should not back his truck close to the fire, but should dump the brush some distance to one side where it may be fed to the fire by hand. On large clearing jobs these brush piles may safely be pushed into the fire by small caterpillar or equal tractors with a rake attachment. Care must be exercised to keep the fire under control. Be sure that there is no chance of the fire's spreading to fields, fences, woods, or buildings. Fires must never be left unattended, and all fire must be extinguished before the crew leaves for lunch and before the work is finished for the day. Every crew required to burn brush should be equipped with a few suitable fire tools. Fire rakes and swatters are especially designed for brush, grass, and leaf-litter fires. Fire pumps, which contain 5 gal of water and are carried on the back, are also useful. Brush must never be burned except in places that have been designated by competent authority, and then only when burning conditions are satisfactory and safe. Locate the fires in open areas well away from trees. Why prune the trees only to scorch them later in the burning operations? Ordinarily, poisonous vines should not be burned, because the smoke is likely to affect susceptible persons. If it is absolutely necessary to burn such material, care should be taken to keep workmen and passersby out of the smoke which carries the poison.

If brush is piled on a public dump, the foreman should make sure that he complies with all the requirements of that particular dumping ground.

Transportation

Truck drivers should qualify under all rules which apply to licensing, driving, and maintenance of motor vehicles.

All persons should get on and off the truck on the right (or curb) side of the truck, or the rear. No one should get on or off when the truck is in motion. The driver should be the last one to get on, and before starting the truck must make certain that all riders are safely within the truck bed.

No person should be allowed to ride on any part of the truck except within the cab or bed. No part of the body should extend beyond any part of the truck when it is in motion. Stake sides and tail gates must be in place in trucks carrying persons.

Tools and equipment must not be carried loosely on the truck beds, but in proper boxes or receptacles provided for them. Every truck should be equipped with a fire extinguisher and a good first-aid kit properly stocked with suitable materials. Crewmen should be instructed in the use of both.

Spraying

All spray materials must be used with extreme caution. Arsenic in any form is a deadly poison, and serious injury or discomfort may result from careless use of many materials. Cautions and instructions for any commercially prepared spray material should be carefully read and observed.

Insecticides, fungicides, and their containers must not be left within reach of children or animals. Spray wastes should be buried or drained into a sewer, and containers should be burned or otherwise destroyed as soon after emptying as possible. Sprayer drippings and materials accidentally spilled should be washed off lawns, walks, and roads.

Although it is questionable whether lead arsenate in concentrations normally deposited in ordinary operations is lethal to birds and stock, it is safer to use nonpoisonous substitutes when spraying in or near bird runs and pastures. Spray materials are especially deadly to fish, and extreme care must be exercised to avoid pollution of ponds, streams, and sources of drinking water.

Stomach poisons, such as lead arsenate, should not be used for insect control on fruits or garden vegetables if there is a possibility that poison residues in harmful concentrations may remain until the time of consumption.

To avoid the hazards of poisoning from lead, arsenic, and other spray materials, the following rules should be observed:

1. If possible, every workman should have a medical examination, including a complete blood analysis, before working with spray materials. Workers having blood diseases should not work with lead.

2. Teeth should be brushed daily after work.

3. Hands and face should be well washed before eating and after work.

4. A shower should be taken and clothes changed as soon after work as possible.

5. Lunches should be kept and eaten away from spray materials.

6. When mixing dry spray materials, the worker should keep the nostrils and mouth covered with a respirator or wet cloth. Most spray materials are especially dangerous in concentrated form.

7. During the spraying season, workers should drink plenty of milk to counteract arsenic poisoning.

8. Operators should wear raincoats, hats, and goggles while spraying, and keep out of the drift as much as possible.

Spray crews using lead arsenate may be subjected to both lead and arsenic poisoning. Symptoms of lead poisoning include headache, dizziness, colic, constipation, loss of weight, convulsions, blood changes, anemia, palsy, neuritis, weakness, blue line on gums, joint pains, twitching, and paralysis. Arsenic poisoning symptoms include skin ulceration; loss of nails and hair; inflammation of the nose, mouth, throat, and lungs; brown discoloring of the skin; perforation of the bonelike part of the nose; muscular weakness; paralysis; and diarrhea. Persons suspecting either type of poisoning should immediately consult a doctor.

Care must be exercised, especially when using a solid stream nozzle, to avoid contact of the spray stream or the nozzle with electric wires. Spray apparatus should be kept as clean as possible at all times, not only for general reasons of good management, but to avoid falls of persons from slippery surfaces. Cleats should be attached to the floors of trucks to prevent slipping on slick surfaces. Hose connections on hydraulic sprayers should be checked and tightened before use to prevent blowing. Extreme care is necessary in cranking motors on sprayers; watch for kickback. There should be no smoking around or on mist blowers when oil solutions are being mixed or used.

Fumigation

Fumigation is the practice of killing pests by means of a gas. The gas may be applied directly from suitable containers or formed from chemicals introduced into the area requiring treatment, which may be tree cavities or soil. Special techniques are required in treatments of this kind.

The chemicals employed are usually very poisonous and should be handled and used only upon the advice of and by persons thoroughly familiar with the individual properties of each. Operators should make sure that they comply with all local laws and regulations covering fumigation.

First aid and poisonous plants

Each member of a tree preservation crew should be trained in first aid and the back pressure—arm lift method of resuscitation. First aid kits should be provided for each crew.

Small cuts, scratches, and blisters must be attended to immediately. Even the most minor scratch may easily become infected and lead to serious complications.

A common source of "lost-time" accidents among tree workers is contact with poisonous plants such as poison ivy, poison oak, and poison sumac. Susceptibility to the poison varies with individuals, but it is never safe to assume immunity from it.

Learn to know the poisonous plants on sight and then avoid contact with them. If contact cannot be avoided, the hands, arms, and face should be washed as soon as possible after exposure with strong yellow soap or washing powder, which will often prevent infection, or at least retard it.

There is danger of reinfection through handling or wearing clothes which have been in contact with poisonous species, even after the passage of months or years. Susceptible persons should avoid wearing such clothes.

Poison ivy remedies are numerous, but most are of doubtful value as preventives or cures. They may relieve itching and burning, but frequently a remedy that will give relief to one person may not help another. Some of the newer treatments are reported to be superior to older remedies. However, avoid promiscuous use, particularly with home remedies, as they may tend to spread rather than cure the infection. Susceptible persons should investigate through proper medical channels the latest immunization treatments. A physician should be consulted in all cases of severe poisoning.

Duties of the first-aid man

The trained man possesses the ability to render first aid, and should immediately assume charge of the situation. He should:

1. Keep the patient lying down.
2. Determine the nature and extent of the injuries. Serious bleeding, stoppage of breathing, and internal poisoning demand immediate treatment and take precedence over everything else.
3. Keep the patient warm.
4. Send for a physician or ambulance immediately and do not move the patient unless absolutely necessary in more serious cases. For less serious injuries, prepare the patient for transportation and get him to a doctor.
5. Keep calm.
6. Never give an unconscious person anything to drink.
7. Keep onlookers away from the injured.
8. Make the patient comfortable and cheer him as much as possible.
9. Avoid letting the patient see his own injury.

NURSERY STOCK STANDARDS

There are many times when it becomes necessary to purchase various types of plant materials, either as replacement stock or for expansion of existing plantings. At such times it is necessary to know the relationship between the height, spread, caliper and branching habits of trees and shrubs. Since all reputable nurseries adhere to grading standards as established by the American Association of Nurserymen, it is best to prepare specifications for purchasing plant materials based on these standards.

The standards given here are slightly adapted from the original standards in the "American Standards for Nursery Stock" approved by the American Standards Association.

Deciduous trees

Height measurement: Height shall be given in single feet, up to 6 ft: (5–6 ft) ; over 6 ft height shall be given in double feet: (6–8 ft, 12–14 ft).

Height of branching for street trees: Unless otherwise specified, street trees are to be free of branches to a point not to exceed 60 per cent of their actual height. Height of branching should bear a relationship to size and kind of tree, so that "top" branching will be in good balance with the trunk as the tree grows. Example: Norway maple (6), 2–2½ in. caliper, 12–14 ft branched 6–7 ft. Branching height of trees 11 ft and up may vary from that specified as much as 1 ft, and the tree will be in proper balance. Trees with ascending branches (American elm) may be branched even lower than 12 in. below optimum height and still provide proper clearance. Higher branching is often desired on larger trees, particularly for those planted close to pavements and for types with descending branching habits.

Caliper measurement: Measure caliper 6 in. above the ground; if this measurement is more than 4 in., substitute caliper 12 in. above the ground. Caliper shall be the determining measurement in grading.

Height in relationship to caliper: Actual height measurement expressed as a minimum to a maximum height may be given in listing trees. The grades specified are minimum heights only, for general varieties. See Fig. 3.21.

Type 1. Standard shade trees

Relationship of height to caliper will, for most standard shade trees, be as follows:

Caliper of tree, in inches	Minimum height, in feet
½ – ¾	5 – 6
¾ – 1	6 – 8
1 – 1 ¼	7 – 9
1 ½ – 2	10 – 12
2 – 3	12 – 14
3 – 4	14 – 16
4 – 5	16 – 18
5 – 6	18 and up

Sizes under one inch may be calipered if desired.

Examples:

Ash, American (104)	Linden, bigleaf (298)
Ash, green (105)	Linden, European (295)
Elm, American (302)	Linden, silver (299)
Lindens, American (294)	Maidenhair tree (107)

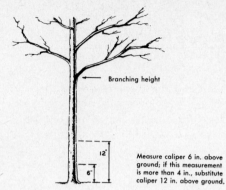

Fig. 3.21   Type I Standard shade trees

Branching height

12"

6"

Measure caliper 6 in. above
ground; if this measurement
is more than 4 in., substitute
caliper 12 in. above ground.

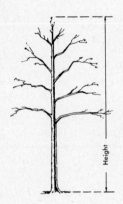

Fig. 3.22   Type II Slow growing shade trees

CALIPER MEASUREMENTS
DETERMINE GRADING

Height in relation to caliper
must not be less than ⅔ that
given in table for Type 1.

Measure caliper 6 in. above
ground; if this measurement
is more than 4 in., substitute
caliper 12 in. above ground.

Height

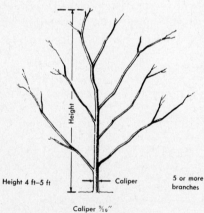

Fig. 3.23   Type III Small and flowering
shrubs

Height

Height 4 ft–5 ft   Caliper   5 or more
branches

Caliper ⅜"

PLANTING AND CARE OF TREES AND SHRUBS

Maple, Norway (6)
Maple, red (9)
Maple, silver (10)
Maple, sugar (11)
Oak, black (218)
Oak, mossy-cup (215)
Oak, pin (216)
Oak, red (217)
Oak, scarlet (214)
Plane tree (194–196)
Poplar (197–200)
Tulip tree (159) (may vary in height)

Numbers following common name refer to master list on pages 152 to 158 for scientific name.

Type 2. Slower-growing shade trees

Trees of slower growth which will not usually attain the height measurement in relation to caliper as in Type 1 would, however, be not less than two-thirds the heights given for Type 1. See Fig. 3.22.
Examples:

Ash, mountain (252)
Beech, American (101)
Beech, European (102)
Birch (30–32)
Chestnut, horse (12)
Hackberry (41)
Hop hornbeam, American (178)
Linden, common (297)
Linden, Crimean (296)
Linden, little-leaf (295)
Oak, swamp-white (212)
Oak, white (211)
Sweetgum (160)
Tupelo or Sourgum (177)
Yellow-wood (49)

Type 3. Small and flowering trees

This is a broad group, including small trees as well as "standard" forms of plants which may be grown as clumps or shrubs. Height is the governing measurement. See Fig. 3.23. For single stem plants, the relationship of caliper and branching will be as follows:

Height of tree (ft)	Caliper of tree (in.)	Minimum no. of branches
2 – 3	5/16	3
3 – 4	7/16	4
4 – 5	9/16	5
5 – 6	11/16	6
6 – 9	7/8	6

Examples:

Crab apples (167–174)
Dogwood, flowering (55–56)
Flowering-almond (205)
Golden rain tree (145)

Great silver ball (110)
Hawthorns—upright types (77–80)
Hornbeam, American (39)
Laburnum (146)
Magnolias (165)
Maple, amur (5)

Maple, hedge (4)
Redbud (43)
Shrub-althea (114)
Snowbell, fragrant (263)
Snowbell, Japanese (262)
Sourwood (179)

Many of the above trees classified as single-stem, or tree-form, may be grown with two or more stems.

Deciduous trees for other uses

Trees for other uses should be branched naturally, according to type. Where a form of growth is desired which is not in accordance with normal growth habit, this form should be so specified.

Bush form: Trees which start to branch close to the ground in the manner of a shrub.

Clumps: Trees with three or more main stems starting from the ground.

Cut back or sheared: Trees that have been pruned back so as to multiply the branching structure and to develop a more formal effect.

Topiary: Trees sheared or trimmed closely in a formal, geometric pattern.

Top-worked trees: Height of stem and age should be specified.

Grading tolerance: The growing of plant material cannot be standardized because of varying conditions of growth, methods of handling, by climate, soil, and other conditions beyond the control of the grower.

DECIDUOUS SHRUBS—HEIGHT MEASUREMENT

Dwarf shrubs: State height in inches up to 24; usually in 3-in. series (3–6 in., 6–9 in., 12–15 in. etc.). State heights greater than 24 in. in feet, with .5 ft series (2–2.5 ft, 2.5–3 ft).

Strong growing shrubs: Grade shrubs up to 24 in. in a 6-in. series (12–18 in., 18–24 in.). Grade shrubs over 24 in. by single feet up to 6 ft; then in double feet above 6 ft.

Quality definitions: Quality, density, and condition of the shrubs are more important considerations than the actual physical measurement of height, number of canes, and root development. If a plant is well grown with single stem, well-shaped, and bushy, and has sufficient well-spaced side branches to give it weight equal to one grown with numerous canes, it should be an equally acceptable plant. See Fig. 3.24 and 3.25.

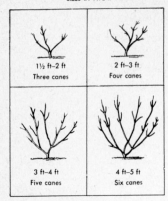

Fig. 3.24   Deciduous shrubs

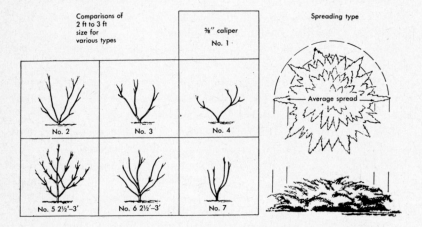

Fig. 3.25   Deciduous shrubs

A cane is defined as a primary stem which starts from the ground or close to the ground at a point not higher than one-fourth the height of the plant.

Clumps indicate plants with at least double the number of canes needed for standard material.

Type 1. Shrubs: Dwarf and semidwarf

Height of shrub (in.)	Minimum number of counted canes	Minimum height of counted canes (in.)
12 – 15	3	12
15 – 18	4	15
18 – 24	5	18
24 – 30	6	24
30 – 36	7	30

Examples:

Cinquefoil, shrubby (201)   Rose, bristly (238)
Currant, mountain (232)   Rose, Virginia (242)
Deutzia, Lemoine (84)   St. Johnsworth, kalm (120)
Deutzia, rose panicle (83)   Spirea, Anthony Waterer (254)
Deutzia, slender (82)   Spirea, fortune (255)
Huckleberry (106) dwarf types

Type 2. Shrubs

Height of shrub (ft)	Minimum number of counted canes	Minimum height of counted canes (ft)
1.5 – 2	3	1.5
2 – 3	4	2
3 – 4	5	3
4 – 5	6	4

Examples:

Beautyberry, Chinese (36)   Mockorange, Lemoine (184)
Bush clover (148)   Privet, amur (151)
Buttonbush, common (42)   Privet, European (157)
Deutzia (85)   Privet, ibolium (152)
Dogwood, coral (62)   Privet, ibota (153)
Dogwood, gray (59)   Redbud (43)
Dogwood, red osier (63)   Rose, Japanese (237)
Dogwood, silky (54)   Rose, prairie (241)
Dogwood, tatarian (52)   Spirea (256)
Honeysuckle, southern bush   Stephanandra, cutleaf (260)
  (86)   Sweetspice (130)
Jetbead (223)

Type 3. Shrubs

Height of shrub (ft)	Minimum number of counted canes	Minimum height of counted canes (ft)
1.5 – 2	2	1.5
2 – 3	3	2
3 – 4	4	3
4 – 5	5	4

Examples:

Alder, smooth (14)
Almond (203)
Aralia, five-leaved (3)
Arrowwood (310)
Bayberry (176)
Blueberry, highbush (304)
Buckthorn, common (219)
Buckthorn, glossy (220)
Chokeberry, red (18)
Chokeberry, black (19)
Coralberry, common (268)
Cotoneaster, Peking (68)
Cranberrybush, European (316)
Deerberry (305)
Euonymous, brook (92)
Elder, American (245)
Elder, European (246)
Forsythias (103)
Hydrangea, snowhill (115)
Hydrangea, peegee (117)
Honeysuckle, bush (161)
Hazelnut, American (64)
Kerria (144)
Lilac, Chinese (270)
Lilac, Manchurian (269)
Lilac, Japanese tree (271)
Lilac, Hungarian (272)
Lilac, Persian (273)
Lilac, late (274)
Mockorange (183–184)
  (all standard varieties)
Privet, regal (156)
Plum, myrobalan (204)
Plum, flowering (207)
Quince, Japanese flowering (45)
Rosemallow (113)
Rose, meadow (234)
Spirea, false Kashmir (249)
Spirea, tree (250)
Spirea, false Ural (251)
Snowberry, spreading (266)
Snowberry, western (267)
Snowberry, Chenault (265)
Snowball, Japanese (318)
Sumac, fragrant (226)
Sumac, shining (227)
Viburnum, Kentucky (314)
Viburnum, double-file (323)
Winterberry, smooth (127)
Winterberry, common (129)
Wayfaring tree (312)
Weigela, Eva Rathke (327)
Withe rod (309)
Witch hazel (111)

Type 4. Shrubs

Height of shrubs (ft)	Minimum number of counted canes	Minimum height of counted canes (ft)
1.5 – 2	2	1.5
2 – 3	3	2
3 – 4	4	3
4 – 5	5	4

Examples:

Bladder-senna, common (51)
Bush clover (148)
Buckthorn, common (219)

Buckthorn, glossy (220)
Blackhaw (319)
Burningbush, European (94)

Chaste tree (325)
Dogwood, coral (62)
Dogwood, Pagoda (53)
Elder, scarlet (247)
Eleagnus, autumn (89)
Euonymus, winged (90)
Euonymus, winterberry (93)
Euonymus, yeddo (99)
Fringetree, white (48)
Groundsel-bush (24)
Indigo bush (16)
Lilac, common (275)
Lilac, common white (276)

Nannyberry (313)
Olive, Russian (87)
Pea-tree, Siberian (38)
Pearlbush, common (100)
Smoketree, American (66)
Smoketree, common (67)
Summersweet (50)
Silverbell, great (110)
Spicebush (158)
Sumac, shining (227)
Tamarix (277)
Weigela, Eva Rathke (327)

Type 5. Shrubs, heavy and treelike

Height of shrubs (ft)	Minimum number of counted canes	Minimum height of counted canes (ft)	Caliper (in.)
1.5 – 2	1	1.5	$5/16$
2 – 3	1	2	$3/8$
3 – 4	1	3	$1/2$
4 – 5	1	4	$5/8$
5 – 6	1	5	$7/8$

Examples:

Sumac, cutleaf (229)
Sumac, shredded (231)

Sumac, smooth (228)
Sumac, staghorn (230)

Type 6. Barberry, common (27)

Height of shrub (in.)	Minimum number of counted canes	Minimum height of counted canes (in.)
12 – 15	3	12
15 – 18	3	15
18 – 24	4	18
24 – 30	4	24
30 – 36	5	30
Over 36	6	36

Type 7. Privet in variety (151–157)

Height of shrub (ft)	Minimum number of counted canes	Minimum height of counted canes (in.)
1.5 – 2	3	1.5
2 – 3	4	2
3 – 4	5	3
4 – 5	6	4

Note: For other species of privet, see Types 2 and 3.

Grading tolerance for shrubs: The growing of plant material cannot be standardized because of varying conditions of growth and methods of handling due to climate, soil, and other conditions beyond the control of the grower.

Quality definition for shrubs: A plant with smaller number of canes, yet well-shaped and bushy, and with sufficient side branching to give it weight equal to one with numerous canes, should be equally acceptable. The recommended grades apply to plants grown under average soil and climatic conditions, which have been transplanted, root-pruned and trimmed according to regular nursery practice.

EVERGREENS—CONIFERS

Specimen: Used to indicate exceptionally heavy, well-shaped plants which have been cut back or trimmed to form a symmetrical, tightly knit plant. The letters X, XX, or XXX may be used to designate an extra heavy grade.

Collected: Natural seedling or fully grown plants dug from native stands or forest plantings must be so designated.

Type 1. Spreading type

Measurement designates spread; height is not considered. See Fig. 3.26 and 3.27.

Height (in.)	Measurement interval (in.)
18 or less	3
18–48	6
48 or more	12

Measurement should be average, not greatest, diameter. Plants properly trimmed and transplanted should measure the same in any direction. An uneven plant measuring 15 in. at the greatest diameter and 9 in. at the least diameter should be classified as 12-in. stock.

Example: Spreading junipers (133, 134, 137, 138, 139)

Type 2. Semispreading type

Measurement designates spread.

Height (in.)	Measurement interval (in.)
18 or less	3
18–48	6
48 or more	12

Measurement should be average, as in Type 1.

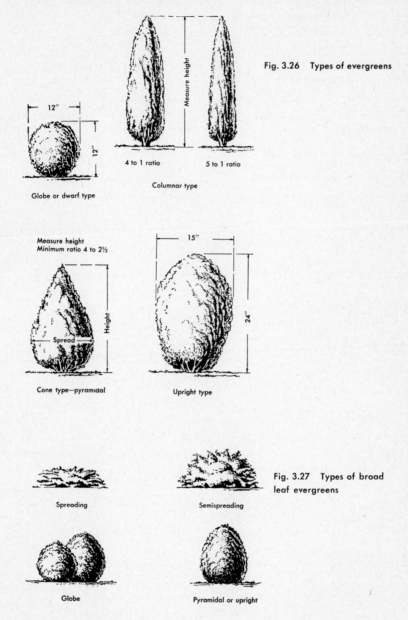

Fig. 3.26   Types of evergreens

12"

12"

Globe or dwarf type

Measure height

4 to 1 ratio

5 to 1 ratio

Columnar type

Measure height
Minimum ratio 4 to 2½

Height

Spread

Cone type—pyramidal

15"

24"

Upright type

Spreading

Semispreading

Fig. 3.27   Types of broad
leaf evergreens

Globe

Pyramidal or upright

Relationship of height to spread

For first-class material height will be at least one-half of spread. Above 3 ft height will be less than spread, varying somewhat with the natural growth of the species and the method of handling.

Spread (in.)	Height (in.)
6 – 36	(same as spread)
36 – 48	30 – 42
48 – 60	36 – 48

Examples: Pfitzer juniper (133); Japanese yew (282)

Type 3. Globe or dwarf type

Measurement designates height.

Height (in.)	Measurement interval (in.)
18 or less	3
18 – 48	6
48 or more	12

Spread will usually be equal to height in well-grown material up to 12 in. In taller specimens there will be variation depending upon variety.

Spread (in.)	Height (in.)
(same as height)	6 – 12
10	12 – 15
12	15 – 18
15	18 – 24
18	24 – 30
21	30 – 36
24	36 – 42

Many broad spreading and globe types in this classification will usually have the same spread as height, even in larger sizes.

Examples: Arborvitae, globe (288); Globe red cedar (142); Spruce, dwarf ball-shaped types (188)

Type 4. Cone type (Pyramidal)

Height (ft)	Measurement interval (in.)
1.5 or less	3
1.5–5	6
5–8	12
8 or more	24

The ratio of height to spread of properly grown material should not be less than 4 to 2.5.

Spread (in.)	Height (in.)
8–12	12–15
9–15	15–18
12–18	18–24
15–21	24–30
18–24	30–36
21–30	36–48
30–36	48–60
36–48	60–72

Examples:

Arborvitae, American (289)

Arborvitae, giant (293)

Arborvitae, Oriental (292)

Fir, Douglas (209)

Hemlock, Canadian (300)

Hemlock, Carolina (301)

Pine (except dwarf types) (191–192)

Retinospora, sawara (46)

Spruce, Norway (187)

Yew, upright (283)

Type 5. Columnar type (Pyramidal)

Measurement designates height. Use same measurement intervals as for Type 4. This group includes all upright-growing evergreens which naturally develop a straight-sided form or one that tapers slightly from the ground to a point more than half the height. See Fig. 3.26.

The broader types will usually have a ratio of height to spread of four to one.

Spread (in.)	Height (in.)
3–6	12–15
4–7	15–18
5–8	18–24
6–9	24–30
7–10	30–36
9–12	36–48
12–15	48–60
15–18	60–72
18–21	72–84
21–24	84–96
24–30	96–120

Examples:

Arborvitae, American (289)

Arborvitae, oriental (292)

Arborvitae, Rosenthal (291)

Juniper, common (135)

Juniper, Irish (136)

Juniper, red cedar (141)

Yew, Hicks (285)

EVERGREENS—BROADLEAF

Five general types or groups (See Fig. 3.27) are considered separately as follows:

Type 1. Spreading type

Measurement designates spread; height is not considered.

Spread (in.)	Measurement interval (in.)
24 or less	3
24–48	6
over 48	12

Examples: Cotoneaster, rock—all varieties (72, 73)

Type 2. Semispreading type

Measurement designates spread; height is not considered.

Spread (in.)	Measurement interval (in.)
24 or less	3
24–48	6
over 48	12

Examples:

Abelia (1)
Andromeda, mountain (189)
Azalea, amoena (20)
Azalea, hiryu (22)

Barberry, warty (29)
Cotoneaster, franchet (71)
Cotoneaster, willowleaf (75)
Daphne, winter (81)

Type 3. Globe or dwarf type

Measurement designates height.

Height (in.)	Measurement intreval (in.)
less than 24	3
24–48	6
over 48	12

Up to 12 in. (height), the spread will usually be equal to or only slightly less than the height. In specimens over 12 in., the spread may be less than the height, but the height will never be more than twice the spread.

Height (in.)	Minimum spread (in.)
6–9	5
9–12	6
12–15	7
15–18	9
18–21	10
21–24	12
24–30	14

Examples:

Boxwood, common (33)
Holly, Japanese (122)
Leucothoe, drooping (150)

Myrtle, sand (147)
Speedwell (evergreen type) (306)

Type 4. Pyramidal or upright type

Measurement designates height.

Height (in.)	Measurement interval (in.)
less than 18	3
18–36	6
over 36	12

This group includes all of the larger growing upright "broadleaves" which vary considerably in ratio of spread to height. Well-grown material will in most cases have a height equal to if not greater than the spread. However, the spread should not be less than two-thirds of the height.

Height (in.)	Minimum spread (in.)
12–15	8
15–18	10
18–24	12
24–30	16
36–48	24
48–60	28

Examples:

Andromeda, Japanese (190)
Barberry, wintergreen (25)
Holly, Japanese (122)
Holly, American (128)

Hollygrape, Oregon (166)
Privet, glossy (154)
Rhododendrons (221)
Viburnum, leatherleaf (320)

General

Measurement of height should be where the branches start, and not at the ground, if the plant is leggy. It should stop where the main part of the plant ends and not extend to the tip of a thin shoot.

TABLE 3.13 RECOMMENDED BALLING AND BURLAPPING SPECIFICATIONS

Type 1 Spreading coniferous broadleaf evergreens		Type 2 Broadleaf coniferous evergreens		Type 3 Columnar coniferous evergreens		Type 4 Shrubs and small trees		Type 5 Standard shade trees	
Spread (ft)	Min. diam. ball (in.)	Height (ft)	Min. diam. ball (in.)	Height (ft)	Min. diam. ball (in.)	Height (ft)	Min. diam. ball (ft)	Caliper (ft)	Min. diam. ball (in.)
1.5–2	11	1.5–2	11	1.5–2	11	1.5–2	10	1.25–1.5	18
2–2.5	13	2–3	13	2–3	12	2–3	12	1.5–1.75	20
2.5–3	15	3–4	15	3–4	13	3–4	13	1.75–2	22
3–3.5	16	4–5	17	4–5	14	4–5	15	2–2.5	24
3.5–4	18	5–6	19	5–6	16	5–6	16	2.5–3	28
4–5	21	6–7	21	6–7	18	6–7	18	3–3.5	32
5–6	24	7–8	24	7–8	20	7–8	20	3.5–4	36
6–7	28	8–9	27	8–9	22	8–9	22	4–4.5	40
7–8	32	9–10	30	9–10	24	9–10	24	4.5–5	44
8–9	36	10–12	33	10–12	27	10–12	26	5–5.5	48
		12–14	36	12–14	30				
		14–16	40	14–16	33				
		16–18	44	16–18	36				
		18–20	48	18–20	40				

Note: For upper limits of various sizes, the minimum sizes of ball should be proportionately increased to meet the lower limits of ball sizes for the next higher classification.

BALL DEPTHS

The ball of earth used for transplanting should be deep enough to encompass the fibrous and feeding root system necessary for the full recovery of the plant. See Fig. 3.28.

Ratios for ball depths

Diameter (in.)	Depth, in per cent of diameter
less than 20	75
20–30	66⅔
31–48	60

For larger diameters, depth percentages will be scaled down in similar progression.

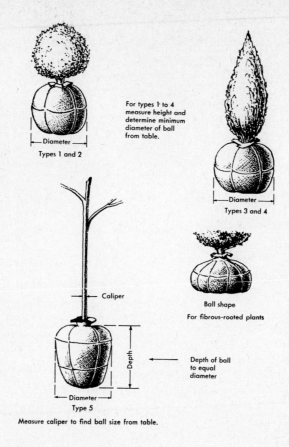

For types 1 to 4 measure height and determine minimum diameter of ball from table.

Diameter
Types 1 and 2

Diameter
Types 3 and 4

Caliper

Ball shape
For fibrous-rooted plants

Depth

Depth of ball to equal diameter

Diameter
Type 5

Measure caliper to find ball size from table.

Fig. 3.28   Balling and burlapping recommendations

Ball sizes for collected plants

Collected material will require a larger ball than that recommended for transplanted nursery stock, because trees and shrubs which have grown in natural surroundings have unrestricted root development and varying soil conditions. For such material the minimum size ball should be at least one-third greater than those specified above.

Examples, Type 1, Spreading conifers and broadleaf evergreens:

Arborvitae, globe (288)   Juniper, pfitzer (133)
Azaleas (20–23)   Rhododendron (221–222)
Cotoneaster (68–76)   Yews, spreading (281–282)

Diameter—48 in.
Depth—29 in.
Ratio—60 per cent

Fig. 3.29   Ball depth ratio

Diameter—30 in.
Depth—20 in.
Ratio—66⅔ per cent

Diameter—20 in.
Depth—15 in.
Ratio—75 per cent

Examples, Type 2, Broad coniferous and broadleaf evergreens:

Cypress—fast growing,
    upright varieties (46)
Hemlock (301–302)
Laurel (143)

Magnolia (165)
Spruce, Norway (187)
Pine (191–193)

Examples, Type 3, Columnar and coniferous evergreens:

Arborvitae—upright
    varieties (289–293)
Holly (128)

Juniper (135 and 141)
Yew—upright (283)

Examples, Type 4, Shrubs and small trees:

Cherry, flowering (208)
Dogwood (52–63)

Hawthorn (77–80)
Viburnum (307–324)

Examples, Type 5, Standard shade trees:

Birch (30–32)
Maple (5–11)

Oak (211–218)

ROSE GRADES

All grades of roses must have well-developed root systems and weight and
caliper appropriate to grade and variety. All No. 1 grades and No. 1½
grades should be tied 10 to a bundle, and No. 2 grades 20 to a bundle. Grade
specification and two printed variety labels should appear on each bundle.

Grade specifications for roses

(Varieties covered: Tea, hybrid tea, and everblooming; rugosa hybrids; hybrid perpetuals, and miscellaneous bush roses)

	Minimum strong canes	No. strong canes minimum height	Minimum height (in.)	Height of branching above bud union (in.)
Grade No. 1	3	2	18	
No. 1 light-growing	3	2	16	3
Grade No. 1½	2	2	15	
No. 1½, light-growing	2	2	13	3
Grade No. 2	2	2	12	
No. 2, light-growing	2	2	10	3

Grade specifications for floribunda roses

	Minimum strong canes	No. strong canes minimum height	Minimum height (in.)	Height of branching above bud union (in.)
Grade No. 1	3	2	15	
No. 1, light growing	3	2	13	3
Grade No. 1½, (medium)	2	2	14	
No. 1½, light-growing	2	2	12	3

Grade specifications for polyantha—baby roses

	Minimum canes	Minimum height (in.)	Height of branching above bud union (in.)
Grade No. 1	4	13	3
Grade No. 1½ (medium)	3	10	3
Grade No. 2 not recognized.			

Grade specifications for climbing roses

	Minimum strong canes	Minimum height (in.)	Height of branching above bud union or crown (in.)
Grade No. 1	3	24	
Grade No. 1 Wichuriana	4	24	3
Grade No. 1½ (medium)	2	18	
Grade No. 1½ Wichuriana	3	18	3

VINES

Type 1. Fast-growing vines

Fast-growing vines, which normally produce a number of vigorous woody runners in one or two years, are graded and designated as follows:

	Tops	No. runners of minimum length	Minimum length of runners (in.)	Root system
2–yr, No. 1	Heavy, well-branched	3	18	Vigorous, well-developed
2–yr, No. 2	Lighter, but no serious defects	3	12	Commensurate with top

Older vines should be designated according to age, heavy or light grade, length of runners, and other characteristics such as standard, grafted, potted, or tubbed.

Examples:

Bittersweet, American
Bittersweet, oriental
Creeper, Engelman
Honeysuckle, Japanese

Honeysuckle, Hall's
Honeysuckle, trumpet
Wisteria

Type 2. Medium growing vines

Woody vines, usually starting with a single cane or runner should be designated by age and grade (heavy and light).

	Tops	Root system
2–yr, No. 1	Heavy, well-branched	Vigorous, well-developed
2–yr., Medium	Lighter, less well-branched, but no serious defects.	Commensurate with top

Older vines should be designated according to age, heavy or light grades, length of runners, and other characteristics such as standard, grafted, potted, or tubbed.

Examples:

Actinidia
Boston ivy
Dutchman's pipe
English ivy

Grapes
Trumpet vine
Wintercreeper (and varieties)

Type 3. Clump type

Clump type should be designated by age and heavy or light grade. Dormant plants may or may not have live runners. In this group a well-developed root system and healthy, well-developed crown are important considerations.

Examples:

Clematis and Kudzu vine.

Type 4. Dwarf vines, ground cover

Dwarf vines and ground cover are to be designated or described by age, size of clump and length of runners, and other characteristics peculiar to the particular species offered.

Examples:

Bearberry
Bunchberry

Periwinkle
Spurge, Japanese

Plants in pots or containers: Plants in pots or other containers of adequate size for size of plant and which have been acclimated to outside conditions, should be equal to and acceptable for field grown stock.

Collected vines (Coll.): Plants collected from the wild must be so designated.

STANDARDS FOR SEEDLING TREES AND SHRUBS

Plantings for forests, game refuges, erosion control, shelter belts, or farm woodlot plantings, under natural conditions, should be selected from the following classifications. Actual conditions of soil, climate, and environment will necessarily govern minimum size for any particular species required. Tolerance of not more than 10 per cent under grade should be accepted so long as it is not intentional and the under-graded specimens are close to the grade required.

Deciduous or hardwoods

When caliper is important, measurements are taken at root collar or ground line.

Caliper (in.)	Minimum height (in.)	Minimum root length (in.)
$1.5/16$–$2.5/16$	6	8
$2.5/16$–$3/16$	8	8
$3/16$–$3.5/16$	10	10
$3.5/16$ and over	12	10

Tops and roots are not trimmed unless specified by growers or requested by purchaser in the above.

When height is to govern, measurements are taken from root collar or ground line.

Height (in.)	Minimum caliper (in.)	Minimum root length (in.)
6–12	$1.5/16$	8
12–18	$2.5/16$	10
18–24	$3/16$	10
24–36	$3.5/16$	12

The above standards are suggested for commercial nurseries furnishing or purchasing stock for the retail trade, which still wish to comply with demands for calipered stock.

It should be understood that when heights are to govern the caliper specification is minimum, and when caliper is to govern the height specification is minimum.

Conifers (Evergreens)

Height (in.)	Minimum caliper (in.)
6–9	$1.5/16$
9–12	$2.5/16$
12–15	$3/16$

Note: Age is not important when height or caliper is specified; however it may be used in listings or demanded by purchaser

DESIGNATIONS

Transplantings: One "T" is used to represent each time transplanted.
Root-pruned: "RP" (6 in. maximum for conifers).
Seedlings: "S."

GENERAL SPECIFICATIONS

All plants should have well-developed root systems; be free of insects, diseases, and mechanical injuries; and be suitable in all respects for field planting. All conifers must have dormant buds (except in the South) and secondary needles. At the option of the purchaser, other special restrictions may be specified.

BULBS, CORMS, AND TUBERS

General

Bulbs and corms are generally sold under grade names such as forcing size, top-size, large, etc. In the case of narcissus and daffodils, the designations of "double nose" to indicate a split bulb with probably two flower buds, and "rounds" are used.

With some groups, for example hyacinths, the grade names indicate usage such as exhibition and forcing sizes and sizes more suitable for outdoor bedding purposes.

Some grade measurements have normally been given in centimeters of circumference, since this measurement allows closer grading. This system is in vogue and is generally accepted in the trade for the smaller size bulbs such as crocus and grape hyacinth, while for larger and particularly for the flat type corms, such as gladioli, tuberous begonias, and caladiums, inches in diameter is the generally accepted measurement.

For such items as peonies, bleeding heart, and cannas, the number of "eyes" or buds on the tuber is designated.

The following grades conform in substance to generally accepted trade usage. Both grade names and sizes in inches or centimeters should be given; size in inches or centimeters must be designated.

Offers of bulbs, corms and tubers (except peony divisions) which cannot reasonably be expected to bloom in the season after planting should not be made to the public, but if they are, they should be clearly indicated as "non-blooming" sizes for naturalization or other similar plantings.

1. Size grades for tulips

Grade	Circumference (centimeters)	Circumference (in.)
Top size	12 and over	4¾ and over
Large	11–12	4⅜–4¾
Medium	10–11	4 –4⅜
Small	9–10	3⅝–4

Note: Some botanical and species tulips are smaller than the sizes designated in the table. Such bulbs should be identified as botanical or species, and the sizes given.

2. Size grades for hyacinths

Grade	Circumference (centimeters)	Circumference (in.)
Top exhibition forcing	19 and over	7⅝
Large exhibition forcing	18–19	7¼–7⅝
Medium exhibition forcing	17–18	6¾–7¼
Top bedding or garden	16–17	6⅜–6¾
Large bedding or garden	15–16	6 –6⅜
Medium bedding, miniature, or garden	14–15	5½–6

3. Size grades for grape hyacinths

Grade	Circumference (centimeters)
Top size	9–11
Large	8–9
Medium	7–8

4. Size grades for crocuses

Grade	Circumference (centimeters)	Circumference (in.)
Top size	9 and over	3⅝ and over
Large	8–9	3⅛–3⅝
Medium	7–8	2¾–3⅛
Small	6–7	2 –2¾

5. Size grades for narcissus and daffodils

Grades: Top size round, large round, medium round; top size double-nose, large double-nose, medium double-nose. No standard sizes have been established.

"Round" means single-nosed bulbs which are fairly circular in cross-section and show evidence of producing one flower. Slabs are not permitted in this grade.

"Double-nose" means bulbs that show indications of producing two or more flowers. Because bulbs are double, circumference measurements are variable.

There are certain varieties which normally have smaller bulbs than others. These varieties have not been officially graded, and therefore name grade designations as indicated and accepted by the trade should be used.

6. Size grades for narcissus (paper white)

Bulbs of this type are normally smaller than other varieties, and are therefore listed separately.

Grade	Circumference (centimeters)	Circumference (in.)
Top size	16 and over	6⅜ and over
Large	15–16	6 –6⅜
Medium	14–15	5½–6
Small	12–14	4¾–5½

7. Size grades for gladioli

Gladioli are designated by inches in diameter.

Grade	Diameter (in.)
Jumbo	Over 2
Large	
No. 1	1½–2
No. 2	1¼–1½
Medium	
No. 3	1 –1¼
No. 4	¾–1
Small	
No. 5	½– ¾
No. 6	⅜–1
No grade name	
No. 7	Under ⅜

8. Size grades for amaryllis

Grade	Diameter (in.)
Fancy	3½ and over
Top size	3¼–3½
Large	3 –3¼
Medium	2¾–33
Small	2¼–2¾
(Sizes under 2¼ in. are not acceptable.)	

9. Size grades for lilies (regal and Easter)

Grade	Circumference (in.)
Giant	10 and over
Fancy	9–10
Extra large	8–9
Large	7–8
Standard	6–7
Medium	5–6

10. Size grades for caladium (fancy-leaved)

Grade	Diameter (in.)
Giant	3½ and over
Large	2½–3½
Standard	2 –2½
Medium	1½–2
Small	1 –1½

11. Size grades for tuberous begonias and gloxinias

Grade	Diameter (in.)
Giant	2½ and over
Extra large	2 –2½
Large	1½–2
Medium	1¼–1½
Small	1 –1¼

12. Size designations for tuberoses

Grade	Circumference (in.)
Top size	4–6
First size	3–4

13. Size grades for callas and other miscellaneous bulbs

			Diameter (in.)			
	Giant	Top	Extra large	Large	Medium	Small
Callas	–	2½ or over	–	2 –2½	1½–2	1¼–1½
Ranunculus	1 or over	–	⅞–1	¾– ⅞	⅝– ¾	½– ⅝
Freesia	–	–	⅞ or over	¾– ⅞	⅝– ¾	½– ⅝
Anemones	–	–	⅞ or over	¾– ⅞	⅝– ¾	½– ⅝

14. Grades for peonies and bleeding hearts
Number of "eyes," or buds, per division should be indicated.

Grade	No. of "eye" divisions
Select	5–7
Standard	3–5
Small	2–3

15. Grades for cannas
Number of "eyes" or buds per root should be indicated; for example 2–3 eye roots. Roots with less than 2 "eyes" should not be offered for sale, although they may be used for special purposes in the nursery.

16. Grades for dahlias
Because the character of division in dahlias varies so widely from one variety to another no size designations can be listed. Each division should have a portion of live crown and at least one "eye" or bud.

TABLE 3.14/A MASTER LIST OF TREES AND SHRUBS

Key	Botanical Name	Common Name
1.	*Abelia grandiflora*	Glossy abelia
2.	*Abies* species	Fir
3.	*Acanthopanax pentaphyllum*	Five-leaved aralia
4.	*Acer campestre*	Hedge maple
5.	*Acer ginnala*	Amur maple
6.	*Acer platanoides*	Norway maple
7.	*Acer platanoides columnare*	Columnar Norway maple
8.	*Acer pseudo platanus*	Sycamore maple
9.	*Acer rubrum*	Red maple
10.	*Acer saccharinum*	Silver maple
11.	*Acer saccharum*	Sugar maple
12.	*Aesculus* species	Horsechestnut
13.	*Ailanthus glandulosa*	Tree of heaven
14.	*Alnus rugosa*	Smooth alder
15.	*Amelanchier canadensis*	Downy shadblow or shadbush
16.	*Amorpha fruticosa*	Indigobush
17.	*Aronia* species	Chokeberry
18.	*Aronia arbutifolia*	Red chokeberry
19.	*Aronia melanocarpa*	Black chokeberry
20.	*Azalea amoena*	Amoena azalea
21.	*Azalea hinodegiri*	Hinodegiri azalea
22.	*Azalea obtusa*	Hiryu azalea
23.	*Azalea kaempferi*	Torch azalea
24.	*Baccharis halimifolia*	Groundsel-bush
25.	*Berberis julianae*	Wintergreen barberry
26.	*Berberis* species	Barberry
27.	*Berberis thunbergii*	Japanese barberry
28.	*Berberis triacanthophora*	Threespine barberry
29.	*Berberis verruculosa*	Warty barberry
30.	*Betula alba*	European white birch
31.	*Betula papyrifera*	Canoe birch
32.	*Betula populifolia*	Gray birch
33.	*Buxus sempervirens*	Common boxwood
34.	*Buxus suffruticosa*	Dwarf English box
35.	*Callicarpa japonica*	American beautyberry
36.	*Callicarpa purpurea*	Chinese beautyberry
37.	*Calycanthus floridus*	Sweetshrub, Carolina allspice
38.	*Caragana arborescens*	Siberian pea-tree
39.	*Carpinus betulus*	European hornbeam
40.	*Carpinus caroliniana*	American hornbeam
41.	*Celtis occidentalis*	Hackberry
42.	*Cephalanthus occidentalis*	Buttonbush
43.	*Cercis canadensis*	American redbud
44.	*Cercis chinensis*	Chinese redbud
45.	*Chaenomeles japonica*	Japanese quince
46.	*Chamaecyparis pisifera*	Sawara cypress
47.	*Chamaecyparis thyoides*	White cedar
48.	*Chionanthus virginicus*	White fringe-tree
49.	*Cladrastis lutea*	Yellow-wood
50.	*Clethra alnifolia*	White-alder, summersweet
51.	*Colutea arborescens*	Bladder-senna
52.	*Cornus alba*	Tatarian dogwood
53.	*Cornus alternifolia*	Pagoda dogwood

Key	Botanical Name	Common Name
54.	*Cornus amomum*	Silky dogwood
55.	*Cornus florida*	Flowering dogwood
56.	*Cornus florida rubra*	Pink flowering dogwood
57.	*Cornus kousa*	Kousa dogwood
58.	*Cornus mas*	Cornelian cherry
59.	*Cornus paniculata*	Gray dogwood
60.	*Cornus sanguinea*	Red dogwood
61.	*Cornus sibirica*	Coral dogwood
62.	*Cornus stolonifera*	Red-osier dogwood
63.	*Cornus stolonifera lutea*	Yellowtwig dogwood
64.	*Corylus americana*	American hazel
65.	*Corylus avellana*	European hazel
66.	*Cotinus americanus*	American smoke-tree
67.	*Cotinus coggygria*	Common smoke-tree
68.	*Cotoneaster acutifolia*	Peking cotoneaster
69.	*Cotoneaster dielsiana*	Diels cotoneaster
70.	*Cotoneaster divaricata*	Spreading cotoneaster
71.	*Cotoneaster francheti*	Franchet cotoneaster
72.	*Cotoneaster horizontalis*	Rock cotoneaster
73.	*Cotoneaster horizontalis perpusilla*	Ground cotoneaster
74.	*Cotoneaster microphylla*	Rockspray cotoneaster
75.	*Cotoneaster salicifolia*	Willowleaf cotoneaster
76.	*Cotoneaster simonsii*	Simons cotoneaster
77.	*Crataegus coccinea*	Thicket hawthorn
78.	*Crataegus cordata*	Washington hawthorn
79.	*Crataegus crus-galli*	Cockspur thorn
80.	*Crataegus oxyacantha*	English hawthorn
81.	*Daphne odora*	Winter daphne
82.	*Deutzia gracilis*	Slender deutzia
83.	*Deutzia gracilis rosea*	Rose panicle
84.	*Deutzia lemoinei*	Lemoine deutzia
85.	*Deutzia* (tall growing varieties)	Deutzia
86.	*Diervilla sessilifolia*	Southern bush honeysuckle
87.	*Eleagnus angustifolia*	Russian olive
88.	*Eleagnus longipes*	Cherry eleagnus
89.	*Eleagnus umbellata*	Autumn eleagnus
90.	*Euonymus alata*	Winged euonymus
91.	*Euonymus alata compacta*	Dwarf winged euonymus
92.	*Euonymus americana*	Brook euonymus
93.	*Euonymus bungeana*	Winterberry euonymus
94.	*Euonymus europaea*	European burningbush
95.	*Euonymus fortunei*	Fortune euonymus
96.	*Euonymus patens*	Spreading euonymus
97.	*Euonymus radicans vegeta*	Bigleaf winercreeper
98.	*Euonymus radicans*	Wintercreeper
99.	*Euonymus yedoensis*	Yeddo euonymus
100.	*Exochorda racemosa*	Common pearlbush
101.	*Fagus americana*	American beech
102.	*Fagus sylvatica*	European beech
103.	*Forsythia*, all varieties	Forsythia
104.	*Fraxinus americana*	White ash
105.	*Fraxinus pennsylvanica*	Green ash
106.	*Gaylussacia*	Huckleberry

Key	Botanical Name	Common Name
107.	*Ginkgo biloba*	Maidenhair-tree
108.	*Gleditsia triacanthos inermis*	Thornless honeylocust
109.	*Gleditsia* varieties	Honeylocust
110.	*Halesia tetraptera*	Great silverbell
111.	*Hamamelis*	Witchhazel
112.	*Hedera helix*	English ivy
113.	*Hibiscus*, bush form	Hibiscus, rose mallow
114.	*Hibiscus syriacus*	Shrub-althea
115.	*Hydrangea arborescens grandiflora alba*	Snowhill hydrangea
116.	*Hydrangea macrophylla Otaksa*	Otaksa hydrangea
117.	*Hydrangea paniculata grandiflora peegee*	Peegee hydrangea
118.	*Hydrangea quercifolia*	Oakleaf hydrangea
119.	*Hydrangea petiolaris*	Climbing hydrangea
120.	*Hypericum kalmianum*	Kalm hypericum
121.	*Hypericum moserianum*	Goldflower
122.	*Ilex crenata*	Japanese holly
123.	*Ilex crenata rotundifolia*	Round leaved holly
124.	*Ilex crenata convexa (bullata)*	Convex leaved holly
125.	*Ilex crenata microphylla*	Littleleaf Jap. holly
126.	*Ilex glabra*	Inkberry
127.	*Ilex laevigata*	Smooth winterberry
128.	*Ilex opaca*	American holly
129.	*Ilex verticillata*	Common winterberry
130.	*Itea virginica*	Sweetspire
131.	*Jasminum floridum*	Summer flowering jasmine
132.	*Jasminum nudiflorum*	Winter jasmine
133.	*Juniperus chinensis pfitzeriana*	Pfitzer juniper
134.	*Juniperus chinensis sargenti*	Sargent juniper
135.	*Juniperus communis*	Common juniper
136.	*Juniperus communis hibernica*	Irish juniper
137.	*Juniperus horizontalis Bar Harbor*	Bar Harbor juniper
138.	*Juniperus horizontalis douglasii*	Douglas juniper
139.	*Juniperus horizontalis plumosa*	Andorra juniper
140.	*Juniperus squamata Meyeri*	Meyer juniper
141.	*Juniperus virginiana*	Red cedar
142.	*Juniperus virginiana globosa*	Globe red cedar
143.	*Kalmia*	Mountain laurel
144.	*Kerria japonica*	White kerria
145.	*Koelreuteria paniculata*	Golden rain-tree
146.	*Laburnum*	Laburnum
147.	*Leiophyllum*	Sandmyrtle
148.	*Lespedeza bicolor*	Shrub bushclover
149.	*Lespedeza thunbergii*	Thunberg lespsdeza
150.	*Leucothoë catesbaei*	Drooping leucothoe
151.	*Ligustrum amurense*	Amur privet
152.	*Ligustrum ibolium*	Ibolium privet
153.	*Ligustrum ibota*	Ibota privet
154.	*Ligustrum lucidum*	Glossy privet
155.	*Ligustrum ovalifolium*	California privet
156.	*Ligustrum regelianum*	Regel privet
157.	*Ligustrum vulgare*	European privet

Key	Botanical Name	Common Name
158.	*Lindera Benzoin*	Spicebush
159.	*Liriodendron tulipifera*	Tuliptree
160.	*Liquidambar styraciflua*	Sweetgum
161.	*Lonicera* (bush forms)	Bush honeysuckle
162.	*Lonicera fragrantissima*	Winter honeysuckle
163.	*Lonicera Morrowii*	Morrow honeysuckle
164.	*Lonicera tatarica*	Tatarian honeysuckle
165.	*Magnolia glauca*	Sweetbay
166.	*Mahonia aquifolium*	Oregon hollygrape
167.	*Malus arnoldiana*	Arnold crabapple
168.	*Malus atrosanguinea*	Carmine crabapple
169.	*Malus baccata*	Siberian crabapple
170.	*Malus coronaria*	Wild sweet crabapple
171.	*Malus floribunda*	Japanese flowering crabapple
172.	*Malus ioensis plena*	Bechtel crabapple
173.	*Malus sargenti*	Sargent crabapple
174.	*Malus scheideckeri*	Scheidecker crabapple
175.	*Myrica caroliniensis*	Northern bayberry
176.	*Myrica pennsylvanica*	Bayberry
177.	*Nyssa sylvatica*	Tupelo, sourgum
178.	*Ostrya virginiana*	American hophornbeam
179.	*Oxydendron arboreum*	Sourwood
180.	*Pachysandra terminalis*	Japanese spurge
181.	*Phellodendron chinense*	Chinese corktree
182.	*Phellodendron* species	Corktree
183.	*Philadelphus coronarius*	Sweet mockorange
184.	*Philadelphus lemoinei*	Lemoine mockorange
185.	*Photinia villosa*	Oriental photinia
186.	*Physocarpus opulifolius*	Common ninebark
187.	*Picea abies* (*excelsa*)	Norway spruce
188.	*Picea* (dwarf)	Dwarf spruce
189.	*Pieris floribunda*	Mountain andromeda
190.	*Pieris japonica*	Japanese andromeda
191.	*Pinus nigra austriaca*	Austrian pine
192.	*Pinus strobus*	White pine
193.	*Pinus sylvestris*	Scotch pine
194.	*Platanus acerifolia*	London planetree
195.	*Platanus occidentalis*	American sycamore
196.	*Platanus orientalis*	European planetree
197.	*Populus*	Poplar
198.	*Populus alba Bolleana*	Bolleana poplar
199.	*Populus eugenei*	Carolina poplar
200.	*Populus maximowiczii*	Japanese poplar
201.	*Potentilla fruticosa*	Shrubby cinquefoil
202.	*Potentilla* varieties	Cinquefoil
203.	*Prunus amygdalus*	Almond
204.	*Prunus cerasifera*	Myrobalan plum
205.	*Prunus glandulosa*	Flowering almond
206.	*Prunus maritima*	Beach plum
207.	*Prunus triloba*	Flowering plum
208.	*Prunus subhirtella pendula*	Weeping Japanese cherry
209.	*Pseudotsuga taxifolia*	Douglas fir
210.	*Pyracantha coccinea Lalandii*	Laland firethorn

Key	Botanical Name	Common Name
211.	*Quercus alba*	White oak
212.	*Quercus bicolor*	Swamp white oak
213.	*Quercus borealis*	Northern red oak
214.	*Quercus coccinea*	Scarlet oak
215.	*Quercus macrocarpa*	Mossycup oak
216.	*Quercus palustris*	Pin oak
217.	*Quercus rubra*	Common red oak
218.	*Quercus velutina*	Black oak
219.	*Rhamnus cathartica*	Common buckthorn
220.	*Rhamnus frangula*	Glossy buckthorn
221.	*Rhododendron*	Rhododendron
222.	*Rhododendron maximum*	Rosebay rhododendron
223.	*Rhodotypos kerrioides (scandens)*	Jetbead, white kerria
224.	*Rhus Cotinus*	Common smoke tree
225.	*Rhus* in variety	Sumac
226.	*Rhus aromatica (canadensis)*	Fragrant sumac
227.	*Rhus copallina*	Shining sumac
228.	*Rhus glabra*	Smooth sumac
229.	*Rhus glabra laciniata*	Cutleaf sumac
230.	*Rhus typhina*	Staghorn sumac
231.	*Rhus typhina laciniata*	Shredded sumac
232.	*Ribes alpinum*	Mountain currant
233.	*Robinia hispida*	Black locust
234.	*Rosa blanda*	Meadow rose
235.	*Rosa hugonis*	Hugonis rose
236.	*Rosa lucida*	Virginia rose
237.	*Rosa multiflora*	Japanese rose
238.	*Rosa nitida*	Bristly rose
239.	*Rosa palustris*	Swamp rose
240.	*Rosa rubiginosa*	Sweetbrier
241.	*Rosa setigera*	Prairie rose
242.	*Rosa virginiana*	Virginia rose
243.	*Rosa wichuriana*	Wichurian rose
244.	*Salix* in variety	Willow
245.	*Sambucus canadensis*	American elder
246.	*Sambucus nigra*	European elder
247.	*Sambucus pubens*	Scarlet elder
248.	*Sophora japonica*	Chinese scholartree
249.	*Sorbaria aitchisonii*	Kashmir false spirea
250.	*Sorbaria arborea*	Tree spirea
251.	*Sorbaria sorbifolia*	Ural false-spirea
252.	*Sorbus aucuparia*	European mountain ash
253.	*Spiraea bumalda*	Bumalda spirea
254.	*Spiraea bumalda Anthony Waterer*	Anthony Waterer spirea
255.	*Spiraea japonica Fortunei*	Fortune spirea
256.	*Spiraea*, tall varieties	Spirea
257.	*Spiraea thunbergii*	Thunberg spirea
258.	*Spiraea tomentosa*	Hardhack
259.	*Spiraea vanhouttei*	Vanhoutte spirea
260.	*Stephanandra flexuosa*	Cutleaf stephanandra
261.	*Stephanandra incisa*	Stephanandra
262.	*Styrax japonica*	Japanese snowball
263.	*Styrax obassia*	Fragrant snowball

Key	Botanical Name	Common Name
264.	*Symphoricarpos albus* (*racemosus*)	Common snowberry
265.	*Symphoricarpos chenaultii*	Chenault snowberry
266.	*Symphoricarpos mollis*	Spreading snowberry
267.	*Symphoricarpos occidentalis*	Western snowberry
268.	*Symphoricarpos orbiculatus* (*vulgaris*)	Coralberry
269.	*Syringa amurensis*	Manchurian lilac
270.	*Syringa chinensis*	Chinese lilac
271.	*Syringa japonica*	Japanese tree lilac
272.	*Syringa josikaea*	Hungarian lilac
273.	*Syringa persica*	Persian lilac
274.	*Syringa villosa*	Late lilac
275.	*Syringa vulgaris*	Common lilac
276.	*Syringa vulgaris alba*	Common white lilac
277.	*Tamarix* species	Tamarix
278.	*Tamarix parviflorum*	Algerian tamarix
279.	*Tamarix pentandra*	Five stamen tamarix
280.	*Taxus*	Yew
281.	*Taxus baccata*	English yew
282.	*Taxus cuspidata*	Japanese yew
283.	*Taxus cuspidata capitata*	Upright yew
284.	*Taxus cuspidata nana*	Dwarf Japanese yew
285.	*Taxus cuspidata Hicksii*	Hicks yew
286.	*Taxus media Browni*	Brown's yew
287.	*Taxus media Hatfieldii*	Hatfield yew
288.	*Thuja* (globe and dwarf forms)	Globe and dwarf arborvitae
289.	*Thuja occidentalis*	American arborvitae
290.	*Thuja occidentalis pyramidalis*	Am. pyramidal arborvitae
291.	*Thuja occidentalis Rosenthalii*	Rosenthal arborvitae
292.	*Thuja orientalis*	Oriental arborvitae
293.	*Thuja plicata*	Giant arborvitae
294.	*Tilia americana*	American linden
295.	*Tilia cordata*	Littleleaf European linden
296.	*Tilia euchlora*	Crimean linden
297.	*Tilia europaea*	Common linden
298.	*Tilia platyphylla*	Bigleaf European linden
299.	*Tilia tomentosa*	Silver linden
300.	*Tsuga canadensis*	Canada hemlock
301.	*Tsuga caroliniana*	Carolina hemlock
302.	*Ulmus americana*	American elm
303.	*Ulmus pumila*	Dwarf Asiatic elm
304.	*Vaccinium corymbosum*	Highbush blueberry
305.	*Vaccinium stamineum*	Deerberry
306.	*Veronica*, evergreen types	Speedwell
307.	*Viburnum acerifolium*	Mapleleaf viburnum
308.	*Viburnum americanum*	American cranberrybush
309.	*Viburnum cassinoides*	Withe rod
310.	*Viburnum dentatum*	Arrowwood
311.	*Viburnum dilatatum*	Linden viburnum
312.	*Viburnum lantana*	Wayfaring tree
313.	*Viburnum lentago*	Nannyberry
314.	*Viburnum molle*	Kentucky viburnum
315.	*Viburnum nudum*	Smooth withe rod

Key	Botanical Name	Common Name
316.	*Viburnum opulus*	European cranberrybush
317.	*Viburnum opulus nanum*	Dwarf cranberrybush
318.	*Viburnum plicatum*	Japanese snowball
319.	*Viburnum prunifolium*	Blackhaw
320.	*Viburnum rhytidophyllum*	Leatherleaf viburnum
321.	*Viburnum Sieboldii*	Siebold viburnum
322.	*Viburnum theiferum*	Tea viburnum
323.	*Viburnum tomentosum*	Doublefile viburnum
324.	*Viburnum wrightii*	Wright viburnum
325.	*Vitex*	Chaste-tree
326.	*Vinca minor*	Periwinkle
327.	*Weigela Eva Rathke*	Red Flowering weigela
328.	*Zanthorhiza apiifolia*	Yellowroot

CHAPTER FOUR

THE SELECTION, USE,

AND MAINTENANCE

OF EQUIPMENT

The selection, use, and maintenance of all types of grounds equipment is important to all park or grounds maintenance programs. Good equipment, plus a well-rounded supply of materials and equipment and an efficient maintenance program, determines the difference between economical and efficiently operated programs and costly and inefficient programs utilizing old and outmoded methods.

The best maintenance is, of course, preventive maintenance. A program of preventive maintenance reduces the number and extent of repairs, and in the long run will save money. Many budgets are less than adequate when it comes to purchasing new equipment. It therefore is necessary to get as much use out of a piece of equipment as is possible. By efficient preventive maintenance the life of most equipment can be extended considerably.

SELECTION OF EQUIPMENT

There is a wide variety of equipment on the market today, all designed to speed up the job of grounds maintenance. The following list and descriptive material give some indication of the type of equipment required to do an efficient job. This list is designed as a general outline of the kinds of equipment available. The management of each individual area or plant must determine which of the equipment is suitable for its particular use, and must make its own selection of make or manufacturer.

Spraying equipment

Each year new insects and diseases develop which add to the already heavy burden of park maintenance. The development of spraying and dusting equipment has therefore taken on greater significance. Fortunately there have been many recent advances in chemical control.

Spraying and dusting equipment must be selected to suit the conditions and problems involved. There is no one size of sprayer or duster which will meet all control needs of any one specific area or park. There is, however, a wide variety of models and sizes of equipment and accessories available to meet most anticipated needs.

The first consideration in selecting the equipment to be used is the jobs for which the equipment will be used. The following list presents some of the jobs the spraying equipment is expected to perform:

1. Weed control
2. Brush control
3. Plant disease control
4. Insect pest control on trees and shrubs
5. Insect pest control for flies, mosquitoes, chiggers, etc.
6. Application of liquid fertilizers
7. Application of wood preservatives
8. Control of grass, brush, and forest fires.

In order to select the proper model of sprayer or duster, the extent or frequency of use must first be determined. For jobs in which the equipment will be in almost constant seasonal use, heavy duty models should be selected for the most economical operation. Certain types of chemicals may affect the selection of equipment. Application of spray materials such as wettable powder insecticides, some of the common fungicides, whitewash, or water base paints will require a unit with enough mechanical agitation to keep the spray material properly mixed in the tank. Since there is a certain amount of abrasive action, the sprayer must have a pump which will withstand such action.

Another consideration in selecting the proper sprayer is the amount of coverage required. Tall shade trees will require hydraulic sprayers with pump capacities of 20–50 gal per minute at pressures from 500–800 lb per sq in. to cover them adequately with the required spray material. On the other hand, for weak spraying a pump capacity of 4–10 gal per minute at pressures under 100 lb per sq in. is sufficient.

Hand equipment will be required for small spraying jobs, for spraying in areas inaccessible to power equipment, and for fighting grass, brush, or forest fires. Hand-operated dusters are used in greenhouses and nurseries, and in protecting floral displays.

Power sprayers

The three most commonly used types of power sprayers used in grounds maintenance work are: (1) conventional hydraulic sprayers, (2) mist blowers or concentrate sprayers, and (3) aerosol generators or fogging machines. The conventional hydraulic sprayer is the mainstay of most spraying programs. The mist blower or concentrate sprayer is used primarily for shade tree work, and to a lesser degree for fly and mosquito control. The aerosol generator, or fogging machine, is used for applying space sprays in the control of adult flies, mosquitoes, and other pests.

Hydraulic sprayers

There is a wide selection of types and models of hydraulic sprayers now available, differing primarily in size of tank, size and type of pump, method of agitation, power source, and type of mounting. The conventional unit of this type consists of a tank containing an agitator, a pump, a power source, a combination pressure regulator and relief valve, and a discharge system consisting of one or more hand guns, or a multiple nozzle boom.

Fig. 4.1 General purpose sprayer
The gun makes it possible for the operator to direct the spray to areas particularly susceptible to plant diseases.

Fig. 4.2 Boom attachment for general purpose sprayer
With boom attachment shown here, the sprayer shown in Fig. 4.1 can be used to control roadside weeds.

Fig. 4.3 50-gal sprayer
This small unit can be used for spraying trees and shrubs as well as for weed control in lawns.

Fig. 4.4   10-gal sprayer
This small power sprayer is useful to nurserymen and can also be used for control of pests in industrial plants and public buildings.

A surge tank or air chamber is provided with these pumps to assure a constant pressure at the nozzle, and a mechanical agitator to keep the spray materials properly mixed in the tank.[1] (See Fig. 4.1–4.4).

The most common types of hydraulic sprayers in use today are the power wheelbarrow and estate sprayers, the skid mounted sprayer, and the trailer or wheel-mounted sprayer. The power wheelbarrow sprayers have tank capacities of 10–20 gal, and are equipped with piston type pumps delivering 1–1.5 gpm at pressures up to 250 lb. Power can be furnished by a small air-cooled engine, or by a 0.5 hp heavy-duty electric motor.

The estate or small wheel-mounted sprayer has a tank capacity of 15–50 gal, with piston type pump discharging from 1 to 4 gpm at pressures up to 250 to 300 lb. Standard equipment with this type of sprayer is a hand gun with a 25-ft length of hose.

[1] Earl D. Anderson, National Sprayer and Duster Association, Chicago, Ill.

Fig. 4.5 Large mist sprayer
Besides having greater capacity, working faster, and making more effective use of spray materials than smaller models, this sprayer covers greater distances and is less affected by wind deflection. It is useful for sanitation spraying, shade tree spraying, and leaf windrowing. Output is 28,000 cu ft of air per minute; velocity is 100 mpm; engine 70 hp. Spray outlet is 23 in. in diameter, tank capacity is 100 gal, and the pump capacity is 7 gpm and 400 psi pressure, the engine is a Willys 70 hp, developing 700 cu ft of spray per horsepower.

The skid models are made in a wide range of sizes suitable for transporting in a jeep, truck, or trailer. The smallest of this class is the estate or small wheel-mounted sprayer. The largest skid models range in capacity of 500 gal and up, and have a pump capacity of 50 gal per minute with pressures up to 800 lb. The power plant ranges in size from 1 hp to about 30 hp.

The most versatile of the skid or wheel-mounted models is a multiple use sprayer commonly available with a pump of 4–8 gpm capacity, developing pressures in the range of 30–250 or even 800 lb, and tank capacity of 50–250 gal. Most are equipped with field booms for turf insect and weed control, and hand guns and hose for selective area spraying. If they are equipped with oil- and chemical-resistant hose and gaskets, plus a mechanical agitator, these sprayers will apply almost any spray material successfully.

The tractor- or jeep-mounted type of hydraulic sprayer has proved satisfactory in applying sediment-free sprays (such as certain weed control chemicals) in the low gallonage range, at pressures under 100 lb. Such sprayers (Fig. 4.5) are commonly equipped with a rotary gear pump operated by the power takeoff on the tractor or jeep.

Mist blowers or concentrate sprayers

Concentrate sprayers are used primarily for treating shade trees and for residual and larvicidal treatment of large areas for mosquito control. The effective coverage is from fifty to several hundred feet, depending upon the size of the machine, the terrain, density of foliage, and the direction and velocity of the wind.

The use of concentrates, of course, requires lesser volume of water to be handled, and therefore may result in some operating economies. The concentrate sprayer consists essentially of a low-volume, low-pressure sprayer which is incorporated with an engine-driven fan or blower. The spray material is pumped under relatively low pressure to an outlet side of a fan, where it is sprayed into the air stream. The air blast aids in breaking up the liquid, and carries the small droplets to the surface to be covered.[2]

The smaller models are usually mounted on wheelbarrow or cart chassis and have high-velocity, low-volume blowers delivering about 5000 cfm at over 150 mph. The larger models have velocities from 5000 to 25,000 cfm at velocities from 100 to 150 mph. Such models are usually mounted on skids for ease in transport by truck, trailer, or boat.

Aerosol or fog generators

Temporary control of adult mosquitos in restricted areas such as picnic grounds, ball parks and camping areas is the chief use for aerosol or fog generators.

A unit of this type dispenses liquid insecticides in the particle size range classified as aerosol or fogs (1–50 microns). They are usually operated at a time when the most favorable temperature, humidity and wind conditions prevail. . . . The essential parts of the typical machine consist of a self-contained power source, a tank for insecticides, a means of breaking up the liquid into the desired droplet size either mechanically or thermally, and a force to impart an initial velocity to fog as it leaves the machine. This may be either skid or wheel-mounted. The smallest units are suitable for treating a few acres—the

[2] Earl D. Anderson, National Sprayer and Duster Association, Chicago, Ill.

Fig. 4.6 Duster with high speed fan
Fan speed of 3200 rpm assures an easy flow into the mixing tube. This unit holds 14 lb of dust.

largest several square miles. The net effective width of coverage is usually 400 to 500 ft maximum, depending upon the wind movements which are relied upon to carry the fog over the area.[3]

Power dusters

There is now available a tractor-mounted type of power duster, light enough to be carried on small farm tractors and powerful enough to cover a swath several times the tractor width. They can be used with a multiple nozzle boom or with a single nozzle outlet on the fan case.

A duster of this type (Fig. 4.6) is used for control of turf insects, dusting ornamental plantings, and for distributing insecticide pellets for mosquito larvae control.

[3] Earl D. Anderson, National Sprayer and Duster Association, Chicago, Ill.

Fig. 4.7   The sickle-bar mower
This model is available with 5-ft or 6-ft cutter bar. It is ideal for highways, rights of way, cemeteries, factory grounds, school grounds, curbed areas, and parks.

Hand equipment

There is always room for hand operated equipment to supplement the power equipment. The common type compressed air sprayer is available in several different sizes ranging in capacity from 1.5–5 gal. Some of the latest models are equipped with rechargeable CO_2 cylinders, which eliminate hand pumping.

The knapsack sprayers have capacities of 4–6 gal and have lever, pump, or telescopic operation. Both types of sprayers are supplied with oil- and chemical-resistant hose and gaskets. Multiple nozzle booms, also available, will speed up many hand spray jobs. Hand dusters, both crank and knapsack styles, are useful for quick application of insecticides and fungicides on floral or other ornamental plantings.

Power mowers

There is a very wide selection of power mowers on the market today. They range from the small 18-in. mower, used principally for small areas, to the larger tractor-drawn rotary or gang mowers. Practically all mowers are the rotary, sickle bar, or reel type, and it is a matter of judgment which type is best suited to the particular use (Fig. 4.7–4.12).

Fig. 4.8   The rotary cutter

Cutting width is 5 ft; transport clearance 11 ft; cutting height 2 to 10 in. This cutter mows grass, brush, or heavy weeds. Front and rear shields protect operator and the public from blades and flying debris.

Fig. 4.9   General purpose tractor

With dump-bed attachment, this tractor can be used for mowing, plowing, and disking. Mower attachment greatly reduces cost of mowing scattered areas, because the machine can mow and transport simultaneously. Width of cut is 5 ft 8 in. for 3 unit; 10 ft for 5 unit.

Fig. 4.10 Reel mower for large lawn areas
This model, especially suitable for estates and institutions, will mow up to 26 acres per day. It trims close to obstacles, climbs hills, and can be adjusted from ⅜ in. to 2½ in. Ground speed is 4.4 mph.

Generally speaking, the rotary mower is used and built for rough and heavy work. It will cut weeds and grasses so coarse that the reel type of mower will hardly touch them. The rotary mower should be used in meadows where a close even cut is not essential, or on large grass areas, such as golf fairways. The sickle bar mower is generally found in use on highway shoulders and slopes, or in meadows or pastures if a hay crop is desired. The reel type, single or gang, is used principally on lawns, in parks, on golf courses, and on industrial grounds, where a smooth even cut is desired (Fig. 4.13).

A hand power scythe developed by TVA is ideal for use on steep side slopes. This mower is a standard sickle bar power unit with a bicycle wheel attachment to maintain balance on the slope. This device eliminates the need for a second man to assist the operator in holding the machine on the slope. When mowing direction is reversed, the stabilizing bar unhooks from the other end of the frame and the entire unit swings on a pivot shaft to opposite side of the machine (Fig. 4.14).

Fig. 4.11 Small rotary mower
Small areas and strips adjoining walls can be trimmed with this 18-in. rotary mower.
Height of cut can be adjusted from 1 in. to 3 in., and mowing capacity is 21,000 sq ft
per hour at 3 mph.

Soil shredders

The soil shredders are useful in any grounds maintenance program. They
come in sizes to suit practically every type of job for greenhouses, nurseries,
golf courses, parks, college campuses, and municipal sewage treatment
plants. Soil shredders are used principally for preparing top-dressing materials. They produce a top-dressing that is loose, fluffy, and of small particle
size; free of sticks, stones, roots and other trash. They are also used to prepare compost for flower and shrub beds, shred composted leaves, prepare
topsoil, blend commercial fertilizers with top-dressing and topsoil, and to
sterilize topsoil by blending in weed seed poisons (Fig. 4.14).

In cities where the disposal of leaves becomes a problem, the shredder will
clean and shred them so they can be bagged and sold for leaf mold. Sewage
sludge can also be ground or shredded and sold for fertilizer.

Fig. 4.12   Reel mower with power handle
This power unit can be used for a number of maintenance operations. It will operate reel or rotary mowers, snow plows, sprayers, generators, pumps, tillers, edge-trimmers, and aerators.

Fig. 4.13   Mower for steep slopes
A standard sickle bar power unit can be equipped with a bicycle wheel attachment to maintain balance on steep slopes.

Fig. 4.14 Soil shredder
Soil is dumped into the hopper from a front end loader and processed into a loose, pliable dressing material. The shredder will process up to 50 cu yd of material per hour.

Fig. 4.15 Power chain saw
A single-cylinder, two-cycle, two-port air-cooled engine runs this chain saw, which can cut trees up to 3 ft in diameter.

Power saws

All grounds maintenance programs need some power saw equipment. The power saw is useful in clearing brush, dead, down and diseased timber from forest areas. It is useful in cutting wood for picnic areas and in clearing away storm damage. The one man chain saw will cut practically all size timber found in most wooded areas and is probably the most useful piece of equipment (Fig. 4.15). One piece of equipment which is exceedingly useful for park or any type of grounds maintenance work is a light weight shoulder unit. This unit is extremely versatile, it will cut grass, weeds, briars, brush, trees and will cultivate shrub beds and edge walks and around shrub and specimen trees (Fig. 4.16).

Fig. 4.16   Power unit with cutter bar attachment

Aerating equipment

As stated previously the aerating of turf areas is becoming increasingly popular, especially on golf courses, and more recently on large industrial and government reservations. As illustrated below proper aerifying of the turf will do many things all beneficial to the turf.

There are several types of aerifiers all designed for specific purposes. The small power aerifier suitable for home and industrial lawns, athletic field, school grounds and smaller golf courses and some landscape work has a

Fig. 4.17   Aerifier and vertical grass cutter (Verti-Cut)
At the left the Aerifier is ventilating the soil; at the right the vertical grass cutter (Verti-Cut) is pulverizing the cores of soil scooped up by the Aerifier spoons.

Fig. 4.18   Brush chipper
One truckload of chips from this chipper is equal to four truckloads of brush.

cultivating width of 18 inches, operational speed up to 4 MPH and cultivation depth up to 3 inches.

A larger model is the junior aerifier (Fig. 4.17) for use on golf greens and for fast coverage of large turf areas in parks, athletic fields, golf course fairways, military installations and lawns around industrial plants and Institutions. Use a unit cultivating a width of 6 feet and powered by standard farm tractor. A new type of mower, the Verti-Cut, has come into general use in connection with the aerification principle.

Regular mowers make a horizontal cut, removing the tips of grass blades to control the height of grass. But close to the soil, the surface stems and old grass leaves accumulate, and this excess growth is removed by the Verti-Cut. The blades cut down into the turf, trim through runners and outspread leaves. There is no pulling or tearing such as occurs when material is torn out with rakes.

Brush chippers

More and more cities, towns, parks and industrial plants—especially highway departments, utility companies and line clearance contractors—are finding the brush chipper useful in fast and economical disposal of brush and tree limbs. The chipper will reduce brush to chips up to 4 in. in diameter (Fig. 4.18). Brush chips can be either loaded directly into trucks and hauled to a central location for use later as a mulch, or spread in place as the chipper moves along. The chips can be used for many things: mulching, erosion control, soil conditioners, weed control in shrub beds, and as cushion material under slides and swings in playground areas. After severe storms when cities and towns find their streets clogged with broken branches and trees the chipper will dispose of such hazards much faster than the conventional methods of loading, hauling, and burning. You can load many more trees to a truck as chips than as brush. At Christmas time the chipper permits faster and more economical disposal of Christmas trees and provides useful mulching material for acid-loving plants such as rhododendrons and laurels. The larger size chippers will cut trees and brush up to 10 in. in diameter.

Post hole digger

Like an electric drill in any workshop, a post hole digger is a real saver of time and muscle power. There are several types; the tractor equipped with an auger extension; the jeep equipped similarly; and a power tool for earth boring and tunneling. The tractor and jeep equipped with an auger can bore holes for fence posts, guard posts, power and telephone poles, holes for planting trees and shrubs, and practically anything that requires a hole in the ground. Most of this equipment is hydraulically operated from the power

Fig. 4.19 Post hole digger
With an auger extension, holes up to 48 in. deep can be drilled quickly with this implement, which is run from the power take-off of the tractor and raised and lowered hydraulically. Auger sizes from 4 to 24 in. in diameter are available.

take-off shaft. Control levers to raise and lower the auger are within easy
reach of the operator. See Fig. 4.19.

Another useful hole digging device is the Hole-a-matic, a one-man operated, lightweight earth-boring and tunneling machine which operates from a
portable 2 KW AC or DC power generator. It will dig through soft shale and
at any angle. It bores holes 2 in. to 16 in. in diameter as deep as 100 ft and
is useful for digging earth sampling holes, shallow wells, post holes, tree
fertilizing holes, concrete pier and guard post holes; for conduit and sewer
lines up to 30 ft or more, and for soil testing down to 100 ft or more. See
Fig. 4.20.

Portable generators

The portable generators are ideal for operating portable tools (such as the
earth boring machine described above) for contractors, public utilities,
grounds maintenance work in cemeteries and parks, yard maintenance in
industrial plants, and for police and fire departments, campers, etc. To determine the size of generator needed use Table 4.1.

Fig. 4.20   One-man operated earth boring machine

TABLE 4.1/APPROXIMATE POWER REQUIREMENTS

Power tool	Required watts
¼-in. drill	400–600
½-in. drill	700–1200
¾-in. drill	1000–1500
1-in. drill	1400–2000
Hole-a-matic	1700–2200
Portable floor planer	700–1200
1½-hp radial saw	3000–3500
3-hp radial saw	3600–5000
7½-hp radial saw	8000–12000
6-in. electric saw	1200–1700
7-in. electric saw	1400–2000
8-in. electric saw	2000–2500
10-in. electric saw	2400–3000
pipe threading machine	2200–2500
portable router	600–1500

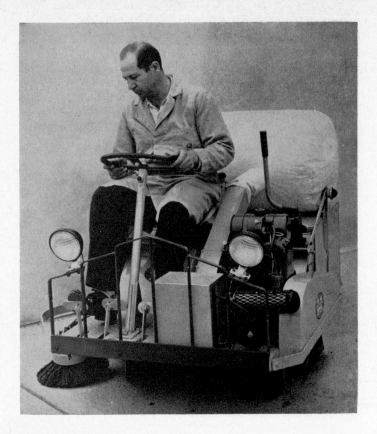

Fig. 4.21   Power sweeper

The above recommendations take into account starting and operating loads normally imposed by the equipment listed. Table and photographs furnished by the Gen-A-Matic corporation, Van Nuys, Calif.

Miscellaneous equipment

Labor saving machines are important wherever large acreages are to be maintained. Disks, cultivators, fertilizer and lime spreaders, sweepers, road repair equipment, tractors equipped with earth moving and snow removal attachments, and an assortment of small tools, shovels, picks, axes, and pruning equipment are some of the items needed. Sweeping equipment is essential for large industrial plants both inside and outside. The modern power sweeper will clean a swath 36 in. to 48 in. wide. A special side brush for cleaning along walls and curbs adds an additional 11 in. to the cleaning swath. The 36-in. machine covers 80,000 sq ft in an hour. Labor savings

Fig. 4.22 Equipment for litter removal

alone soon pay for the sweepers, since it would take 20 men with brooms to cover the same area in an hour. Outdoors the sweeper picks up grass cuttings, leaves, and brush, and is equipped with special dust control features. See Fig. 4.21.

Sod-cutting equipment is also essential in many park operations, military installations, and in much contractors' work. The sod cutter is an efficient, easy-to-operate machine that will cut from 70 to 150 ft per minute, or one man can cut up to 1000 yd of sod per hour. Sod cut mechanically will be easier to handle and relay. The sides are cut smoothly and evenly, permitting neat and even laying.

Maintenance management connected with large cities and towns, parks and industrial grounds, golf courses, cemeteries, and highways, will find the job of litter, dust, refuse, leaves, and other debris removal much easier with the latest in motorized equipment. Such equipment, operated like a giant vacuum cleaner, will clean up bottles, cans, rags, cartons, and leaves and twigs —wet or dry. It operates dust-free, which is essential for city use. All debris is drawn into a large 12 cu yd hydraulic, self-dumping hopper for quick disposal at dumping sites. It requires a 2-man operating crew, who can cover more territory than 10 or 12 men using conventional methods. See Fig. 4.22.

Fig. 4.23 Rotary cutter
This cutter, mounted on a jeep, will cut and shred any growth the jeep can travel over, including brush and small trees. A heavy flywheel gives steady cutting action, mowing a 5-ft swath. Cutting height can be adjusted from 1 in. to 12 in.

The jeep is a versatile machine, useful for many purposes. When equipped with four-wheel drive it will go where many machines are not considered safe. For use in forests it is unsurpassed. It can be used for fire fighting, servicing fire towers, and transporting men and equipment over rough mountain and forest roads, and to haul materials and logs. Equipped with power takeoffs it can be used in logging operations. With proper accessories it can mow grass, brush, and heavy weeds. It will do light grading, loading, or trenching, or snow removal, hauling, terracing, and towing and servicing. For airport operations and maintenance it can be used for servicing and fueling planes, loading baggage, and clearing runways of snow. Equipped with generator units it provides a source of power for starting planes, or it can be equipped for emergency use as a crash wagon. See Fig. 4.23 and 4.24.

For use in fire protection it can be equipped to fight all kinds of fires in inaccessible areas. Rural and forested areas benefit principally from the extra traction and mobility of jeep units. For public utilities it provides weed and brush control, and can be used for digging trenches, drilling holes, and carrying mobile generators to remote locations. It can also be equipped as service truck.

Fig. 4.24   Dirt blade for use with jeep

New equipment is constantly being introduced on the market. In the past few years, methods of seeding, fertilizing, and mulching steep slopes and large areas have undergone radical changes. For instance, the old methods of applying straw and hay mulches by hand and then staking and tying the mulch down became so expensive that it was rapidly becoming necessary to stop mulching altogether, or to devise more economical ways of getting the job done. As a result, new machines were invented that did the job quickly and economically.

Mulch spreader

Since mulching of newly seeded slopes was an absolute must in most areas, the mulching machine was developed first. The mulch spreader is simply a machine equipped with a chute into which bales of hay or straw are fed. The straw is forced into a hopper where it is beaten apart and blown by a powerful fan into a discharge tube. The straw emerging from the end of the discharge tube is distributed evenly over the ground, with a minimum of bunching. To hold the mulch in place on the ground, the spreader is equipped with three jets at the end of the discharge tube. These jets are connected to a drum of asphalt mounted on the side of the machine. The operator of the

Fig. 4.25 Mulch spreader
As it leaves the tube the straw is being sprayed with asphalt. Note hose connection to asphalt tank.

discharge tube can control the amount of asphalt discharged through the jets by means of a lever which opens or closes the jets. The asphalt is applied to the straw as it comes out of the discharge tube. Just enough asphalt adheres to the straw to form a mat after it falls on the ground. Approximately 100 gal of asphalt per acre is required to do an effective holding job on mulch spread at the rate of 2 tons per acre. Normally the mulch can be spread to a distance of 50–75 ft effectively. See Fig. 4.25. Specifications for asphalt emulsions used on vegetative mulch are given in Chapter 2.

Hydro seeder

The hydro-seeder is principally a truck-mounted tank into which is mixed a slurry consisting of 100 gal of water mixed with a ton of fertilizer and from 200 lb to 300 lb of seed. The slurry is kept in motion by an agitator. This mixture will cover approximately two acres.

Connected to the tank truck, but a separate unit, is the pumping unit and nozzle tower. The tower permits a 360-degree swing and a 90-degree vertical travel, and the pump will force the slurry a distance of 100 ft. For fast, economical seeding and fertilizing of slopes, ditches, shoulders, and large open areas this method is unsurpassed. Combined with the mulch spreader it can do the entire operation of liming, fertilizing, seeding, mulching and anchoring the mulch in two operations.

Fig. 4.26 Hydro Seeder
With this equipment, seed, fertilizer, and lime can be applied in one operation, saving as much as 50 per cent in labor costs.

Hydraulic boom

One piece of equipment that has proved extremely useful to the tree pruner on large scale jobs is a hydraulically operated boom for carrying workers aloft and maintaining them on constant work base at any required level (Fig. 4.27). It rotates upon a turret mounted on a truck, dolly, trailer or tractor. It provides a working height above ground of up to 41 ft. The turret is equipped with power tools, and all positions of the turret can be controlled by the operator in the turret. Some of the work this machine can perform is as follows:

1. Trimming for proper distribution of new light system
2. General tree pruning
3. Pruning and topping Dutch elm diseased trees
4. Trimming city trees from power and telephone lines
5. Telephone line work
6. Electric utility work

Fig. 4.27 Hydraulic boom tree trimmer
Pruning along power and telephone lines can be done quickly and safely with this boom trimmer.

New methods of preparing seed beds are constantly being introduced. Two such pieces of equipment are the Landscape Finish Rake and the Pulverizer and Seeder (Fig. 4.28 and 4.29).

The finish rake will grade, level, and finish rake a full 7-ft path and will, if used properly, put hard and compacted soils into good condition for seeding.

The pulverizer and seeder will also grade, scarify, and level soil surface, and in addition it will seed and roll the surface. Used in connection with the finish rake it can prepare a seed bed from practically any type of soil.

Tractors

Every efficient grounds maintenance program must have one or more tractors, depending upon the size of the area to be maintained. The tractor is a very versatile machine, and with attachments it can perform almost every

Fig. 4.28 Pulverizer and seeder

The different sizes of rollers and seedboxes available for this machine can be combined or selected for grading, scarifying, leveling, clod-breaking, pulverizing, rolling, and seeding. Scarifying teeth cut soil every 2 in., and rollers penetrate the soil 1 in. with pressure up to 600 lb. For extremely cloddy ground, spring tension can be increased with jam nuts to produce an extra 300 lb of pressure. As little as 3 lb of seed per 1000 sq ft is needed for use in the seeder.

Fig. 4.29 Landscape finish rake

This rake grades, levels, spreads, finish rakes, and scarifies hard rutted soils. Positions are controlled by a hand pitch control wheel, which can be adjusted from the rear seat of the tractor.

conceivable job of grounds maintenance, including moving earth from one place to another; light grading and scarifying; drilling holes in earth; cutting grass; asphalt paving; loading with fork lift; hauling; rolling; trenching; logging; sweeping; sawing wood; turf seedbed preparation; snow removal; spraying; and many others.

Some of the attachments available to do the above work are disk plows, disk tillers, subsoilers, harrows, cultivators, combines, balers, mowers, cranes, rakes, front and rear loaders, lime and fertilizer spreaders, scoops, wagons, cordwood saws, post-hole diggers, and rotary cutters.

Maintenance of the tractor and its equipment is described below. These procedures should be followed for all types of equipment.

MAINTENANCE PROCEDURES AND SCHEDULING

Maintenance designed to prevent costly breakdowns contains two basic activities: (1) a periodic inspection of equipment to uncover conditions which may lead to breakdowns or excessive depreciation and, (2) upkeep to remedy such conditions, while still in a minor stage. By following these two basic activities through proper lubrication, job planning, and scheduling of repairs, certain major returns can be expected—fewer breakdowns, with a corresponding decrease in production downtime; fewer large scale or repetitive repairs; lower costs for simple repairs made before breakdowns (because less manpower, fewer skills, and fewer parts are needed); less overtime pay on ordinary adjustments and repairs than for breakdown repairs; and less standby equipment.

The best way to achieve a maintenance program based on preventive maintenance is through periodic inspections to discover and correct unsatisfactory conditions. Frequency of inspections depends upon the amount and degree of use, and will vary from one area to another. To establish the best frequency cycle, begin with an analysis of the equipment as to such factors as age, condition, value, amount of use, safety requirements, number of hours or mileage operated, and susceptibility to wear, damage, and loss of adjustment.

Most maintenance programs can be divided into three groups: routine upkeep, periodic inspections, and contingent work. The latter includes work at irregular intervals when the equipment is down for other reasons, so the more work which can be squeezed into this category, the less costly it will be.

Routine upkeep of vehicular equipment includes such chores as lubrication, oil change, checking tires and batteries, washing, tune-up, checking spark plugs and points, brake inspection etc. Most of these chores should be the responsibility of the operator, and if he finds anything which should be corrected he should report it to the main service garage.

Periodic inspections should be done at the garage by personnel trained in this kind of work. During these inspections, every moving part of the equipment should be checked and worn parts removed and replaced. Following inspection the equipment should be thoroughly cleaned and lubricated.

Contingent work consists of repairs for major breakdowns or general overhaul of the equipment. At this time the equipment should be inspected as for a regular inspection period, and all worn or broken parts removed and replaced.

Scheduling maintenance work can be done by the use of over-all charts for all equipment, and individual cards for each piece of equipment. The over-all chart will give a quick picture of the workload. The chart should list the days or months across the top border and an itemized list of the equipment down the left side. A system of symbols to show various types of repairs, adjustments. etc. should be devised so they can be marked under the date and opposite the piece of equipment.

TABLE 4.2/SAMPLE OVER-ALL CHART FOR VEHICLE MAINTENANCE

| Truck No. | January | | | | | | | | | | | |
	1	2	3	4	5	6	7	8	9	10	11	12
1			wa		o.c.				tu			
		√	lu									
2								sp				
			√	tu				wa				
3												
						√						

Symbols
√   inspection   o.c.   oil change
wa   wash   sp   spark plugs
lu   lubrication   tu   tune-up

The individual cards should provide more details for each piece of equipment. Both major and minor repairs should be listed on the card, plus the time and materials used.

One important factor in achieving good maintenance practices or in making preventive maintenance effective is the proper training of the driver or operator. Improper driving or operation is a major factor in mechanical failures of motor vehicles. Carelessness can nullify all efforts at proper maintenance. Wherever it is practicable, a regular driver or operator should be assigned to each piece of equipment. The operator should be made responsible for such preventive maintenance as daily checks on fuel, oil, and water levels, on tires for inflation, unusual wear, and penetration of foreign ob-

TABLE 4.3/SAMPLE CARD FOR INDIVIDUAL VEHICLE MAINTENANCE

Material used			Name of park			
Name or no. of part	Amount					
			Unit no.	Description		Mileage in
			Date start	Job ordered		Mileage out
			Date finish	by		miles
			Oper. no.	Repair order instructions		
			Tires and batteries		Item	Quantity	Amount	Total
			Ticket no.	Amount	Gasoline			
					Diesel oil			
					Lube oil			
					Grease			
					Parts			
					Tires			
					Item	Hours	Amount	
			Total		Labor			
			Processed by		Overhead on labor			
			Cost		Overhead on stores			
			Foreman		Total labor and overhead			

jects; on lights, horns, windshield wipers, and other equipment accessories; and on indications of fuel, oil, water, gear oil, or brake system leaks. While the equipment is in operation the operator should observe the operation of the various instruments, brakes, steering, engine, and power driven units, and report any defects immediately to his foreman or supervisor. The operator should also make weekly checks on the carburetor, generator, regulator, starter, water pumps, fan and drive belts, battery, and battery connections.

Operating rules

The operator of any power unit should know a few fundamental principles in order to get the best service possible:

1. All excess grease, oil, and dust should be wiped clean from the unit before it is placed in operation after a long period of idleness.

2. The crankcase should always have a sufficient supply of the recommended grade of oil. The oil should be changed periodically, or after every 25 hours of operation. Oil depth in the crankcase should be checked after every five hours of operation to make sure it is at the recommended level.

3. All moving parts should be properly lubricated. Lubrication should not be overdone, however, since an excess of grease will collect dirt and do more harm than good.

4. Use only the regular commercial gasoline mixtures as fuel. High test gas or special fuel mixtures should be used only if specifically recommended by the manufacturer.

5. Always allow the motor to warm up after first starting it and before placing it in operation. If the engine will run smoothly with the choke wide open (not pulled out) it is warm enough for safe operation. On cold or damp days, an engine that is difficult to start can be started more easily by priming.

6. After the unit is placed in operation, the motor should be run at the proper speed for the conditions and job to be done. The operator should never strain the unit by running it at excessively high speeds when the extra power is not needed.

7. All power tools are designed to do the work. An operator need only guide the power tool he is using and should not force it.

8. The operator should clean up the unit immediately after it has been used. Dirt and grime can be removed more easily at this time than if they are allowed to dry and harden.

9. When the unit is not in use it should be stored in a dry, level, dirt-free area and covered with a protective cover to keep out dust and dampness.

10. If the unit is equipped with different attachments, the attachments should receive as good care as the unit itself.

Safety Rules

The operator of power mowers and similar equipment should know a few basic safety rules:

1. Keep feet and hands away from the moving blades.

2. With self-propelled models, hold the mower down firmly with the foot, safely placed before starting the engine; disengage the clutch, and then be careful not to engage it accidentally.

3. Don't touch the spark plug of a running mower; it can give you a nasty shock.

4. Keep your hold on the handle at all times when the mower is going or in a position to start moving.

5. Stop the engine when you leave the mower or equipment.

6. Do not add fuel while the engine is hot.

7. Before starting to mow, rake the area free of loose objects that might be thrown by the blades.

8. Treat a running rotary mower as you would a gun; never allow its discharge opening to point at anyone. The fewer people around when a mower is used, the less chance that someone will be injured by a flying object.

9. If you are going to move the blade of a rotary mower by hand for any reason, disconnect the spark plug wire and make sure it cannot touch the plug while you are near the blade. Rotating the blade cranks the engine, and if the plug is connected, the mower could conceivably start running.

CHAPTER FIVE

DISEASE

AND INSECT

CONTROL

The control of diseases and insects of trees and shrubs is becoming an ever increasing problem on public lands of all categories. A well rounded maintenance program should have the skill, materials, and equipment to control all kinds of diseases and insects. Many new chemicals are proving effective, and many of the old standby formulas are still good.

CONTROL OF DISEASES

The control of diseases in trees and shrubs is based largely on eradication and protection. For example, collecting and burning fallen leaves from diseased plants will eliminate one source of trouble. Pruning infested branches and burning them also removes a source of subsequent infections. Spraying with dormant or delayed dormant sprays at the point where infection occurs is another commonly used method of control. The removal of decayed wood from trees is only partially successful in eradicating disease, since the fungi usually extend well beyond the zone of decay.

Spraying

The successful control of disease by spraying is dependent upon three factors:

1. Sprays must be applied at the proper time. All protective sprays must be applied before rainy periods, because fungi and bacteria penetrate plant tissues when the plants are wet.

2. The spray must be applied as a fine mist in order to cover the plant. Complete coverage by an even protective film is essential for effective control.

3. The sprays must contain the proper ingredients. Copper and sulfur are the two chemical elements most often used in protective sprays. They can be used safely on plants without injury to the tender leaves.

Copper sprays

The most commonly used copper spray is Bordeaux mixture, which adheres well to most shade tree leaves without the addition of a spreading and sticking agent. When copper sprays are used on conifers, however, casein soap or fish oil soap should be added at the rate of 2 lb in 50 gal of spray. Surplus spray should not be stored for future use, since it deteriorates rapidly.

There are two objectionable features about Bordeaux mixture: (1) it forms an unsightly residue on the leaves and (2) it may burn foliage during extended periods of cool, wet weather.

Other copper sprays which may be used are: Basicop, Bardow, Copocil, Copper Hydro 40, Copper Phosphate, Cupro-K, Cupracide 54, Pyrox and Triogen. Complete instructions for use are given by manufacturer. Since most copper sprays are corrosive to metals, spraying machines and accessories should be thoroughly cleaned with water after each operation.

Sulfur sprays

Sprays containing sulfur as the active ingredient are also used for disease control. The most common is a lime sulfur solution, which is used also as a contact insecticide and as a disinfecting spray. When it is used as a dormant disinfecting spray, a strength of one part in 10 parts water is recommended. The powdered form should be mixed at the rate of 20 lb in 50 gal water. For a protective spray on leaves, use 1 gal of the concentrated liquid or 4 lb of powder in 50 gal of water. Never use a lime sulfur spray on trees near a house, since it reacts very strongly on house paint.

Other sulfur compounds, known as wettable and flotation sulfurs, are Flotex wettable sulfur, Kolofog, Koppers flotation sulfur, micronized wettable sulfur, Mike sulfur, sulfocide, and Sulfrox. Sulfur sprays are used to treat mildew, rust diseases, and the diseases of the rose family. Do not use a sulfur spray when the air temperature is $90°$ F or higher.

Combination sprays

Protective sprays may be combined with insecticides to control fungus or bacterial diseases and insects in one operation. However, care should be taken to mix compatible materials together in order to avoid injury to the plant or to reduce the efficiency of one or several of the materials in the mixture. The following rules for mixing should be observed:

1. Copper sprays and Bordeaux mixture may be mixed with lead arsenate for chewing insects and with nicotine sulfate for sucking insects.
2. Lime sulfur may be mixed with calcium or lead arsenate and nicotine sulfate. To prevent burning the foliage, be sure the quantity of lime added is equal to that of the calcium or lead arsenate.
3. Do not mix lime sulfate with Paris green, soaps, Bordeaux mixture, or oil emulsions.
4. Wettable sulfurs may be mixed with arsenicals or nicotine sulfate.
5. Do not mix wettable sulfurs with oil emulsions or soaps.

CONTROL OF INSECTS

Insects are usually classified into five categories: leaf-chewing, sucking, leaf-mining, borers and bark beetles, and root-infesting.

Stomach poisons are generally most effective against chewing pests. The most widely used stomach poison is arsenate of lead.

For use as a spray, mix as follows:

Large quantity: 2–3 lbs arsenate of lead; 50 gal water.
Small quantity: 2–3 level tablespoons arsenate of lead; 1 gal water.

For use as a dust, mix one part of arsenate of lead to nine parts of dusting sulphur, hydrated lime, or other suitable carrier.

Other common stomach poisons are Paris green, calcium arsenate, magnesium arsenate, sodium fluosilicate.

Pyrethrum sprays are contact sprays, but some are effective against chewing pests. Rotenone is effective both as a stomach poison and as a contact insecticide. Both rotenone and pyrethrum are nonpoisonous to man and warm-blooded animals. They should not be used near water, as they may kill fish. The directions of the manufacturer should be followed.

Insecticides for sucking insects

Contact sprays are usually used for sucking insects. They kill by acting on the nervous system, clogging the breathing pores, or caustic action on body tissues.

The most common of these sprays are made with one of the following materials as the active agent: nicotine, pyrethrum, rotenone, soap, oil, or lime sulphur.

Nicotine spray: Ordinarily nicotine is used one part to 500 to 800 parts water. Add 2–5 lb of soap to each 50 gal of spray to increase its effectiveness. For small quantities, use 1–1½ teaspoonfuls of nicotine and 1 oz of soap to each gallon of water.

Nicotine dust is effective against aphids and leafhoppers.

Pyrethrum and rotenone: Follow manufacturer's recommendations on the package.

Soap: Applications of fish oil soap, or other good soaps in mixtures of 1 lb in 20–40 gal of water, are effective on some soft-bodied insects.

Oil: Summer oil emulsions are oils with most of the chemically active material removed, and are safe on most foliage. Summer oils (white sulfonated oils) may be used in concentrations of up to 2 per cent actual oil and may be applied to plants in foliage.

Dormant spray oils are not safe on foliage, and should be used for dormant spraying only. Dormant spray oils may be either miscible oils or oil emulsions. Miscible oils are diluted one part to 15 parts water for scale insect control. Oil emulsions are diluted so that the final spray will contain 3 per cent actual oil. Most oil emulsions contain from 66 per cent to 80 per cent oil.

Insecticides for borers and bark beetles

Borers are hard to control because they attack only weak and devitalized trees. The best preventive is to keep the trees in good health and vigor.

Carbon bisulfide: This compound may be injected into the burrow with an oil can. After the injection the burrow should be closed with putty or some similar substance. The fire hazard of carbon bisulfide can be eliminated if a mixture of ethylene dichloride and carbon tetrachloride is used instead.

Pine oil: Effective control of boring insects and bark beetles has been obtained with a soluble pine oil containing one pound of paradichlorobenzene to the quart. Paradichlorobenzene is dissolved in the pine oil by heating it to 120° F. To use, dilute this mixture with 2 qt water and paint on the infested bark.

Repellent Washes: One formula for a repellent wash consists of 1 gal soft soap dissolved in 1 gal hot water, with 1 pt crude carbolic acid stirred in. The mixture is left overnight and then diluted with 8 gal water and applied to the trunk. Another formula consists of 25 lb potash soap, 1½ gal water, 12 lb naphthalene, and 1 lb flour. Soap and water are heated together until temperature reaches 180°F, and the flour is stirred in followed by the naphthalene. After being reheated to 180°F, and stirred until thoroughly mixed, it can be removed from the fire, cooled quickly with occasional stirring, and painted on tree trunks.

Best results with washes are obtained when trees are painted in late spring (May or June, or at the time adults are emerging) and applications repeated at several two-week intervals.

Protectors: Damage by borers may be prevented by wrapping trees with protectors made of newspaper, building paper, or another suitable paper.

Cylinders of fine-meshed wire screen give protection, if the tops are plugged with cotton.

Sprays: Spraying with arsenicals is helpful in the control of adult borers that chew foliage. Spraying should be done at the time the adults are emerging and before they lay eggs.

Carbon bisulfide: This compound is useful in killing ants and other insects in the soil. Make several holes about 4 in. apart in the infested area and place in each hole a tablespoonful of the material; close with soil. This mixture is extremely flammable and should be handled with great care.

Insecticides for leaf-mining insects

Leaf-miners are insects, mostly Lepidoptera and Diptera, which in the larval stages burrow in and eat the parenchyma of leaves. Leaf-mining insects are not easily controlled because neither contact nor stomach poisons can be used against them. Some may be controlled by fumigation with cyanide and treatment with hot water. Hand-picking infested leaves is also of value.

Insecticides for root-infesting insects

Carbon bisulfide emulsion: This emulsion can be prepared by mixing (parts by volume) one part of rosin fish oil soap (other soaps may be used), three parts water, and 10 parts carbon bisulfide. Place soap and water in container and stir until mixture is uniform. Add carbon bisulfide and agitate until mixture is creamlike. Mix 1 qt emulsion in 50 gal water and apply this mixture to the soil at rate of 1 qt per sq ft. Avoid fires of any kind and do not smoke when using this mixture. This treatment kills Japanese beetle grub, white grub, earthworms, and burrowing bees.

Arsenate of lead: Use 5 to 15 lb to 1,000 sq ft of surface, depending on the degree of infestation. Spread evenly over the surface of the ground by mixing the material with 25 times its volume of moist sand or soil. Wash material into the soil by running water sprinkler in one spot for half an hour to one hour. This application will protect the lawn for years against root infesting insects.

To grubproof a lawn during construction, use 35 lb of lead arsenate to 1,000 sq ft of surface. Apply as above and mix into the soil to a depth of 3 in.

USE OF CHLORDANE FOR SUBTERRANEAN CONTROL OF TERMITES

For fast initial control and extended protection against reinfestation, 0.5 to 1.0 per cent chlordane-water emulsions are recommended. The strength of insecticide required varies with the soil: sandy soils require the least, clays and loams more, and peats and mucks the most.

This solution will not damage nearby foliage, and a water emulsion eliminates the fire hazard of oil sprays, but care should be taken not to contaminate wells or other water supplies. Annual inspection of the treated areas is recommended, to check for reinfestation.

Treatment of exposed soil areas

Outside surfaces of foundation walls are usually exposed by trenching to a soil depth of 1 or 2 ft, but no lower than the footings. Both trench and backfill should be treated with 2 gal of the chlordane emulsion per lin ft.

Exposed soil areas under porches and other structures should be treated with 1 gal of the chlordane emulsion per 10 sq ft.

Treatment of unexposed soil areas

Under sidewalks and driveways which border foundation walls, the emulsion may be applied through shrinkage cracks or through specially drilled holes.

Under structures the inside surface of the foundation should be treated wherever the soil is exposed. Dig a shallow trench about 6 in. wide, and treat as described for other trenching. Depth of penetration will depend upon the relationship between inside and outside soil level. If the soil is not exposed, remove or drill through the covering, treat with chlordane emulsion, and replace the covering.

Other contact points to be checked and treated are tree stumps and fence posts, wooden stairs, stoops, supports, trellises, and possible termite entrances around basement windows and pipes, chimney bases and supporting piers, and points where beams, joists, and sills rest on foundations.

Concrete slab construction

Termites have been found infesting baseboards, partitions, closets, and all types of interior wood construction in many recent houses built on concrete slabs. They gain access through cracks in the slabs, and through wooden stakes or forms not properly removed during construction.

The best way to prevent such infestations is to treat the fill beneath the slab with a 1 per cent chlordane-water formulation before the concrete is poured. The method of application is described under "B" below.

Rates of application

A. Buildings with crawl spaces

1. Apply 2 gal per 5 lin ft to critical areas under the house, such as along the inside surfaces of foundation walls and around piers and service entrances. Do not make an over-all treatment of the area.

2. Along the outside of foundation walls, (including the part opposite entrance platforms, porches, etc.) apply 2 gal per 5 lin ft where the foundation is shallow. Apply 4 gal per 5 lin ft where the foundation is deep.

3. Apply 1 gal per 10 sq ft of soil surface as an over-all treatment only when the attached porches, entrance platforms, utility entrances, and similar constructions are slabs on fill or ground.

B. Buildings with concrete slab on the ground

1. Apply 1 gal per 10 sq ft as an over-all treatment under attached porches. Over-all treatments applied to washed and ungraded gravel fills, or fills of absorbent materials such as cinders, should be increased by ½ gal per 10 sq ft over that specified above.

2. Apply 2 gal per 5 lin ft to critical areas under the slab, particularly along the inside of foundations walls and around service entrances.

3. Apply 2 gal per 5 lin ft along the outside of the foundation.

C. Buildings with basements

1. Follow instructions under "A" above for buildings with crawl spaces.

D. Voids of unit masonry walls

All voids of unit masonry walls and piers should be treated with 1 gal per 5 lin ft from grade to footing. Oil solutions should not be used under slabs unless an impervious oil-stable vapor barrier separates the treated soil from the slab.

Architectural plans

Termite protection should start with the design of the building. The architect can indicate on the plans the spots where entrances may develop and chlordane treatment should be applied. He can also design termite shields and other barriers.

TABLE 5.1/CHLORDANE DILUTION GUIDE*

Chlordane in finished formulation (per cent)	Volume of finished formulation (gal.)	Required amounts of chlordane emulsifiable concentrates			
		40 per cent concentrate	44–46 per cent concentrate	60–62 per cent concentrate	72–75 per cent concentrate
1.00	5	1.00 pt	14.00 fl oz (or .875 pt)	9.00 fl oz	7.00 fl oz
1.00	50	1.50 gal	4.25 qt	5.5 pt	4.25 pt
1.00	100	2.25 gal	8.50 qt	11.00 pt	4.25 qt
0.50	5	8.00 fl oz	7.00 fl oz	4.00 fl oz	3.00 fl oz
0.50	50	2.50 qt	4.25 pt	2.75 pt	2.125 pt
0.50	100	1.25 gal	4.25 qt	5.50 pt	4.25 pt

* To obtain 5, 50, or 100 gal of a 1.00 or .50 formulation (columns 1 and 2) measure out amount of concentrate specified in columns 3–6, and add water to make up desired volume.

Notes of general interest

1. Neither highly alkaline soils nor high alkaline plaster and plaster board scraps found at building sites affect the stability of chlordane.

TABLE 5.2/DILUTION GUIDE FOR 20 PER CENT CHLORDANE LIQUID CONCENTRATES*

Per cent chlordane in finished formluation	Add to 1 gal 20 per cent chlordane concentrate in kerosene:		Add to 1 gal 20 per cent chlordane concentrate in No. 2 diesel oils:
	Kerosene IBO ** (gal)	No. 2 diesel oil IBO (gal)	No. 2 diesel oil IBO (gal)
1	21.0	18.0	20.0
2	10.0	8.50	9.50
2½	7.75	6.50	7.50
5	3.25	2.75	3.125

* By permission of the Velsicol Chemical Corporation.

Example: To prepare 2.5 per cent chlordane oil solution from 20 per cent chlordane concentrate in deodorized kerosene using No. 2 diesel oil, mix 1 gal of the 20 per cent concentrate with 6.5 gal of No. 2 diesel oil.

When using 40 per cent chlordane oil concentrate, use 0.5 gal of concentrate to the same amount of IBO. The approximate weight of kerosene is 6.6 lb per gal and No. 2 diesel oil is 7.8 lb per gal.

**Insecticide base oil.

2. Chlordane water-emulsion formulations have been recommended for soil treatment because experimental field tests and practical applications have shown no harmful phyto-toxic effects to plants and shrubbery. Such formulations also eliminate fire hazard.

3. Chlordane formulations properly applied to the soil do not produce obnoxious odors.

4. One application at proper concentration and satisfactorily applied will control termites for five years or longer. Case histories of over 10 years of continuous effective control are on record.

5. Reference: "Protection against Decay and Termites in Residential Construction" No. 448, NAS, 1956, The Building Research Advisory Board, National Academy of Science, National Research Council, 2101 Constitution Avenue, Washington 25, D.C.

6. Consult pest control operators on termite problems.

SAFETY IN CHLORDANE HANDLING[1]

Chlordane, when given to laboratory animals in sufficient quantities, may produce an acute toxic state, recognized by signs of irritation of the central nervous

[1] Adapted, by permission, from a publication of the Velsicol Chemical Corporation.

system. Symptoms of acute intoxication are usually not so clearly defined as those of acute, but in general are similar and slowly progressive. In addition, a history of the loss of appetite, loss of weight, and headaches may be noted. If intoxication, either acute or chronic, is suspected, a detailed history of conditions of exposure must be obtained, as well as information on the components of the formulations exposed. The above symptoms are in general typical of chlordane exposure, but not necessarily of other components of a formulation. Solvents may produce symptoms such as nausea and vomiting ,and irritation to the skin, eyes, throat, and lungs.

Precautionary measures

1. Personal hygiene

a. Remove materials spilled on the skin immediately by thorough washing, but not scrubbing, with soap and water.

b. After routine contact with chlordane, wash the face and hands before eating in order to avoid repeated ingestion of small quantities.

2. Clothing

a. Avoid the wearing of clothing contaminated with chlordane. Do not wipe chlordane on clothing where it could soak through and come into contact with the skin.

3. Protective equipment

a. Respirators provide protection against inhalation of sprays, fogs, or dust. The extent to which they should be used depends upon the conditions and methods of insecticide application, but respirators are recommended for persons treating confined areas.

b. Gloves are suggested if there is danger of unsuspected exposure to chlordane during formulation or application.

Treatment

1. If chlordane is spilled on the skin, wash thoroughly, without scrubbing, with large amounts of soap and water. Always change if clothing has been contaminated.

2. If chlordane is splashed or spilled into the eyes, wash repeatedly with water.

3. If chlordane has been swallowed, induce vomiting immediately by inserting fingers into throat, or by drinking a tumbler of warm water containing a tablespoonful of salt or a teaspoonful of mustard. If patient is unconscious, do not give anything by mouth.

4. Persons exhibiting symptoms of chlordane intoxication following excessive exposure should be given a doctor's care immediately. The doctor must be told what materials the formulation contained, how it was applied, and how long the patient was exposed.

TABLE 5.3/DILUTION GUIDE FOR CHLORDANE EMULSIFIABLE CONCENTRATES

(By permission of the Velsicol Chemical Corporation)

Per cent chlordane in finished formulation	Gal. of finished formulation	Required amounts of chlordane emulsifiable concentrate (Balance of final volume is water.)	
		Using 44 to 46 per cent chlordane emulsifiable concentrate (4 lb tech. chlordane per gal)	Using 72 to 75 per cent chlordane emulsifiable concentrate (8 lb tech. chlordane per gal)
1	5	0.875 pt	7 fl oz
	50	4.25 qt	4.25 pt
	100	8.5 qt	4.25 qt
2	5	1.75 pt	0.875 pt
	50	8.5 qt	8.5 pt
	100	17.0 qt	8.5 qt
2.5	5	1.0 qt	17 fl oz
	50	10.5 qt	10.5 pt
	100	5.25 gal	21 qt
5	5	2 qt	1 qt
	50	5.25 gal	10.5 pt
	100	10.5 gal	21 qt

Example: To make 100 gal of 2 per cent chlordane using 72 per cent chlordane emulsifiable concentrate, mix 8.5 qt of 72 per cent concentrate with sufficient water to make 100 gal of finished formulation (water used would be 97.875 gal)
1 fluid ounce (fl oz) = 2 tablespoonfuls
16 fluid ounces = 1 pint
2 pints (pt) = 1 quart (qt) = 32 fluid oz
4 quarts = 1 gallon (gal) = 8 pints = 128 fl oz

Note to attending physician

Treatment for chlordane intoxication is primarily symptomatic. The following measures have been suggested:

1. An attempt should be made to control nervous symptoms and convulsions by use of sedatives and anticonvulsants. Suggested materials are phenobarbital, sodium pentabarbital, chloral hydrate plus magnesium sulfate, and cannabis. Use at levels that relieve symptoms but do not interfere with eating or excretion.

2. Definite measures should be taken to encourage appetite. Parenteral feeding should be given if patient is comatose.

3. In cases of intoxication by ingestion, oily laxatives and enemas should be avoided.

4. Provide a quiet place as free from noises or other sources of irritation as possible.

5. Supportive treatment should be given consistent with that used in liver or central nervous system impairment.

GROUNDS MAINTENANCE HANDBOOK

TABLE 5.4/FORMS OF DDT AND METHODS OF USE WITH MIST SPRAYERS

Technical (100 per cent) DDT powder (commercial)
Cannot be added directly to water. Must first be dissolved in a solvent, and then combined with an oil soluble emulsifier (like Triton X-100).
Solvents: Sufficient amounts of Kerosene, No. 2 fuel oil. xylene, benzene and other DDT solvents.
Wettable DDT powders containing 25–50 per cent DDT (commercial)
Add directly to water to make a suspension for mist blowers or for hydraulic sprayers. Do not add oil.
Wettable DDT powders containing 10 per cent DDT (commercial)
Use as a dust. Do not use in sprays.
Emulsifiable DDT containing 25–40 per cent DDT (commercial or homemade)
For general use. Add to water or to oil to make any concentration desired for mist blowers or for hydraulic sprayers. Dilute to 4–12 per cent DDT concentration for mist blowers. For hydraulic sprayers use 1–2 pt per 100 gal water. These DDT solutions are ones to which an emulsifier has been added.
DDT solutions containing 4–40 per cent DDT (commercial or homemade)
Do not add directly to water. Do not use "as is" in hydraulic sprayers. Can be added directly to oil for use in mist blowers at 4–12 per cent DDT concentration. Can be diluted with water for mist blowers or hydraulic sprayers after adding one part by volume of emulsifier to each 20 parts of the solution before adding the water.

TABLE 5.5/QUANTITIES OF MATERIALS TO USE IN MAKING GIVEN CONCENTRATIONS OF DDT FOR MIST BLOWERS

Type of DDT spray	Ingredients	Quantities of material for		
		1 gal	10 gal	100 gal
6 per cent suspension	Water	1 gal	10 gal	100 gal
	Wettable powder (50 per cent DDT)	1 lb	10 lb	100 lb
5 per cent solution	Kerosene	1 gal	10 gal	100 gal
	100 per cent technical DDT powder	6.4 oz (0.4 lb)	4 lb	40 lb
6 per cent solution	No. 2 fuel oil	1 gal	10 gal	100 gal
	100 per cent technical DDT powder	0.5 lb (8 oz)	5 lb	50 lb
12 per cent emulsion	Xylene	2.25 pt	2 gal 3 qt	28 gal
	100 per cent technical DDT powder	1 lb	10 lb	100 lb
	Triton X-100	2 fl oz	1.25 pt	12.5 pt
	Water	5.33 pt	6.66 gal	67 gal
6 per cent emulsion	Xylene	1 pt 2 fl oz		14 gal
	100 per cent technical DDT powder	0.5 lb	11.25 pt	50 lb
	Triton X-100	1 fl oz	10 lb	6 pt
	Water	6.5 pt	3 gal	83 gal

Control of mosquitoes, flies and small flying insects

To control mosquito larvae in standing water, apply malathion emulsifiable liquid at rate of 13 fl oz (approximately .5 lb actual malathion) per acre. Mix in sufficient water or oil to obtain even coverage when applied by air or ground equipment. For control outdoors, use 2 per cent malathion fog, aerosol or space spray. For spray, dilute 1 part 57 per cent emulsifiable liquid in 28 parts of a mixture consisting of 4 parts kerosene solvent and 1 part aromatic hydrocarbon solvent. Repeat applications as necessary.

TABLE 5.6/DILUTION TABLE FOR DDT SOLUTIONS AND EMULSIONS MADE FROM 25 PER CENT EMULSIFIABLE DDT SOLUTION FOR MIST BLOWERS

Per cent	Ingredients	Quantities for			
		1 gal	10 gal	50 gal	100 gal
4	DDT solution (water or oil)	1.25 pt 6.75 pt	11 pt 8 gal 3 pt	6 gal 6 pt 43 gal 2 pt	13.5 gal 86.5 gal
5	DDT solution (water or oil)	1 pt 10 oz 6 pt 6 oz	2 gal 8 gal	10 gal 40 gal	20 gal 80 gal
6	DDT solution (water or oil)	1 qt 3 qt	2.5 gal 7.5 gal	12.5 gal 37.5 gal	25 gal 75 gal
10	DDT solution (water or oil)	3 pt 3 oz 4 pt 13 oz	4 gal 6 gal	20 gal 30 gal	40 gal 60 gal
12	DDT solution (water or oil)	4 pt 4 pt	5 gal 5 gal	25 gal 25 gal	50 gal 50 gal

Avoid applying oil based formulations to valuable ornamental plants; they may be injured. Malathion may be toxic to certain species of fish, particularly in shallow water.

TABLE 5.7/PREPARATION OF EMULSIFIABLE STOCK FORMULA CONTAINING 0.37 LB. OF DDT PER PINT, OR 32 PER CENT DDT BY WEIGHT

Ingredient	Quantity for lots of		
	1 gal	10 gal	100 gal
Xylene (xyolo)	6.75 pt	8.5 gal	84.4 gal
100 per cent technical DDT powder	3 lb	30 lb	300 lb
Triton X-100	6 fl oz	3 pt 12 oz	4 gal 5.5 pt

TABLE 5.8/PORTIONS OF EMULSIFIABLE STOCK FORMULA TO USE WITH WATER TO MAKE GIVEN CONCENTRATIONS OF DDT

Per cent of DDT in finished spray	Quantity for lots of			
	1 gal	10 gal	50 gal	100 gal
12	2.7 pt solution 5.3 pt water	3 gal 3 pt solution 6 gal 5 pt water	16.87 gal solution 33.13 gal water	33.3 gal solution 66.25 gal water
10	2.25 pt solution 5.75 pt water	2.8 gal solution 7.2 gal water	14 gal solution 36 gal water	28 gal solution 72 gal water
6	1.35 pt solution 6.65 pt water	13.5 solution 8.5 gal water	8.5 gal solution 41.5 gal water	17 gal solution 8 gal water
5	1.125 pt solution 6.875 pt water	11.25 pt solution 8.6 gal water	7 gal solution 43 gal water	14 gal solution 8 gal water
4	0.9 pt (14.4 oz) solution 7 pt 16 oz water	9 pt solution 8.78 gal water	5.62 gal solution 44.4 gal water	11.25 gal solution 88.75 gal water

TABLE 5.9/GALLONS OF 6 PER CENT DDT SOLUTION OR EMULSION TO APPLY PER ACRE (MIST BLOWER APPLICATION)

Insect Species	Gal per acre
Sawflies on pines	2
Green birch leaf aphid (1)	10
Brown-tail moth	2
May beetles	2
Lace bugs on oak and sycamore	2
Green-striped maple worm	3
Tussock moth	2
Fall webworm	1
Orange-striped oak worm	3
Forest tent caterpillar	2
Eastern tent caterpillar	2
Spiny elm caterpillar	2
Gypsy moth	2
Japanese beetle	3
Cankerworm	2
House fly (out of doors)	3
Horn fly (out of doors)	2
Black fly (out of doors)	2
Mosquito (out of doors)	2

TABLE 5.10/AMOUNTS OF 12 PER CENT DDT SOLUTION OR EMULSION[1] PER TREE FOR ONE MIST BLOWER APPLICATION

Insect	Tree height (ft)							Dates for application (Northeastern states)
	90–80	80–65	65–50	50–35	35–20	20–10		
Brown-tail moth				1 pt	8 oz	4 oz		Aug. 10–25 April 25–May 20
May beetles	2 pt	1 pt 8 oz	1 pt	11 oz	8 oz	4 oz		As soon as adults are abundant
Lace bugs on oak and sycamore	3 pt	2 pt	1 pt	11 oz	8 oz	4 oz		As soon as nymphs are abundant
Green-striped maple worm	1 pt 8 oz	1 pt 8 oz	1 pt	1 pt	1 pt	8 oz		July 15–31
Tussock moth	2 pt	1 pt 8 oz	1 pt	1 pt	8 oz	4 oz		Start treatment when eggs start hatching
Fall webworm	1 pt	1 pt	8 oz	4 oz	2 oz	1 oz		Aug. 1–30
Orange-striped oak worm	1 pt 8 oz	1 pt 8 oz	1 pt	1 pt	1 pt	8 oz		Aug. 1–Sept. 10
Japanese beetle	2 pt	2 pt	2 pt	1 pt	11 oz	8 oz		(a) July 1–15 (b) Aug. 15–30
Forest tent caterpillar	1 pt 8 oz	1 pt	11 oz	8 oz	4 oz	2 oz		Apr. 20–June 7
Eastern tent caterpillar	2 pt	1 pt 8 oz	1 pt	1 pt	8 oz	5 oz		Apr. 5–June 7
Spiny elm caterpillar	2 pt	1.5 pt	1 pt	8 oz	8 oz	4 oz		May 15–June 15
Gypsy moth	1 pt	1 pt	2 pt	4 oz	8 oz	2 oz		Apr. 20–June 10
Canker worm	2 pt	1.5 pt	1 pt	1 pt	5 oz	3 oz		Apr. 25–May 20
Elm leaf beetle	4 pt	3 pt	2 pt	1 pt	8 oz	4 oz		May 1–June 15

1 When using 6 per cent DDT concentration, double the volume of liquid given.

TABLE 5.11/LIST OF SPRAY FORMULAS

Spray Formula No. 1: 2 gal dormant miscible oil (Sunoco or Scalecide), 1 pt nicotine sulfate (Black leaf 40) mixed in 100 gal of water. Apply before the buds open. Caution: Do not drench plants, and do not repeat dormant oil sprays. Do not use when temperature is below 40° F or over 70° in the sun.

Spray Formula No. 2: 6 gal dormant miscible oil mixed in 100 gal water. Caution as above.

Spray Formula No. 3: 2 gal summer oil emulsion, or 4 oz Vatsol, 1 pt nicotine sulfate, mixed in 100 gal of water.

Spray Formula No. 4: 10 gal lime-sulfur (liquid) mixed in 100 gal water. Caution: Do not use this formula near buildings, because it will discolor painted surfaces as well as stone and brick. Do not use after an oil spray has been applied to the same plant in the same season.

Spray Formula No. 5: 25 lb dry lime-sulfur in 100 gal water. Caution: Do not use near buildings; see No. 4.

Spray Formula No. 6: 4 lb DDT 50 per cent wettable powder, 2 lb Ovotron 50 per cent wettable powder, 8 oz sticker and spreader (Filmfast) mixed in 100 gal water. Apply just before buds open in the spring. Caution: Heavy applications of DDT may injure the buds and result in a thinning of the foliage.

Spray Formula No. 7: 1 qt DDT 25 per cent emulsion mixed in 100 gal of water. Apply when main leader elongation begins.

Spray Formula No. 8: 1 gal Dinitro Slurry mixed in 100 gal water. Caution: Do not use on evergreens.

Spray Formula No. 9: 3 lb lead arsenate powder, 8 oz spreader and sticker, mixed in 100 gal of water.

Spray Formula No. 10: 5 lb lead arsenate powder, 8 oz spreader and sticker (calcium caseinate) mixed in 100 gal of water. Caution: Magnolias, hemlocks, and box are susceptible to injury by heavy sprays of lead arsenate. Keep away from pastures.

Spray Formula No. 11: 5 lb lead arsenate powder, 1 pt nicotine sulfate, 1 gal summer oil emulsion (Nursery Volck) mixed in 100 gal water. Two sprays are needed for New England conditions, the first about the middle of June and the second 10 days later. The spray should be applied forcibly downward into the bud and needle clusters.

Spray Formula No. 12: 2 lb DDT 50 per cent wettable powder, 2 lb Ovotran 50 per cent wettable powder (or 1 lb 8 oz Aramite 15 per cent wettable powder), 8 oz sticker and spread, mixed in 100 gal water. Caution: Do not use DDT near pools or streams; it is very toxic to fish and aquatic animals. Also keep spray away from grazing animals. Substitute Aramite for Ovotran where dogwood, holly, roses, or privet are included.

Spray Formula No. 13: 4 lb DDT 50 per cent wettable powder, 2 lb Ovotran 50 per cent wettable powder (or 1 lb 8 oz Aramite 15 per cent wettable powder). 8 oz sticker and spreader, mixed in 100 gal water. Two sprays are necessary, the first in May, the second three weeks later, when eggs are hatching. Apply the spray to the underside of leaves where larvae of beetles are feeding. The use of DDT is likely to build up a mite population; therefore include a miticide where necessary.

Spray Formula No. 14: 1 pt nicotine sulfate, 6–8 qt summer oil or 7 lb soap flakes, or 8 oz Vatsol mixed in 100 gal water. Vatsol should be used where insects with a protective covering are to be controlled, or hairy-leaf trees or shrubs are involved. Caution: Do not use oil if the temperature is over 85° F. When soap is used as a spreader, do not apply this combination where there is an arsenical residue on the foliage. It is safer to spray conifers with the above solution during a cool and cloudy day.

Spray Formula No. 15: 2 lb Ovotran 50 per cent wettable powder, or 1 lb 8 oz Aramite 15 per cent wettable powder mixed in 100 gal water. Caution: Foliage may be injured if Ovotran is used on dogwood, holly, roses, or privet. Aramite is fast-acting and is recommended for a quick clean-up of a heavy infestation. Ovotran is slow acting but has a residual action of a month or more.

Spray Formula No. 16: 1 lb lindane 25 per cent wettable powder mixed in 100 gal of water.

Spray Formula No. 17: 16 lb Bordeaux mixture, 8 oz spreader and sticker (potassium oleate), mixed in 100 gal of water. Two or three applications are usually required: first as buds are breaking; second, two weeks later; and third, when leaves are half grown. Caution: Do not use on fruit trees.

Spray Formula No. 18: 3 lb methoxychlor 50 per cent wettable powder, 2 lb DDT 50 per cent wettable powder, 1 lb Ferbam 50 per cent wettable powder, 5 lb micronized sulfur, 1 pt nicotine sulfate, mixed in 100 gal water. Caution: Do not add the nicotine sulfate until time to use the spray.

Spray Formula No. 19: 4 lb chlordane 50 per cent wettable powder mixed in 100 gal water.

Spray Formula No. 20: 8 oz chlordane 50 per cent wettable powder mixed in 100 gal water, to 1000 sq ft of soil, or 5 lb of chlordane 5 per cent dust to 1000 sq ft of soil. This is the soil treatment for grubs and black vine weevil larvae.

Spray Formula No. 21: 6–8 lb toxaphene 25 per cent wettable powder mixed in 100 gal water.

Spray Formula No. 22: Carbon bisulfide (disulfide) or Cyanogas (a calcium cyanide compound). Use carbon bisulfide to control borers tunnel below the point of entry. Close opening with putty, gum, or plastic wood, after fumigant has been injected. Caution: Carbon bisulfide is highly flammable and explosive. Cyanogas releases hydrocyanic gas, one of the fastest and most powerful poisons known.

Spray Formula No. 23: 1 teaspoonful emulsifiable liquid malathion per gal water. Thorough, full-coverage applications should be made and repeated as necessary.

Spray Formula No. 24: 2 teaspoonfuls emulsifiable liquid malathion per gal water. Thorough, full-coverage applications should be made and repeated as necessary.

Spray Formula No. 25: 4 teaspoonfuls emulsifiable liquid malathion per gal water. Thorough, full-coverage applications should be made and repeated as necessary.

TABLE 5.12/CHART FOR THE CONTROL AND DESCRIPTION OF INSECTS AND DISEASES

Abbott's pine sawfly: Larvae are yellowish, black-headed, black spotted, and nearly 1 in. long when full grown.
Control: Use Spray Formula 10, 12, or 18.

Fig. 5.1   Aphid

TABLE 5.12/CHART FOR INSECTS AND DISEASES (cont.)

Alder blight aphid: The leaves fold downward, and in the folds are found large wooly masses covering bluish-black aphids.
Control: Use Spray Formula 14 when aphids are young.

Ambrosia beetle: Small beetle, about ⅛ in. long, which attacks the trunks of soft maples. It makes a vertical gallery about 1/16 in. in diameter, which extends directly into the wood for several inches, and then divides into several branches.
Control: Use Spray Formula 4, 5, or 14. Formula 22 is also effective in the galleries.

Antlered maple caterpillars: Caterpillars hatch about mid-July and attain full growth in September. They are about 1½ in. long, greenish, and variably marked with reddish brown.
Control: Use Spray Formula 10, 11. 12, or 18.

Ants: Any type of oil solution, water emulsion dusts, or wettable powders at 2 per cent concentration can be used to control the Argentine ant, crazy ant, fire ant, lawn ant, red harvester ant, and Pharaoh's ant. Since chlordane does not repel ants, complete destruction of the colonies may be obtained. A 3 per cent concentration applied to the nests of the mound building prairie ant has given 100 per cent control of the entire colony.

Army cutworm: Apply 5 per cent chlordane dust at the rate of 20 to 30 lb per acre; sprays of 1 lb chlordane per 100 gal water have also been found effective.

Aphids: These are small, soft-bodied insects, generally wingless. They may be green, yellow, red, or black, and produce a sweetish liquid known as honeydew .
Control: Use Spray Formula: 2, 5, 11, 14, 18, or 23.

Ash borer: This insect works just a little below the surface of the soil, frequently producing irregular dead areas surrounded by deformed bark tissues. The young borers work first in the sapwood and later enter the hardwood.
Control: Use Spray Formula 22. Cut and burn all infested shoots.

Fig. 5.2   Bagworm: larva, pupa, and adult

TABLE 5.12/CHART FOR INSECTS AND DISEASES (cont.)

Ash timber beetle: The females of this species usually tunnel the cambium in opposite directions from the entrance point and quickly girdle the infested limb. The young grubs make slender longitudinal galleries from ½ in. to nearly 2 in. long.
Control: Trim all weak branches and burn the infested wood.

Asiatic garden beetle: This beetle is less than ½ in. long, dull chestnut brown, and looks somewhat like a coffee bean. Adults hide in soil during the day and appear at dusk, feeding only at night. Foliage becomes ragged; sometimes only the midribs are left.
Control: Use Spray Formula 10, 12, or 18. Or apply 10 lb actual chlordane per acre as a spray or dust and work into the soil by cultivation or watering.

Azalea leaf miner: A small yellowish caterpillar, this insect is about ½ in. long when full grown. Until nearly half grown it mines inside the leaves, but after this it folds over the tip or margin of leaf and feeds on surface within this fold. The mined leaves turn yellow and drop. The small moths, yellow with purplish markings, deposit their eggs on the leaves.
Control: Use Spray Formula 10, 14, or 18.

Bagworms: These pests can be recognized by spindle-shaped bags hanging on trees, each inhabited by a worm. Young (one brood per year) appear in May; adults are moths.
Control: Use Spray Formula 10, 18, 21, or 24. Small infestations can be hand picked and destroyed.

Banded ash borer: The beetle is about ½ in. long, mostly dark purple with narrow yellow lines on the thorax and three yellow bands on the wing covers. Its grub bores in dying trees and logs of black ash.
Control: As for ash borer.

Fig. 5.3   Black vine weevil

TABLE 5.12/CHART FOR INSECTS AND DISEASES (cont.)

Barberry aphid: This small yellowish-green aphid is usually found on under sides of leaves and tender shoots, where it sucks the sap and weakens the plant. It has a soft, pear-shaped or nearly globular body, and has three pairs of comparatively long legs. It is usually not over ⅛ in. long.
Control: Use Spray Formula 11, 12, 14, or 18.

Barberry worm: Barberry worm caterpillars are black with white spots, and when full grown are about 1½ in. long. They form webby, excrement-filled masses on the tips of the shoots, which remain through the winter. Moths fly about the first of July, and caterpillars feed on leaves in late summer and fall.
Control: Use Spray Formula 10, 11, or 18.

Bark beetle: Seepage of balsam from the trunk, reddening of the needles, and death of the upper parts of the tree result from attacks by this beetle, which is about ⅒ in. long.
Control: Prune and burn infested parts. Spray Formula 6 may also give some control.

Beech blight aphid: This aphid is a blue insect covered with a white cottony substance. It punctures the bark and extracts the juices.
Control: Use Spray Formula 2, 14, or 18.

Beech leaf miner: The larvae of this species are small, white worms. The adult is a small black sawfly.
Control: Use Spray Formula 19 or 23.

Black-banded leaf roller: The leaf roller moth is light brown with dark brown bands obliquely across the fore wings. At rest it is flat, somewhat triangular in shape, and about ½ in. long. The larvae feed within rolled or folded leaves.
Control: Use Spray Formula 10 or 11.

Black spot: Spots produced by this parasite lead to defoliation and retarded growth.
Control: Use Spray Formula 5 or 18.

Black vine weevil: The white, grub-like larvae of this weevil feed on rootlets and later strip or girdle bark from outer roots. Adults are about ⅖ in. long, and black with patches of yellowish hair scattered over the otherwise roughened body. Wingless adult females emerge in June and July.
Control: Use Spray Formula 10, 18 or 20.

Bladder gall mite: Globular, bladder-like galls, ⅒ in. in diameter, on the upper leaf surfaces are produced by these white, pink or red mites, which are ¹⁄₁₂₅ in. long. Galls are first green, then red, and finally black. Mites live in the galls and leaf tissues. They winter in scars and wounds on the bark.
Control: Use Spray Formula 4 or 5.

Bladder maple gall: Small bladder-like galls about ⅒ in. in diameter. green at first, later turning red, are produced by a tiny plant mite. They sometimes practically cover the upper surface of the leaves.
Control: Use Spray Formula 4 or 5 during or immediately after the blossoming period.

Black walnut curculio: This pale, reddish weevil is ¼ in. long and covered with a grayish pubescence. It causes dropping of young nuts in June, each with a crescent-shaped scar.
Control: Collect and destroy infested nuts.

Blight: The sudden browning and death of single leaves in the spring is the first blight symptom. Later, brown, dead areas along and between the veins appear in other leaves. Leaves fall prematurely, and the disease completely defoliates the tree.
Control: Collect and burn all fallen leaves and twigs. Infected parts should also be cut and burned. Apply Formula 4 in spring before the buds break. Fertilize the tree heavily to increase its vigor.

Blue pine borer: This bluish flattened beetle is about ½ in. long, and bores into dead branches of pine.
Control: Cut and burn badly infested wood.

Box-elder bug: The adult is a stout grayish-black bug ½ in. long, with three red lines on the back. All stages are clustered on bark and branches in the early fall. Eggs are deposited in bark crevices in the spring.
Control: Use Spray Formula 14 or 18.

Boxwood leaf miner: Injury is denoted by oval swelling on under side of leaves, each containing one or more small yellowish-white maggots about ⅛ in. long. Adults are small yellowish-orange flies resembling gnats or mosquitoes, appearing in early May.
Leaves show a mottled appearance above and below; a raised blister-like effect which may be light yellow or brown. Plants lose leaves first year. They become under-nourished, have thin foliage, make poor growth, and have an unsightly appearance.
Control: Use Spray Formula 14, 16, 18, or 24. Keep plants covered with spray during the period the adults emerge, usually the month of May.

Boxwood psyllid: The adult of this species is a small dark greenish insect ⅛ in. long, with transparent wings. Young are covered with a white, waxy material. Leaves cupped.
Control: Use Spray Formula 14 or 18.

Broad-necked prionus: Full-grown grubs are 3 in. long, legless, and white with a brown head. They have a diameter of ½ in. or more. Infested shoots are easily broken off at or a little below the surface of the ground, or pulled out. The base of the stem and the thicker roots are full of large, irregular, blackened galleries.
Control: Remove and destroy all infested plants.

Bronze birch borer: This borer has a white, legless larva, ¾ in. long. Adult beetles ½ in. long. appear in June and are bronze colored.
Control: Use Spray Formulas 11 and 22 in the tunnels. Remove and burn infested parts.

Brown-tail moth: The small, firm-webbed nests on the tips of the twigs in midwinter are characteristic of the brown-tail moth. The small reddish caterpillars, about ¼ in. long, begin feeding as the leaves push out from the buds.
Control: Use Spray Formula 10, 11, 12, or 18.

Brown wood borer: Winding galleries in the wood are made by white-bodied, black-headed borers, 1¼ in. long. Tiny holes in the bark are made by emerging shiny brown beetles ¾ in. long.
Control: Treat all open wounds and avoid mechanical injuries to the bark. Use Formula 22 in galleries.

Buck or maia moth: The caterpillars are black, spiny, and feed on the leaves of various oaks, especially in swampy places.
Control: Use Spray Formula 10, 11, 12, or 18.

Bud gall: Hard, globular, woody galls in the vicinity of the buds are formed by a small jumping louse.
Control: Use Spray Formula 14 with soap when leaves are one quarter grown and the adults are about.

Bull's-eye spot: Spots of this disease show a distinct target pattern with layers of concentric rings occuring on red, sugar, and silver maples.
Control: Use Spray Formula 17. Gather and burn all diseased leaves in fall.

Butternut curculio: This insect is about ¼ in. long, reddish-brown, and ornamented with golden and silvery hairs. Grubs work in young shoots and stems in early summer. Nuts drop after the grubs have fed for about 10 days or 2 weeks.
Control: Collect and destroy infested nuts. Cut off and destroy infested shoots.

Cabbage looper: Caterpillar is a delicate pale green when first hatched; when full grown it is about 1⅜ in. long and green with a white stripe along each side of the body. Adult is medium-sized, grayish brown moth.
Control: Use Spray Formula 10, 11, or 18.

California oak moth: The longitudinally striped caterpillars are olive green, black, and yellow and measure 1 to 1½ in. in length. The moths appear in May and June, and second brood in November.
Control: Use Spray Formula 10, 11, 12, or 18.

Fig. 5.4 Cabbage looper

Fig. 5.5 Carpenter worm

TABLE 5.12/CHART FOR INSECTS AND DISEASES (cont.)

Callous borer: This borer causes ugly scars on the trunks and produces irregular, blackish, gall-like growths on the smaller branches. Moths are in flight from the latter part of May to the middle of June. The full-grown caterpillars are whitish, brown-headed, and about ½ in. long.

Control: Keep the trunks and limbs as smooth as possible. Borers should be dug out and the wound treated. Formula 22 may also be used.

Canker: The most obvious symptom is the reduction in number and size of leaves. The tree usually dies within a year or two. Elongated cankers or sunken areas in the bark cause girdling. Wood beneath the cankers is marked by reddish-brown to bluish-black streaks.

Control: Diseased trees should be removed and burned. Avoid injuries to sound trees.

Carpenter worm: Large scars along the trunk and irregularly circular galleries about ½ in. in diameter are produced by a 3-in. pinkish-white caterpillar. The adult moth has a wingspread of nearly 3 in., and deposits eggs in crevices or rough spots on the bark during June and early July.
Control: Use Formula 22 in the tunnels and seal the openings. Spray the trunks and branches in the fall with ¼ lb sodium arsenite and 1 qt miscible oil in 50 gal water.

Case bearer: The case bearer caterpillar is light yellow to green, ⅕ in. long with a black head. The adult is a brown moth with a wing spread of ⅖ in. The caterpillars mine and shrivel leaves.
Control: Use Spray Formula 5, 12, 16, 18, or 19.

Caterpillars: These caterpillars are green with pale spots and lines along the back and spinelike projections at each end.
Control: Use Spray Formula 10, 12, 16, or 18.

Cecropia moth: Cecropia moth larvae are 4-in. bluish-green caterpillars with rows of red, yellow, and blue tubercles along the body. Adult moth has a wing spread of nearly 7 in.; brown wings have red-bordered white cross-band.
Control: Use Spray Formula 10, 11, or 18.

Chiggers: Water emulsifiable concentrates have given excellent control of chiggers when used at the rate of 2 lb chlordane per acre. Dust applications have also given equivalent control results.

Chinch bugs: Dusts or sprays have given control of chinch bugs when 1 lb actual chlordane is applied per acre. The false chinch bug may be controlled in lawns or turfs by an application of 6 lb or 5 per cent chlordane dust per 100 sq ft.

Cockroaches: A 2 per cent chlordane spray gives approximately 100 per cent kill within 24 to 48 hours. This spray provides a residual surface for 60 to 90 days and is non-repellent.

Citrus whitefly: Adults are very tiny, pale yellow, with white powdered wings, similar to those of the green-house whitefly. Larvae are thin, flat, oval, and about ⅛ in. in diameter. They are nearly transparent, and excrete honeydew, upon which an unsightly sooty mold grows and spoils the appearance of the leaves.
Control: Use Spray Formula 14, 18, or 23. Use 2 or 3 applications at weekly intervals.

Cloaked knotty horn: A dark blue beetle, with the base of the wing-covers orange-yellow. It is about ¾ to 1 in. long. Grubs work in the stems.
Control: Cutting out and burning the infested wood is the most practical control.

Cockscomb gall: The feeding of wingless, yellowish-green aphids causes these elongated galls, resembling the comb of a rooster, to form on the leaves.
Control: Use Spray Formula 1, 5, 14, or 18.

Cone gall: These cone-shaped galls at branch tips are produced by small maggots. The adult is a small fly, and deposits eggs in the opening buds.
Control: Use Spray Formula 3 or 14. Spray when the buds are swelling in the spring; remove and burn galls in the fall.

Cottonwood borer: The small borers cut the bark and prevent the sap flow, while the larger ones tunnel the wood and weaken the tree. The beetle is 1¼ to 1½ in. long, stout, black, with irregular stripes and patches of cream-colored scales, and slender antennae longer than the body.
Control: Screen the base of the trees during July and August and treat the soil at the base with Formula 20.

Cottonwood leaf beetle: The beetles are yellowish, about ½ in. long and variably marked with elongated black spots. The dark blackish grubs are about ⅜ in. long. Beetles appear in early spring and feed on the tender shoots.
Control: Use Spray Formula 10, 12, 16, or 18.

Cottony maple scale: This insect is ¼ in. long, with cottony egg masses protruding from the brown scale. It sucks the under sides of the branches, thereby weakening the tree. Adult female appears in late May or June. Winter is passed in the adult stage.
Control: Use Spray Formula 4, 5, 14, or 18. Use only the soap in No. 14, as oils are not recommended for soft maples.

Crepe myrtle aphid: Foliage attacked by this aphid becomes unsightly, sticky, and blackened, and the tree may be completely defoliated.
Control: Use Spray Formula 14 or 18.

Cutworms: Apply 30 lb of 5 per cent chlordane dust per acre to soil surface or around base of the plant. Sprays containing chlordane have given equal control. Two oz of chlordane added to 50 gal of water have also given control. Chlordane formulations may also be used in preparing baits.

Datana caterpillar: Leaves are chewed by the black, yellowish-white striped larva, 2 in. long. Adult female is cinnamon-brown with dark lines across the wings. The wingspread is 1½ in. Eggs are deposited on under surfaces of leaves.
Control: Use Spray Formula 10, 11, 12, or 18.

Die-back: Upper branches progressively die back; cause is not known.
Control: Prune affected branches to sound wood and fertilize and water heavily to revitalize tree.

Dogwood bark borer: This insect works in the cambium of the older bark. Occasionally an infested area may be over 2 ft long and contain possibly 50 borers. Caterpillars winter in the outer dead bark. Moths appear late in June or July.
Control: Remove and burn old, dead bark after the leaves start and before moths appear. Bark should not be removed in early spring because the dogwood bleeds at that time.

Dogwood borer: This common, flat-headed borer makes flattened galleries just beneath the bark, often completely girdling the tree. Adults lay eggs in bark crevices in June and July. Caterpillars of the clear-winged moth may be encountered working in the cambium of the limbs and trunk. Adults lay eggs in May and June. The twig girdler is indicated by cracked and shrunken areas on the bark, and by dying twigs.
Control: Keep trees in good state of vigor. Cut out and burn infested twigs and branches. Use Formula 22 in burrows.

Dogwood club-gall: This spindle-shaped or tubular swelling, from ½ to 1 in. long, is found at the tips or along the stems of small twigs. It is caused by a tiny, two-winged fly or club-gall midge which deposits eggs in the bark in the spring. The maggot develops inside the swelling and deserts the gall late in summer.
Control: Cut off and destroy galls soon after they have formed.

Dogwood scale: Trunks and limbs heavily infested with dogwood scale have a whitish, scurfy appearance. Female scales are roughly pear-shaped, grayish, about 1/10 in. long; male scales are narrow, with sides parallel and pure white.
Control: Use Spray Formula 1, 3, or 4.

Dutch elm disease: Early symptoms of this disease are wilting of the leaves on one or more branches, followed by yellowing, curling, and dropping of all but a few of the

leaves at the branch tips about midsummer. In winter tufts of dead, brown leaves adhere to the tips of curled twigs. This fungus penetrates the tree only through wounds, most commonly made by the bark beetles that carry the disease.
Control: Prune and burn infested wood promptly. Strip and burn bark from felled trees. Spray with Formula 6 just before emergence of beetles in early spring. Repeat in midsummer.

Eastern spruce gall aphid: Small, cone-like swellings or galls are produced by this aphid on the bases of new shoots. Galls are usually about ¾ in. long and resemble miniature pineapples. The tiny, bluish-gray young aphids winter on twigs at the bases of the buds. In spring they develop into wingless adults, about 1/16 in. long, which are soon covered with a white cottony secretion. In August the galls turn brownish and each cell opens, permitting the escape of the maturing aphids.
Control: Use Spray Formula 1, 3, 5, 14. Measure 1 lb of actual chlordane per 100 gal of water.

Eastern tent caterpillar: Caterpillars construct tents in tree forks or crotches in early spring, and often strip the leaves. Reddish-brown moths emerge in early summer and lay eggs in a dark brown collar-like band that encircles small twigs. Eggs hatch the following spring. Full grown caterpillar is nearly 2 in. long. Color is black to light brown, and some have white and blue markings and a white stripe along the middle of the back.
Control: Use Spray Formula 10, 12, or 18.

Eight-spotted forester: The reddish, black-ringed caterpillars of this insect are about 1½ in. long when full grown. The parent insect is a black moth with 8 large lemon-yellow spots on its wings. Wings are about 1½ in. wide.
Control: Use Spray Formula 10, 12, or 18.

Elm borer: This white grub, 1 in. long, burrows into the inner bark and sapwood and pushes sawdust out through the bark crevices. The adult is a grayish-brown beetle, ½ in. long, with brick-red bands and black spots.
Control: Remove and burn severely infested branches or trees, and fertilize and water weakened trees. Use Formula 22 in the burrows.

Elm case bearer: The tiny larva chews small holes in the leaves and mines angular spots between the leaf veins. Adult is a small moth with a ½-in. wing spread.
Control: Use Spray Formula 5, 10, or 11.

Fig. 5.6 Eastern tent caterpillar larva

Elm leaf aphid: This is an inconspicuous green plant louse, occurring in large numbers. The area under infested trees may be kept damp even in hot, dry weather by the constantly dripping honey-dew.
Control: Use Spray Formula 11, 14, or 18.

Elm leaf miner: The larvae of this small sawfly produce somewhat irregular, circular blister mines. The shining black sawflies, about ⅛ in. long deposit their eggs in the leaves the latter part of May. The legless grubs work between the upper and lower surfaces of the leaves. emerging in the latter part of June or very early in July.
Control: Use Spray Formula 12, 14, 16, 18, or 24.

Elm case bearer: The tiny larva chews small holes in the leaves and mines angular spots between the leaf veins. Adult is a small moth with a ½-in. spread.
Control: Use Spray Formula 5, 10, or 11.

Elm sawfly: This is a cylindrical, coiled, yellowish-white worm with a black line down the middle of its back. The coil has a major diameter of about 1 in. The larva is full grown the latter part of July or in August. Winter is passed in a tough, coarse, silken cocoon at or just below the surface of the ground. The large wasplike female, with a length of about 1 in. and a wingspread of 2 in., has a black head and a steely-blue body.
Control: Use Spray Formula 10, 12, 16, or 18.

Elm span worm: These are brownish-black, yellow-marked, looping caterpillars or measuring worms with dull reddish or reddish-brown heads. They feed in early summer, sometimes defoliating large areas. Moths are snow white, appearing in July.
Control: Use Spray Formula 10, 11, 12, or 18.

English walnut scale: Full-grown female scale is circular, with a diameter of about ⅛ in. The young stay in a circle around the mother scale.
Control: Use Spray Formula 2, 4, 5, or 14.

Euonymous scale: These reddish, woolly-bordered scale insects attack bark. They winter as partially developed larvae. The young emerge in June and settle on leaves, where they develop until fall, and then migrate to the bark. They are usually not over ¼ in. long. Infestation causes yellow spots on foliage and gives twigs and branches a slate-gray color. Severe injury causes leaves to drop off early.
Control: Use Spray Formula 2, 5, 8, 14, or 24.

European bark beetle: The adult female, a reddish-black beetle 1/10 in. long, deposits eggs along a gallery in the sapwood. The small white larvae tunnel out at right angles to the main gallery. Tiny holes are visible in the bark when the adult beetles finally emerge.
Control: Remove and burn severely infested branches or trees, and fertilize and water weakened trees. Use Formula 22 in the galleries.

European canker: These scattered, often numerous, rough, sunken or flattened cankers, form a number of prominent ridges of callus wood on trunks and branches. Some cankers reach a length of 4 ft, a width of 2½ ft, and have as many as 24 ridges.
Control: All badly infested trees should be felled and the cankered tissue cut out and burned. Specimen trees may be saved by removing the canker and shellacking the edges of the wound and coating the wound itself with a good wound dressing. Fertilize and water to build up resistance to other insects.

European elm scale: This is an elliptical, greenish-brown scale, 1/12 in. in diameter, with a woolly fringe around the edge. It causes yellowing and premature defoliation. Young scales appear on foliage in June, and move to the bark in fall.
Control: Use Spray Formula 2, 3, 5, or 14.

European pine mite: Tiny mites are found within the basal sheath of the needle clusters. Infestation can be recognized by the thinner crown of paler foliage, as well as the distinct orange-brown color of the fallen needles.
Control: Use Spray Formula 1, 3, or 15.

European pine shoot moth: This brown-bodied, black-headed caterpillar, ⅔ in. long, feeds on the lateral shoots of pine causing them to wilt. The adult moth has silvery-banded, reddish-orange frontal wings and brown hind wings, which have a spread of ¾ in.
Control: Remove and burn infested shoots in fall, winter, or early spring. Use Spray Formula 11. Two sprays are recommended for New England conditions, the first about the middle of June and the second about 10 days later. The spray should be forced downward into the bud and needle clusters. Use Formula 23.

European willow gall midge: Yellowish, jumping maggots of this pest cause swollen, distorted twigs. Adults appear in early spring.
Control: Prune and burn infested twigs. Use Spray Formula 14 or 15.

Fall canker worm: Wingless females deposit dark gray flowerpot-shaped eggs on the bark in irregular clusters of 10–50 or more. Eggs hatch about the time the leaves begin to push out of the bud. The caterpillars complete their growth the latter part of May and are then about 1 in. long, mostly black, usually with three narrow white stripes and a broader lemon-yellow stripe on each side. They have three pairs of prolegs.
Control: Use Spray Formula 10, 12, or 18.

Fall webworm: Caterpillars spin a tent-like web at ends of branches, enclosing foliage on which they feed. The caterpillars are hairy, with long grayish-brown hairs arising from black and orange spots, and shorter hairs between. When fully grown they are about 1 in. long, with a broad brownish stripe along the back. Two generations are produced each year, the first in late spring and the second in late summer. Cocoons are spun in protected locations or in the soil, and the satiny white moths which emerge from them lay their eggs in masses on the leaves.
Control: Use Spray Formula 10, 12, or 18.

Flat-headed apple tree borers: The rather slender white grubs of this species have the anterior portion of the body greatly enlarged. They make wavy flattened galleries in the wood. The parent insect is an inconspicuous, metallic-colored, grayish, flattened beetle about ½ to ⅝ in. long. It is in flight from the latter part of May into September.
Control: Cut out and burn infested or dying wood. Use Formula 22 in galleries.

False pine webworm: Webworms are about ¾ in. long when full grown and greenish- or yellowish-brown. They have conspicuous antennae and a well developed anal filaments. In late summer they form webbed masses of greenish or brownish excrement on the terminal twigs.
Control: Cut out worms and webs and use Spray Formula 10.

Flathead borer: Adult beetles emerge in late spring and early summer and are attracted to weakened trees, where they lay eggs in bark crevices. Grubs make broad, irregular tunnels filled with boring dust. When nearly full grown, in late fall or spring, they bore into the wood. The yellowish-white and legless grub is about 1 in. long when mature. The body is flattened, and the first segment back of the head is much broader than the rest of the body. The adult is a brownish, metallic, flattened beetle about ½ in. long, blunt at the anterior and more pointed at the posterior end.
Control: Wrap trunks of newly planted trees with burlap or heavy paper to prevent egg laying on the bark. Apply wrapping the first of May and maintain during the first season or two. If borers have entered the wood, use Spray Formula 22.

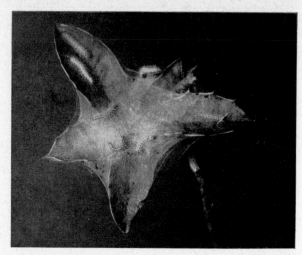

Fig. 5.7 Fall webworm, feeding on holly leaf

TABLE 5.12/CHART FOR INSECTS AND DISEASES (cont.)

Flea beetles: These beetles gnaw small holes through leaves from the under side, giving a shot-hole appearance. When disturbed. they jump away like fleas. Most are of a dark metallic color, very small, and about ⅕ in. long.
Control: Use Spray Formula 12 or 18.

Fleas: Control: Chlordane is very toxic to fleas, and 0.25 per cent spray or dip has proved very effective in flea control. Chlordane dust (2 per cent or 5 per cent) may also be used.

Flower thrips: Thrips enter developing flower buds and feed on tender flower parts, causing the petals to become flecked and discolored and the flowers deformed. The adult is a tiny, slender, brownish-yellow insect with feather like wings, and is extremely active. Young are lemon colored.
Control: Spray flowers with tartar emetic solution prepared as follows: 1 oz tartar emetic, 2 oz brown sugar, and 3 gal water. Repeat applications twice a week until insect is controlled. Use Spray Formula 23.

Forest tent caterpillars: Leaves are chewed by a caterpillar 1½ in. long, bluish-black with white spots down the back. Caterpillars mass in large numbers on the trunk during the day. The adult female is a brown moth with two dark lines across the wings, and a span of 1½ in.
Control: Use Spray Formula 10, 11, 12, 18, or 24.

Fuller's rose beetle: Adult beetle feeds mostly at night; larva attacks roots and beetle feeds on foliage, buds, and flowers. The beetle is brown or grayish, about ⅜ in. long, with a short snout and a white diagonal stripe across each side.
Control: Spray of dust application containing 50 per cent barium fluosilicate or cryolite, or use Spray Formula 18.

Flies: A 2½ per cent chlordane concentration is recommended for general fly control. Apply around baseboards, windows and doors, and in other appropriate parts of buildings. Applications to the surface of the breeding media have given very good control of larvae.

Fusiform maple gall: The gall is about ⅕ in. long, tapers at both ends, and is sometimes very abundant on the upper surface of the leaves.
Control: Use Spray Formula 4 or 5 just after or during the blossoming period.

Giant hornet: This hornet is about 1 in. long, hairy, and black with dark yellowish-orange markings It tears bark from stems, and feeds upon sap flowing from wounds.
Control: Locate nests and destroy them with Formula 22.

Gloomy scale: Gloomy scale is similar to San Jose scale, but is larger and does not cause the reddish discoloration of green tissue. The insect is very prolific, and can encrust a limb in a relatively short time.
Control: Use Spray Formula 2, 4, 5, or 14.

Golden oak scale: Trees infested with golden oak scale have a ragged, untidy appearance. Shallow pits are formed in the bark by circular, greenish-gold scales, $\frac{1}{16}$ in. in diameter.
Control: Use Spray Formula 1 or 2.

Grasshoppers: Use $\frac{1}{2}$ to 1 lb chlordane per acre as a spray, and $\frac{3}{4}$ to $1\frac{1}{2}$ lb per acre as a dust. Also $\frac{1}{2}$ lb chlordane per 100 lb of wet bait or dry bait.

Green maple worm: Full grown caterpillars are smooth, from 1 to $1\frac{1}{2}$ in. long, rather stout, and light green with yellowish-white stripes along the body and a pale, yellowish-green head. Caterpillars are not usually observed until May or early June, when they are about half grown.
Control: Use Spray Formula 10, 11, 12 or 18.

Holly leaf miner: Injury from holly leaf miners is easily recognized by the yellowish or brown serpentine mines in leaves caused by very small fly larvae. Larvae winter in the leaves. Pupation begins around first of April; adults begin to emerge middle of May.
Control: Use Spray Formula 11, 12, 14, 16, 18, or 19.

Holly scale: This scale is circular and flattened, and about $\frac{1}{16}$ in. in diameter, like other scale insects.
Control: Use Spray Formula 2, 3, 4, or 14.

Honeysuckle sawfly: This insect occasionally strips leaves in the spring. Larvae resemble hairless caterpillars about 1 in. long when full grown. They are somewhat grayish, with several yellowish stripes along the body and a row of black spots down the back. After feeding is completed, they spin cocoons in the soil and remain until spring, when the wasplike adults emerge to lay eggs.
Control: Use Spray Formula 10, 12, or 18.

Io moth: The caterpillar is large and pale green, with delicate markings of yellowish-red. It has uniform, rather thick, groups of irritating, sharp, poisonous spines. Its full length, in late summer, is about 2 in.
Control: Use Spray Formula 10, 11, 12, or 18.

Imperial moth: This large, thick, pale green caterpillar is about 3 to 4 in. long when full grown, with a pale orange head and legs and six yellowish spined tubercles behind the head. The moth is yellowish, spotted with purplish-brown, and has a wingspread of $5\frac{1}{2}$ in. It appears late in August through September.
Control: Use Spray Formula 10, 11, 12, or 18.

Ivory-dotted long-horn: The long-horn is a pale brownish-yellow bettle $\frac{1}{2}$ to 1 in. long, with four double ivorylike spots on the wing covers. Grubs are white and over 1 in. long when full grown. They burrow deeply into the limbs and enter the heartwood.
Control: Cut out and burn sick or dying wood. Use Formula 22 in burrows.

Japanese beetle: Beetles are about $\frac{1}{2}$ in. long and approximately the size of potato bugs. Head and thorax are shining brownish-green or coppery, and the wing-covers

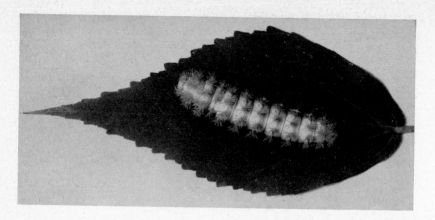

Fig. 5.8   Io moth: caterpillar

Fig. 5.9   Io moth: pupa

Fig. 5.10   Io moth: adult male

Fig. 5.11   Io moth: adult female

Fig. 5.12 Japanese beetle

Fig. 5.13 Japanese beetle: larva

TABLE 5.12/CHART FOR INSECTS AND DISEASES (cont.)

are brown tinged with green at the edges. There are conspicuous whitish spots, usually not concealed, on the sides and at the tip of the hind body or abdomen. Adults emerge from the ground the latter part of June and continue abroad until early in October. Grubs winter in earthen cells 1½ to 12 in. below the surface.
Control: Use Spray Formula 10, (increased to 6 lb), 12, 18, or 23.

Japanese beetle larvae: Control: To secure protection for a long period of time 10 lb of chlordane per acre is recommended. If only initial kill is desired, use 5 lb of chlordane per acre.

June beetles: Adults have been controlled by spraying the foliage of plants with a chlordane spray consisting of 1 lb per 100 gal of water.

Japanese scale insect: This insect is narrower than the common oystershell scale. It is only about 1/16 to 1/12 in. long and a dull grayish-white.
Control: Use Spray Formula 2, 4, 5, or 14.

Juniper webworm: Larvae are small and light brown, striped lengthwise. Moths (or adults) appear in June and lay eggs which hatch within two weeks. There is only one brood per year. Twigs and needles are webbed together, as larvae feed on and web plants throughout the summer, fall, and early spring.
Control: Use Spray Formula 10, 11, 12, or 18.

Kermes scale: This is a globular, light-brown scale, 1/8 in. in diameter. It infests terminal twigs and leaves. Young scales are covered with a white down.
Control: Use Spray Formula 2, 4, or 5.

Lace bug: This small, flattened sucking plant bug has white lacelike wings and a grayish body underneath. Young are flattened like the adult but lack wings. Eggs winter in leaves and bark, hatching in May or early June. Upper surfaces of leaves where they feed take on a mottled grayish green color and may become almost white. Lower surfaces are usually disfigured by black specks.
Control: Use Spray Formula 14, 16, 18, or 23.

Larch case bearer: Affected leaves turn first yellow, then brown, and finally die from the attacks of this dark-brown bodied, black-headed larva, 1/5 in. long. The adult

Fig. 5.15 Lacebug

Fig. 5.14 Leafhopper

TABLE 5.12/CHART FOR INSECTS AND DISEASES (cont.)

female, a silvery gray moth, with a wingspread of ⅓ in., lays cinnamon-colored eggs on the leaves in June. Larvae winter in tiny cases on the branches.
Control: Use Spray Formula 4 or 5.

Laurel psyllid: Leaves of affected shrubs curl and thicken, galls form, and growth is stunted. Young are covered with a white, cottony, waxy layer. The adult, which is ¹⁄₁₂ in. long, is yellowish-brown. Eggs are laid in March or April on the leaves.
Control: Use Spray Formula 3, 4, or 18.

Leaf beetle: Soon after leaves unfurl in spring, rectangular areas are chewed in them by brownish-yellow beetles, ¼ in. long. Later in the season, the leaves are skeletonized, curl, and dry up as a result of attacks on the lower surfaces by black grubs with yellow markings.
Control: Use Spray Formula 10, 12, 13, or 18. Use Formula 20 to kill masses of grubs around the base of the tree.

Leaf blister: Circular, raised areas, ranging up to ½ in. in diameter, are scattered over the upper leaf surfaces. The upper surface of bulge is yellowish-white, and the lower, yellowish-brown.
Control: Gather and burn infected leaves. Use Formula 17 before rainy periods in spring.

Leaf blister fungi: Round galls or blisters are formed on the leaves. The surface of the gall or blister becomes reddish or purplish and is covered with a whitish bloom.
Control: Pick off diseased leaves and burn them, or use Spray Formula 17.

Leaf blotch: Small, irregular, slightly discolored, water-soaked spots appear on leaves in spring. Later the centers of the spots become reddish-brown, surrounded by a yellow zone that merges into the healthy green portion. Numerous minute black specks appear in the center of the spot on the upper surface of the leaf. Tree appears as if scorched by fire, and affected leaves drop prematurely.
Control: Use Spray Formula 17. All leaves should be gathered and burned in fall.

Leaf-cast: Affected needles turn yellow, then brown, and drop prematurely. This disease is a fungus, producing elongated black bodies along the middle vein of the lower leaf surface.
Control: Use Spray Formula 17.

Leafhoppers: Leafhoppers are slender, delicate insects, usually ⅛ in. or less long. They vary from brown to pale green. Eggs are laid in leaf tissue or stalks with two or more broods annually.
Control: Use Spray Formula 12, 18, or 23.

Leaf skeletonizer: The lower leaf surface is chewed and leaf skeletonized, turning brown. Larvae are yellowish-green, and ¼ in. long. Adult moth has white-lined, brown wings with a spread of ⅜ in.
Control: Use Spray Formula 11, 12, or 14.

Leaf miner: Yellow or brown serpentine mines or blotches in leaves are produced by a small yellowish-white maggot, 1/16 in. long. Adult is a small black fly that emerges about May 1 and makes slits in the lower leaf surfaces, where it deposits eggs.
Control: Use Spray Formula 11, 12, 14, 16, 18, 19, or 24.

Leaf mottle: In the spring, small translucent spots surrounded by yellowish-green to white areas appear on the young unfurling leaves. These spots turn brown and dry. Within a few weeks the browned areas multiply until the entire leaf looks scorched and leaves drop prematurely.
Control: Provide adequate fertilization to combat disease. Protect defoliated branches from sun until second set of leaves develops.

Leaf rollers: Several species of leaf roller larvae may be found feeding upon the terminal leaves. They roll and bind the leaves together with a silken web, preventing leaves from developing properly.
Control: Injured twigs should be cut off and burned. Use Spray Formula 12 or 14.

Leaf spot: These are small, gray to brown spots, usually surrounded by a purple margin. They occur almost entirely on two-year-old leaves, and are always more numerous on trees that suffered from drought the previous year, or that are growing in unfavorable soil.
Control: Use Spray Formula 17. Improve soil conditions.

Purple eye spots: These large, irregularly circular brown spots are surrounded by a broad purple border; black pin-point bodies are usually visible in the browned center.
Control: Use Spray Formula 17. Gather and burn all diseased leaves in fall.

Leaf tier: Leaves are tied and matted together by small larvae.
Control: Use Spray Formula 10, 14, or 18 before the leaves are matted together.

Lecanium scale: Branches and twigs covered with brown, downy-covered, half-round scales, ⅛ in. in diameter.
Control: Use Spray Formula 2, 3, 4, or 5.

Leopard moth: The pinkish-white black-spotted larvae, about 2 in. long, tunnel and girdle trunks and branches. The adult female has white wings with metallic blue spots, and a wingspread of 1½ in. Life cycle is completed in two years.
Control: Prune and burn severely infested branches. Use Formula 22.

Lilac borer: This is a whitish caterpillar about 1 to 1¼ in. long when full grown; it bores in the stem, usually near the base. Moths appear in July or August. Larvae

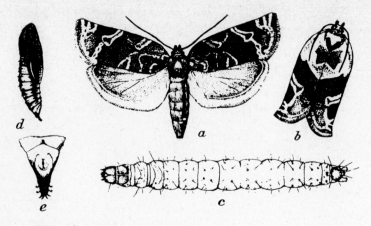

Fig. 5.16   Red-banded leafroller

TABLE 5.12/CHART FOR INSECTS AND DISEASES (cont.)

tunnel beneath the bark and through the stems, often girdling or weakening the stem so that it dies or breaks off.
Control: Cut out and burn infested shoots. Use Formula 22 in tunnels.

Lilac leaf miner: Young caterpillars mine leaves early in June. Toward the end of the month the mines are deserted and the caterpillars web the leaves into curled masses and skeletonize them. The first generation completes its development about second week of July, and the second continues into September.
Control: Use Spray Formula 12, 14, 16, or 18.

Linden borer: A slender white larva, 1 in. long, making broad tunnels beneath the bark near the trunk base or in the roots. The adult is a yellowish-brown beetle, ¾ in. long, with three dark spots on each wing cover. It feeds on green bark.
Control: Use Formula 22 in the tunnels.

Locust borer: Trunks and branches are scarred and gnarled, and tunnels are mined in the sapwood and heartwood by a white larva 1 in. long. The adult, a black beetle with yellow lines crossing the back, emerges in August or September. Severly infested trees die back from the top.
Control: Infested areas on the trunk may be treated in late fall or early spring with Formula 22, or when new growth starts in the spring, the trunk and branches may be sprayed with a solution of 4 oz sodium arsenite in 5 gal of water.

Locust gall maker: Elongated, gall-like swellings. 1 to 3 in. long, are produced on twigs by the feeding of these pale yellow larvae. The adult female is a grayish-brown moth with a wingspread of ¾ in.
Control: Prune and burn infested twigs in August, and gather and burn fallen leaves in fall.

Locust leaf beetle: Holes observed in leaves in late April may be caused by the locust leaf beetle—a black-headed, orange-red beetle, ¼ in. long, with a black stripe down the back. The leaves turn brown and fall in summer.
Control: Use Spray Formula 10, 11, 12, or 18.

Long-tailed mealy bug: These bugs are about ⅕ in. long when full grown. Their oval or elongated bodies are covered with white, waxy or mealy excretion, and they are

usually found in clusters along veins or undersides of leaves, or in crevices at base of leaf stems. They excrete copious quantities of sticky honeydew, in which a black sooty mold grows. Infestations cause loss of color, wilting, and death of affected parts.
Control: Use Spray Formula 3, 14, 18, or 23.

Luna moth: This moth produces a stout apple green caterpillar about 3 in. long when full grown, and with six rows of small pink hairy tubercles. They appear in midsummer feeding on tree leaves. The moth is light green and long-tailed, with a wingspread of about 4 in.
Control: Use Spray Formula 10, 11, 12, or 18.

Magnolia scale: Underdeveloped leaves and generally weak trees result from attacks by this brown, varnishlike hemispherical scale, ½ in. in diameter, with a white waxy covering. Young scales appear in August.
Control: Use Spray Formula 1, 3, 5, or 24. A second application two or three weeks after the first may be necessary.

Maple leaf cutter: Irregular oval holes ⅒ to nearly ½ in. in diameter are produced in foliage by this little caterpillar, which feeds between the upper and lower surface of the leaf. Damage occurs from July until September.
Control: Burn old fallen leaves. Use Spray Formula 11 or 14 in late June or early July.

Maple leaf stem borer: Dropping of sugar maple leaves in June results from the work of this yellowish, nearly legless, sawfly larva. It is about ⅓ in. long when full grown, and tunnels the leaf stalks, causing leaves to drop from lower branches.
Control: Pick and destroy infested leaves about mid-June; gather infested stems and burn them.

Maple nepticula: This insect causes a heavy dropping of Norway maple leaves in June. The very lowest part of the affected leaf stem has a variable sooty-black discoloration, and at a point almost exactly ½ in. from the base of the leaf stem there is a minute, elevated, white oval object. The insect winters in a pale orange-yellow cocoon about ³⁄₁₆ in. in diameter, which is spun mostly on the bark.
Control: Use Spray Formula 1, 3, or 14.

Maple trumpet skeletonizer: Leaves of red maple are folded loosely in August and September. The larva lives in a long, black, tapering, trumpetlike tube near adjacent skeletonized areas.
Control: Use Spray Formula 10, 11, 14, 16, or 18.

Maple and oak twig pruner: The white, cylindrical, conspicuously segmented grub girdles branches 1 in. or less in diameter. The adult is a slender, grayish-brown, long-horned beetle, ½ in. long. Eggs are deposited inside twigs in July, and the larvae winter in the fallen twigs.
Control: Collect and burn all fallen twigs in the summer and fall.

Maple phenacoccus: The cottony masses sheltering the females of this insect are abundant in mid summer on the undersurfaces of sugar maple leaves. The full grown males migrate to the trunk, and when numerous may give it a characteristic chalky appearance. There are three generations, the first brood hatching in June, the second in August, and the third wintering.
Control: Spray with a tobacco-soap preparation when the young are crawling in numbers.

Mildew: Tips of growing canes are halted in growth and the leaves distorted and covered with white spores.
Control: Use Spray Formula 5 or 18.

Mosquitoes: Chlordane applied at the rate of 0.2 to 0.4 lb per acre has given control of both the larvae and adults.

Mottled willow borer: These white legless larvae, ½ in. long, eat through the cambium and wood, producing swollen and knotty limbs. The adult beetle is ⅓ in. long, and has a long snout and grayish-black, mottled wing covers.
Control: Paint the injured area in May or early in June with paradichlorobenzene and pine oil mixture.

Mourning cloak caterpillars: Clusters of these insects strip terminal branches. They are over 2 in. long when full grown, and spiny, with dull red markings. The species is also known as the spiny elm caterpillar.
Control: Use Spray Formula 10, 12, 16, or 18.

Mulberry white fly: Foliage is discolored by these pests, which are found mostly on lower leaf surfaces. The nymphs are oval, black, scalelike, with a fringe of white waxy filaments around the edges, approximately the size of a pin head. Adults resemble tiny white moths. Attacks may occur from spring to fall.
Control: Use Spray Formula 14, 18, or 23.

Norway maple aphid: Large, hairy, greenish-marked aphids appear on undersides of leaves, and excrete large amounts of honey dew. The leaves become badly wrinkled, blackened, and only ⅔ normal size, and heavy midsummer leaf drop follows.
Control: Use Spray Formula 11, 14, or 18.

Northern brenthian: This is a slender grub about ¾ in. long and not quite ½₀ in. thick. It bores into solid wood of white oak.
Control: Cut out and burn sick or dying wood. Use Formula 22 in burrows.

Needle and twig blight: The needles of the current season's growth turn red and shrivel, and new twigs are blackened and stunted by this blight. Severely infected trees appear as if scorched by fire or damaged by frost.
Control: Prune and burn infected twigs and apply Formula 17 as the leaves develop in the spring.

Needle rusts: In late May or early June some of the new leaves turn yellow. Within two weeks the shoots turn yellow and droop. Most of the needles then drop from the shoots. The branch tips look as if they had been scorched by fire. Waxy red linear fungus bodies occur on the lower leaf surface, on the shoots, and on the cones.
Control: Use Spray Formula 5, but reduce to 4 lb to 50 gal water. Apply at weekly intervals in May.

Norway maple leaf hopper: Numerous small yellow hoppers infest the foliage of Norway maples and cause cankerous swelling on twigs. The twig damage is caused by the abundant deposition of eggs just under the tender bark, in small oval cells about ½₅ in. long. The surface of such twigs is slightly ridged, and there are numerous small openings.
Control: Use Spray Formula 12, 14, or 18.

Oak mite: Injuries made by this pest cause mottled yellow foliage. The mites are yellow, brown, or red, and have eight legs.
Control: Use Spray Formula 1, 3, 5, 14, or 15.

Oblique-banded leaf roller: This caterpillar conceals itself by rolling the leaf upon which it is feeding, and by tying terminal leaves together. It varies from yellow to pale green, and is ¾ in. long when mature. There are two generations per year, one in spring and the other late in summer.

Control: Dust plants with a mixture of equal parts tobacco dust and pyrethrum powder. Make two successive applications, separated by a half-hour interval. The first application drives the caterpillars from their hiding places and the second kills them.

Obscure scale: Tiny, circular, dark-gray scales, about $\frac{1}{10}$ in. in diameter, cover bark of twigs and branches.
Control: Use Spray Formula 2, 4, 5, or 14.

Ocellate maple leaf gall: This gall disfigures red maple leaves. Galls are circular, yellow, eyelike spots about $\frac{3}{8}$ in. in diameter, with the center and the margin cherry-red.
Control: Use Spray Formula 4 or 5.

Oleander scale: Heavily infested plants lose vigor, turn pale, and die. The scales are usually circular, somewhat flattened, and about the size of a pin-head. Male scales are tiny and pure white. Female scales are light buff with a faint tinge of purple, and two to three times as large as the males.
Control: Use Spray Formula 2, 3, 5, or 14.

Orange-striped oak worm: The spiny black caterpillars, with four orange-yellow stripes on the back and two along each side, are about 2 in. long when full grown. They commonly occur in clusters and appear in midsummer.
Control: Use Spray Formula 10, 11, 12, or 18.

Oriental moth caterpillar: The sluglike caterpillars appear in midsummer. They are about 3.4 in. long when full grown, and yellowish, red-marked, blue-spotted, green and grayish-brown, with groups of large spiny processes at both ends. They winter in oval cocoons, about $\frac{3}{4}$ in. long and with somewhat irregular broad white markings. Moths appear in late June or early July.
Control: Use Spray Formula 10, 12, or 18 when caterpillars are small.

Oyster shell scale: This scale is the shape of a miniature oyster shell, about $\frac{1}{8}$ in. long. Color is brown to brownish gray. Eggs winter under the female and hatch into the crawling stage about the time the apple blossoms are falling. A second generation is produced in July-August.
Control: Use Spray Formula 2, 3, 5, 14, or 24.

Pacific oak twig girdler: This insect produces numerous small areas of fading yellow, red, or brown on the foliage. It makes a gallery only a few inches long the first year, which may be extended a foot or more in the second year. The burrow spirals around branches not over $\frac{1}{2}$ in. in diameter, killing the part beyond.
Control: Cut and burn infested twigs about April. Use Spray Formula 14 in June to kill the beetles before they deposit eggs.

Pine bark aphid: This aphid causes white woolly patches on the trunks and limbs; adult females winter under the woolly material. Attacks white, Scotch, and Austrian pines.
Control: Use Spray Formula 5, 14, or 18.

Pine leaf miner: The full grown larva, about $\frac{1}{5}$ in. long, is brown and mines the tips of pine needles. Injured tips turn yellow and dry up. There are three generations per year, the first appearing in June.
Control: Use Spray Formula 12, 14, 16, or 18.

Pine needle scale: These tiny elongated white scales appear on the needles during the summer and winter as purplish eggs under female scales.
Control: Use Spray Formula 2, 4, 5, or 25.

Fig. 5.17 Oyster shell scale

TABLE 5.12/CHART FOR INSECTS AND DISEASES (cont.)

Pear leaf blister mite: This tiny elongated four-legged pest, $\frac{1}{125}$ in. long, causes tiny brown blisters on the lower leaf surface, and premature defoliation.
Control: Use Spray Formula 4 or 18.

Peony scale: Usually thin bark grows over these tiny sucking insects, leaving small bumps or swellings on the bark surface. If the swellings are opened, the circular, convex, grayish-brown scales, each about $\frac{1}{10}$ in. in diameter, may be found. When they are removed, a thin layer of white wax remains. The young start hatching about the last of March, and continue for over a month, remaining exposed for about four weeks before the bark covers them. There is only one generation each year.
Control: Use Spray Formula 2, 14, or 18.

Plant mite: These mites cause flower galls, irregular in size and ranging from about $\frac{1}{4}$ to $\frac{3}{4}$ in. in diameter, which eventually dry and remain on the twigs with the starting of growth in spring.
Control: Use Spray Formula 2, 3, 14, or 15.

Pine pitch borer: A white larva 1 in. long causes bark to exude masses of pitch. Adult is a moth with clear wings that have a spread of 1 in.
Control: Remove the pitch in early May and crush the borers. Use Formula 22, or paint the injured bark with pine oil and paradichlorobenzene (moth balls) mixture.

Pine sawfly: Full grown larva is about 1 in. long. Head is black and the body greenish-yellow, with a double stripe of brown down the middle of the back, and on either side a yellow stripe broken with transverse brown. Adults appear in the latter part of April. Two broods of larvae, the first in May and June and the second in August and September.
Control: Use Spray Formula 10, 12, or 18.

Pine tube-moth: Larvae produce cylindrical tubes of needles webbed together, eating off the terminal third of the needles almost to uniform height. Moths emerge from the last of April to the middle of July.
Control: Use Spray Formula 11 or 12.

Poplar borer: Blackened and swollen scars on limbs and trunk and sawdust at base of tree indicate the presence of this borer. The white larvae are $1\frac{1}{4}$ to $1\frac{1}{2}$ in. long at maturity, and upper and lower parts of the body have horny points. The adult female is a bluish-gray beetle, approximately 1 in. long with black spots and yellow patches. Control: Remove and burn badly infested trees. Use Formula 22 in the tunnels.

Poplar curculio: Full grown borer or grub is about ½ in. long, fleshy, white and legless. It ordinarily works within ½ in. of the surface of the branch or trunk. The beetle is about ⅓ in. long, and black with peculiar tufts of black scales or hairs. Tips of the wing covers, sides of the thorax, and portions of the legs are pinkish white. Control: Cut and burn badly infested trees. Use Spray Formula 3 in midsummer.

Poplar sawfly: The orange-yellow larvae are black-spotted and nearly 1 in. long when full grown. Broods hatch in June and August. Control: Use Spray Formula 10, 12, or 18.

Privet mite: Small mites swarm on foliage. Blood red eggs are usually deposited with the long axis perpendicular to the leaf. Life cycle is completed in three weeks, and there are six or seven generations per year. Infestation causes yellowing or fading of leaves. Control: Use Spray Formula 5, 14, or 15.

Promethea moth: The large delicate, bluish-white caterpillars are 2½ in. long when full grown. They have four large yellowish or red tubercles on the posterior segments and large ones on the eighth abdominal segment. They web the leaves firmly to the stem, draw the edges together, and spin a firm cocoon. Control: Pull off and destroy the cocoons. Use Spray Formula 11, 12, 14, or 18.

Red-cedar bark beetle: This insect is a light brown or black beetle about 1/16 in. long. It excavates vertical galleries. Control: Control by liberal watering and feeding.

Red-headed pine sawfly: Larvae are red-headed, dirty yellowish, black spotted, and about 1 in. long when full grown. They feed in clusters near the tips of the branches. The first brood occurs in July and the second in September. Control: Use Spray Formula 10, 12, or 18.

Red-humped caterpillar: Caterpillars are yellowish and black striped with red heads and red humps. Adult is a grayish brown moth with a wingspread of 1¼ in. Caterpillars chew leaves. Control: Use Spray Formula 10, 11, 12, or 18.

Red spider: Leaves assume a gray or yellow cast when severely infested by these tiny green, yellow, or red mites, 1/50 in. long. Infested leaves and twigs are occasionally covered with fine silken webs. Control: Use Spray Formula 1, 5, 14, 15, or 18, or dust with sulfur.

Rhododendron clear wing: Leaves wilt as a result of mining the inner bark and sapwood of branches and stems by this yellowish-white borer ½ in. long. Adult female is a clear-wing moth with a wing expanse of ½ in. Control: Prune and burn dead or dying stems in fall or winter.

Ribbed bud-gall: This gall is conical, strongly ribbed, and about 3/16 in. long. It occurs in crowded masses in longitudinal cracks of the bark. A sweetish secretion exudes from the galls in early summer, attracting many bees and flies. Control: Use Spray Formula 1 or 3.

Ribbed pine borer: The grub is white, broad-headed, and common under the bark of dead trees. Follows the work of the sawyer beetles. The beetle is stout, about ½ in. long, and common in partly rotten bark. Control: Protect logs by barking or placing in water.

Fig. 5.18   Red spider mite

TABLE 5.12/CHART FOR INSECTS AND DISEASES (cont.)

Rose aphid: These are small greenish lice, clustering on buds, stems, and shoots. They deform and kill leaves, buds, and branches.
Control: Use Spray Formula 11, 14, or 18.

Rose chafer: Long-legged grayish-brown beetles, about ½ in. long, appear in swarms about the time grapes are in bloom. Young are grubs and feed on roots and grass.
Control: These beetles are difficult to control. A spray consisting of 4 lb arsenate of lead and 1 gal molasses in 50 gal of water is recommended, or a 5 per cent chlordane dust.

Rose curculio: This black-snouted beetle is about ¼ in. long. It is bright red above, and the snout and under portions of the body are black. It injures roses by puncturing the buds and eating numerous holes in them.
Control: Use Spray Formula 10, 11, or 18. Injured rose buds should be collected and destroyed before September 1.

Rose leaf beetle: This shiny green beetle, about ⅛ in. long, eats buds and partly opened flowers.
Control: Use Spray Formula 10 or 18.

Rose midge: A fragile, two-winged fly about 1/16 in. long, yellowish, with the head and anterior of the body brownish. The tiny, white maggots distort the leaves and blast the buds.
Control: Nightly fumigations with nicotine or cyanide will help. Also keep the soil covered with a layer of tobacco dust about ¼ in. deep.

Rose slugs: There are several species of small greenish sluglike or coiled larvae. Some species feed on upper surfaces of leaves; others on the lower. Adults are four-winged flies, and because some have more than one brood damage may occur throughout the summer.
Control: Use Spray Formula 10, 11, 14, or 18.

Rose stem girdler: Elongated stem swellings are frequently marked with longitudinal lines. The leaves of infested canes turn yellow and finally wither, and the stem dies. The beetle is metallic colored, and is abroad during June and July.
Control: Use Spray Formula 14 or 18. Infested canes should be cut and burned as soon as they are detected.

Fig. 5.19 Rose beetle

TABLE 5.12/CHART FOR INSECTS AND DISEASES (cont.)

Saddle-backed caterpillar: Leaves are chewed by a black, yellowish-white striped larva, 2 in. long. Adult female is cinnamon brown with dark lines across the wings, and has a wingspread of $1\frac{1}{2}$ in. The upper wings are dark reddish brown; the lower, a light grayish brown.
Control: Use Spray Formula 10, 11, 12, or 18.

Sod webworms: See Fall webworm for description.
Control: Use 4 lb of 50 per cent chlordane wettable powder in 100 gal of water. Apply at the rate of 6–7 gal per 1000 sq ft.

San Jose scale: Twigs, branches, or stems are covered with a grayish layer of tiny overlapping waxy scales. Injury is indicated by dead or dying branches, poor vigor, and thin foliage. Waxy scale covering the female insect is circular, grayish, about $\frac{1}{16}$ in. in diameter, with a slight elevation or nipple near the center. Male scale is smaller and more oval. Insects winter in a partly grown condition, and in this stage the scale is nearly black. From two to six generations are produced annually.
Control: Use Spray Formula 2, 3, 5, or 14. Use No. 5 in the spring before the buds open, and No. 14 in the late spring or summer.

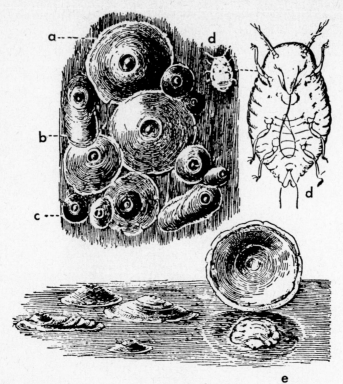

Fig. 5.20 San Jose scale

a: adult female scale; b: male scale; c: young scales; d: larva, just hatched; d′: "d," highly magnified; e: scale removed, showing body of female beneath. All much enlarged.

TABLE 5.12/CHART FOR INSECTS AND DISEASES (cont.)

Satin moth: Moths winter in small very inconspicuous silken pockets on the bark of the branches as well as the trunk. Full grown caterpillars are about 2 in. long, with a bluish-black head and a black body, with irregular white markings and spots down the middle.
Control: Use Spray Formula 10, 12, or 18.

Sawfly: The leaves are chewed by olive-green larvae, ¾ to 1 in. long, covered with small brown spines. The adult is a wasp-like fly with a wing spread of ⅘ in.
Control: Gather and burn fallen needles. Use Spray Formula 10, 12, or 18.

Sawyer: These large white fleshy grubs, about 1½ to 2 in. long, work in the inner bark, sapwood, and heartwood of dying pines. The grayish beetles are about ¾ to 1½ in. long, and the antennae measure from 2 to 3 in. additional.
Control: Protect logs by barking or placing in water.

Scotch pine scale insect: The insect is cherry-red to reddish-brown, about ⅛ in. long.
Control: Use Spray Formula 2 or 4.

Scurfy scale: Irregular white oval, about 1⁄10 in. long. Insects winter in egg stage.
Control: Use Spray Formula 2, 3, or 24. Two applications should be made of No. 3, one just at period when young are appearing and another 10 days later.

Sitka spruce gall: These galls exceed ½ to 3 in. in length, and usually include the entire new shoot. Galls open early in July and cause yellow spots and a bend in the needles.
Control: Use Spray Formula 1, 3, 5, or 14.

Soft scale: This scale, also known as the soft brown scale, is soft, greenish-brown or yellowish-green, often with a marbled or ridged effect across the back. It is oval, rather flat, nearly ⅛ in. long. Twigs and leaves are encrusted and take on a lumpy appearance. The scales produce large quantities of honey dew, on which a sooty fungus develops.
Control: Use Spray Formula 2, 5, 14, or 24 .

Sphinx caterpillars: There are two types. The first is brown, with black and yellow dottings and a short rough tail horn; the second, which may be either green or brown, has a spot resembling an eye at its posterior end. Both types are about 3 in. long when full grown.
Control: These caterpillars are not usually abundant enough to make control measures necessary. However, Spray Formula 10, 12, or 18 will control.

Spider mites: These tiny, yellow, green, or red eight-legged mites are about 1/64 in. long. Foliage of injured plants takes on a grayish, mottled appearance.
Control: Use Formula 18 or 24, or thoroughly dust or spray with sulfur compounds.

Spiny elm caterpillar: This is a spiny pest, black with reddish markings, about 2 in. long when full grown, and possessing conspicuous rows of spines. Parent butterfly is dark maroon, with blue-spotted black wings bordered with yellow. Wingspread is about 3 in.
Control: Use Spray Formula 11, 12, or 18.

Spiny oak worm: The caterpillar is bright tawny or orange with a dusky stripe along its back and prominent spines on the thoracic segments.
Control: Use Spray Formula 10, 11, 12, or 18.

Spittle bug: A spittlelike substance covering the needles and twigs is produced by the young of the spittle bug, a frog-shaped brown insect, ⅜ in. long. Eggs are deposited in the fall, and the young hatch the following spring.
Control: Use Spray Formula 3 or 14.

Spotted hemlock borer: Wide, shallow galleries in the inner bark and sapwood result from boring by white larvae ½ in. long. The adult, a flat metallic-looking beetle with three circular, reddish-yellow spots on each wing cover, deposits eggs in bark crevices.
Control: Prune and burn badly infested branches. Keep the tree vigorous by fertilizing and watering.

Spring canker worms: Yellowish-green oval eggs are deposited in early spring by the wingless females in irregular piles or clusters on the trunks and branches. Eggs are laid about the time the leaves begin to push out of the bud. The caterpillars complete their growth the latter part of May. They are about an inch long, and vary in color from light mottled yellowish brown to dull black. They have only two pairs of prolegs.
Control: Use Spray Formula 1, 3, or 5.

Spruce bud scale: These globular red scales, about ⅛ in. in diameter, occasionally infest the twigs of Norway Spruce.
Control: Use Spray Formula 1, 3, or 5.

Spruce budworm: The mature caterpillar measures about ⅓ in., has a rather thick, dark-brown body with yellowish-white parts. The moth is dull gray with brown or red markings on the wings and flies during June and July. Caterpillars feed by boring into

Fig. 5.21   Spider mite

Fig. 5.22   Gladiolus thrip

Fig. 5.23
Terrapin scale

1: insects in winter, enlarged; 2: insects in winter, natural size; 3: male puparia, enlarged.

the opening buds and later on the needles, which are cut off and held together with silken threads.

Control: Use Spray Formula 10 or 11. Spray as soon as the new shoots begin to develop in the spring, or while the caterpillars are still feeding on the needles.

Spruce cone worm: Cones are disfigured with masses of webbed borings, and occasionally a bunch of cones may be fastened together.

Control: Collect and burn diseased cones.

Spruce gall aphid: Two different galls occur on spruce, the spruce cone gall and Sitka spruce gall. The former occurs as a many-celled gall at the base of Norway spruce shoots. The galls are about ¾ in. long and resemble miniature cones. Sitka spruce galls occur on blue, Sitka and Engelmann spruce. This is also a many-celled gall, but is found on terminal shoots rather than at the base of the shoots.

Control: Use Spray Formula 1, 3, 5, 14, or 18.

Spruce needle miners: The mature caterpillars measure about ⅓ in. and are reddish-brown or green, with shiny yellow-brown heads. Small brown adult moths appear in May and June. They bore into and mine the needles, and later cut off the mined needles and web them together into a nest of silken strands.

Control: Use Spray Formula 11 or 12. Wash the webs loose from the trees with a strong stream of water. Begin at the uppermost webs and work downward. Treatment should be made in March, before the leaf buds begin swelling, or in late fall before cold weather sets in.

Spruce sawfly: This sawfly is about ½ in. long, dark green striped with darker green, and has a dark head. It defoliates trees in midsummer and early fall.

Control: Use Spray Formula 10, 12, or 18.

Spruce spider mite: Plants have a rusty and unhealthy appearance caused by mites' sucking the juices. There is also abundant accumulation of webbing. The mite resembles the common red spider; the young are pale green, the adults dark green or nearly black. They are particularly injurious and abundant during hot dry seasons, and often most serious in spring and fall.

Control: Use Spray Formula 1, 11, 18, or 24.

Stem borer: Grubs are yellow, and less than an inch long. with a swollen thoracic region. The top of the thickened first segment has a crown of short, conspicuous, dark brown spines. The beetles fly about the time the plants are in bloom. The tips of the stem are girdled, usually after plants bloom. Young larvae hollow out the stem and push borings out through surface holes.

Control: Cutting out and burning infested stems is the most practical method of control. Formula 22 may also be used.

Sugar maple borer: Wide channels in the inner bark and sapwood of the trunk and larger branches are made by a pinkish-white larva 2 in. long. The adult beetle is 1 in. long, velvety black with yellow markings. The bark above the infested area dies, leaving large scars.

Control: Prune and burn infested parts by June 1, and inject a nicotine paste into remaining tunnels.

Tar spot: Yellow spots appear on the leaves during late May, then turn reddish-brown and finally black by fall. A narrow border of yellow tissue remains around the darkened spots.

Control: Preventive sprays of Formula 17 applied at two week intervals in late spring should keep this disease in check.

Termites: Use 1 gal of 0.5–2.0 per cent chlordane water solution per lin ft. Apply this to the soil in a trench 1 to 2 ft deep. Treat the soil as the trench is being refilled.

Terrapin scale: This pest is seen as clusters of reddish-brown, terrapin-shaped female scales, ⅛ in. long. A sooty mold develops on the secretions.
Control: Use Spray Formula 4, 5, or 14. Do not use the oil on soft maples.

Thorn-leaf aphid: This aphid, usually pink or yellow-green, attacks young leaves early in the spring, causing them to curl. Aphids are soft, with pear-shaped or nearly globular bodies, and have three pairs of comparatively long legs.
Control: Use Spray Formula 14, 18, or 23.

Thorn limb-borer: Oval swellings, about 1 in. long and marked with four or five longitudinal scars, appear on small limbs and stems. The cinnamon-brown, white-marked beetle appears in the last week of May or early in June. The grub bores in the outer layer of wood.
Control: Prune out the diseased parts and burn them.

Thrips: Sprays using 1 lb chlordane in 100 gal water have been very effective in the control of various species of thrips. Equivalent control results have been obtained by dust applications.

Ticks: Applications of 1 to 2 lb chlordane dust or sprays per acre have proved very effective in controlling ticks. Complete coverage bordering paths and roadways is necessary.

Trunk decay: Trunks often show a white or brown decay of the heartwood. The former forms hard, gray, hoof-shaped fruiting bodies up to 8 in. in width along the trunk in the vicinity of the decay. The latter forms soft, fleshy, shelf-like fruiting structures, which are orange-red above and bright yellow below. The fruiting bodies become hard, brittle, and dirty white as they age.
Control: Clean out the badly decayed portions and apply a good wound dressing. Maintain vigor by fertilizing and watering.

Tulip scale: Trees may be killed by heavy infestations of oval, turtle-shaped, often wrinkled, brown scales, ⅓ in. in diameter. Secretion from the scales drops on leaves and soon is covered by sooty black fungus growth.
Control: Use Spray Formula 1 or 2.

Tulip spot gall: Produced by a minute gall-midge, or fragile yellow gnatlike fly about ⅛ in. long.
Control: Use Spray Formula 1, 14, or 15.

Twig-blight: The tips of the twigs die, turning to a light tan color. Minute black fruiting bodies are pushed through the epidermis of the leaves and twigs and spread from there. This blight is prevalent in wet periods.
Control: Use Spray Formula 17. Prune off and burn the dying twigs.

Twig girdler: A larva ½ in. long girdles twigs, causing them to be broken off by the wind. Adult is a reddish brown beetle ¾ in. long.
Control: Gather and burn severed branches and twigs in the autumn or early spring.

Two-lined chestnut borer: White, flat-headed larvae, ½ in. long, form tortuous galleries underneath the bark. The adult is a slender. greenish-black beetle ⅜ in. long, appearing in late June.
Control: Cut down and burn all badly infested trees. Increase the vigor of the remaining trees by fertilizing and watering.

Fig. 5.24   Twig girdler: adult

Fig. 5.25   Twig girdler: larva and pupa

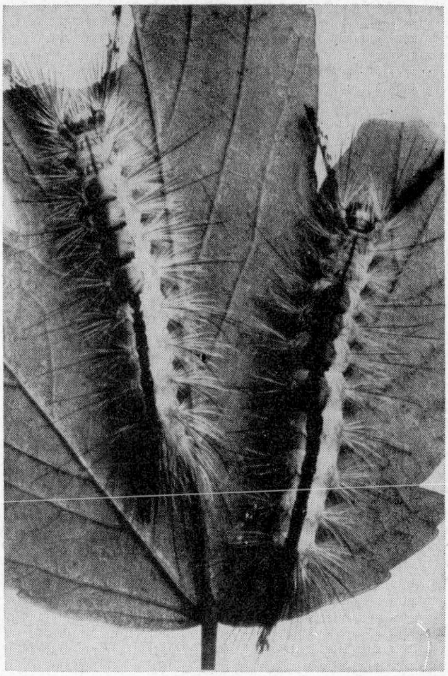

Fig. 5.26   Tussock moth: larva

Fig. 5.27   Tussock moth and egg mass

Two-marked tree hopper: Numerous snow-white frothy masses approximately ¼ in. long and ⅛ in. wide appear on the smaller stems. This is protective matter placed over the point where the eggs are laid. Adults are brownish-black with two white spots, and when resting upon shoots, they look very much like thorns. Eggs hatch in May.
Control: Use Spray Formula 5, 12, 14, or 18.

Walnut aphid: A light yellow plant louse with black markings on the antennae, legs, and abdomen. Winter is passed as eggs, which hatch in February and March.
Control: Use Spray Formula 11, 14, 18, or 23.

Walnut datana: Trees are defoliated by a black caterpillar (growing to 2 in. in length) covered with long white hairs. The adult female moth has a wingspread of 1½ in. The dark buff wings are crossed by four brown lines.
Control: Use Spray Formula 10, 11, or 18.

Wasps (hornets, yellow jackets and mud-daubers), white grubs: Use a 5 per cent or 6 per cent chlordane dust, 2 per cent oil spray, or 2 tablespoons of 75 per cent emulsifiable chlordane solution in 1 qt of water. Apply to nest openings at night. At the rate of 5–10 lb per acre chlordane has given control of the white grubs. The amount of insecticide required depends upon the type of soil.

Wireworms: Chlordane applied at the rate of ½–5 lb per acre gives control of wireworms. The correct dosage depends upon the type of soil. In some areas, a side dressing has been sufficient to give control. A solution of 2–4 oz of chlordane per 50 gal of transplant water has given protection. Chlordane can be incorporated with fertilizers.

Walnut husk-maggot: This maggot produces blackened hulls which are slimy within and contain numerous whitish maggots. Parent fly is dark yellow with brown-banded wings, about the size of a house fly.
Control: Use Spray Formula 10, 11, 12, or 18.

Walnut scale: Round brown scales ⅛ in. in diameter appear in masses. The adult female is frequently encircled by young scales.
Control: Use Spray Formula 2 or 4.

White blotch oak leaf miner: A larva ⅓ in. long feeds between leaf surfaces, producing white, blotched patches on the leaves. The adult female is a small moth with white forewings and silvery hindwings, with a spread of ¼ in.
Control: Gather and burn the leaves. Use Spray Formula 11, 14, 16, or 18.

White fly: Leaves are usually sticky from honey dew secreted by tiny black young, which look like oval scales about 1/35 in. long. Adults are tiny white flies that dart away when the leaves are disturbed.
Control: Use Spray Formula 14 or 18.

White-marked tussock moth: The full-grown caterpillar, nearly 2 in. long, has a red head and is marked with yellow and black. There are three long black tufts, two at at the front end and one at the rear. The insects winter in conspicuous egg masses which are covered by a white frothy substance about half an inch in diameter.
Control: Use Spray Formula 10, 11, 12, or 18.

White peach scale: Bark is covered with tiny white scales. Female scale is circular, nearly 1/10 in. in diameter and gray with a yellow center. Male scales are smaller, more oval, elongated, and pure white. Clusters of these white male scales are often noticeable near the base of branches.
Control: Use Spray Formula 2, 3, or 5.

White pine weevil: The leader shoot wilts and dies as a result of girdling of the inner bark by a white, legless form, ⅓ in. long. The adult is a reddish-brown beetle, about ½ in. long, mottled with brown and white scales. The adult hibernates in ground litter.
Control: Use Spray Formula 5, 7, or 18. Remove and burn infested leader shoots in the spring.

Willow leaf beetle: Holes are chewed in the leaves by the blue metallic adult form, ⅛ in. long, and leaves are skeletonized by the black larva, ¼ in. long.
Control: Use Spray Formula 3, 4, 5, or 14.

Willow scale: A pear-shaped white scale, ⅛ in. long. Eggs winter under the scale of the female.
Control: Use Spray Formula 3, 4, 5, or 14.

Willow-shoot sawfly: The adult is a wasplike insect which lays eggs in the shoots in early spring, then girdles the shoot below the point of deposition. The larva feeds in pith, causing the terminal shoots to wilt.
Control: Prune and burn infested twigs. Use Spray Formula 10 or 12.

Willow scurfy scale: Purplish-red eggs carry the insect over winter, young appearing in late May or early June.
Control: Use Spray Formula 1, 4, or 5.

Wilt: Leaves on one limb or on several limbs suddenly wilt and die, and usually fall. Infection of the entire tree may result in small, sparse, sickly foliage. Sometimes an entire side of a tree is killed during the winter and fails to leaf out in spring. The presence in the sapwood of bright green streaks, turning to bluish-black and brown, is a positive indication of wilt.
Control: Trees showing a severe infestation cannot be saved and should be cut down and burned. Mild cases may be corrected by judicious pruning and the application of high nitrogen fertilizers.

Witches-broom: This pest is visible on buds during the winter. Affected buds are larger, more open, and hairier than normal ones. Branches break off more readily, exposing wood to decay.
Control: Prune back all infected twigs to sound wood, and spray with one part sulfur in 10 parts water in early spring.

Woolly aphids: Clusters of woolly aphids on tips of new shoots will kill tips back to 6 or 8 in.
Control: These insects are more difficult to kill than most common aphids. Make sprays stronger and apply them as a coarse, driving spray in order to penetrate the waxy covering on the body of the aphid. Use Formula 14, 18, or 23.

Woolly beech aphid: Leaves are curled and blighted by an insect with a cottony cover. The cast skins adhere to the lower leaf surface.
Control: Use Spray Formula 2, 14, or 18 before leaves are curled.

Woolly larch aphid: White woolly patches adhering to the needles hide the adult aphids.
Control: Use Spray Formula 4, 5, 14, 18, or 23.

Yellow-spotted willow slug: A greenish-black sawfly or false caterpillar, ½ in. when full grown, with heart-shaped yellow spots on each side. First signs of infestation are blisterlike swellings containing eggs, on the upper surface of the leaves. The young slugs eat small holes and usually feed near each other. Growth is completed in ten days to three weeks. The full-grown caterpillars are slaty-black with lighter spots on the sides. The change to the adult occurs in dark brown cocoons on or near the surface of the ground.
Control: Use Spray Formula 10, 11, 16, or 18.

TABLE 5.13/CHARACTERISTICS, PRUNING, INSECTS, AND DISEASES: EVERGREEN AND DECIDUOUS SHRUBS

Botanical and common name	Description	Conditions and habits of growth	Pruning and other remarks	Insects and diseases
Abela grandiflora— Glossy abelia	4–5 ft Flowers (pink): June–Nov.	Likes either sun or shade, in a light peaty soil. Pendulous growth. Foliage is small, glossy, and is evergreen in South.	Remove old flower heads and thin the plant out occasionally. The shrub needs no regular pruning.	No serious pests or diseases.
Amelanchier canadensis— Downy shadbush	20–25 ft Flowers (white): March–April in South May in North Fruit (purple): May–June	Likes either sun or ½ shade, limestone soil. Open spreading growth. Fruit is sweet.	No specific pruning is necessary.	Pear leaf blister Mite—willow scale
Ampelopis quinquefolia— Virginia creeper	30–40 ft Flowers inconspicuous Fruit (blue): Sept.–Oct.	Likes sun or ½ shade in good loam soil. Has aerial roots and twining stems.	Requires no specific pruning. Has scarlet fall foliage.	Eight-spotted forester. Sphinx caterpillars
Ampelopsis quinquefolia Engelmanni— Engelmann creeper	30–40 ft Flowers inconspicuous Fruit (blue): Sept.–Oct.	Likes sun or ½ shade in good loam soil. Has aerial roots and twining stems.	Requires no specific pruning. Has smaller foliage than type.	Eight-spotted forester. Sphinx caterpillars
Aronia melanocarpa— Black chokeberry	4–6 ft Flowers (white): Apr.–May Fruit (black): June–July	Both like either sun or ½ shade and a dry rocky soil. Upright growth. Good autumn color.	No specific pruning is necessary. Shape plant in winter by removing old or dead branches.	No serious pests or diseases..

Botanical and common name	Description	Conditions and habits of growth	Pruning and other remarks	Insects and diseases
Aronia arbutifolia Brilliantissima Red chokeberry	6–8 ft Flowers (white): Apr.–May Fruit (red): June–July	Both like either sun or ½ shade and a dry rocky soil. Upright growth. Good autumn color.	No specific pruning is necessary. Shape plant in winter by removing old or dead branches.	No serious pests or diseases
		Evergreen azaleas		
Azalea amoena— Amoena azalea	5–6 ft Flowers (purple): Apr.–May	Likes sun or ½ shade, woodsy, humus soil. Browns in winter in North.	Prune only to shape plant. Prune in winter. Where planted outside its native woods habitat, maintain acid soil condition by mulching with acid peat moss, well-rotted sawdust, or oak leaves. Also by application of an acid fertilizer.	Mulberry white fly
Azalea hinodegiri— Hinodegiri azalea	3–4 ft Flowers (carmine-pink): May	Likes sun or ½ shade. Woodsy, humus soil.	as above	Leaf blister fungi
Azalea hinomayo— Kurume azalea	3–4 ft Flowers (pink): May	as above	as above	Peony scale Lace bug
Azalea indica— India azalea	4–5 ft Flowers (pure white): May	as above	as above	Stem borer Azalea leaf miner
Azalea ledifolia— Snow azalea	2–3 ft Flowers (snow white): May	as above	as above	Spider mites

Botanical and common name	Description	Conditions and habits of growth	Pruning and other remarks	Insects and diseases
		Deciduous azaleas		
Azalea calendulacea— Flame azalea	4-10 ft Flowers (yellow to flame) : May–June	Likes sun or ½ shade. Woodsy loam soil. Has an open and delicate growth.	See Azalea amoena	Black vine weevil
Azalea kaempferi— Torch azalea	8-10 ft Flowers (red) : Apr.–May	Same as above but with a dense and spreading growth.	as above	Fuller's rose beetle
Azalea mollis— Chinese azalea	4-6 ft Flowers (wide range of reds) : May	Ditto; will thrive in lime-stone soils.	as above	
Azalea nudiflora— Pinxter bloom	5-6 ft Flowers (pink) : Apr.–May	as above	as above	
Azalea poukhanensis— Korean azalea	3-4 ft Flowers (lavender) : May	as above	as above	
Azalea arborescens— Sweet azalea	6-10 ft Flowers (white) : June–July	Same as above but bushy and fragrant.	as above	
Azalea mucronulata— Manchurian azalea	5-6 ft Flowers (rosy purple) : April	Same as above but up-right and a very early bloomer.	as above	
Azalea rosea— Downy pinxterbloom	6-8 ft Flowers (pink) : Apr.–May	Same as above but spread-ing.	as above	
Azalea schlippenbachi Royal azalea	5-6 ft Flowers (pale pink) : May	Same as above, spreading and with large accented blooms.	as above	

Botanical and common name	Description	Conditions and habits of growth	Pruning and other remarks	Insects and diseases
Azalea viscosa—Swamp azalea	4-6 ft Flowers (white) : June–July	Likes a wet soil and is thick and bushy. Latest azalea to bloom. Fragrant.	as above	
Benzoin aestivale—Spice bush	8-10 ft Flowers (pale yellow) : March–Apr. Fruit (spicy red) : Autumn	Likes moist ground in sun or ½ shade. Is upright and dense. Foliage yellow in fall.	No regular pruning necessary.	No serious pests or diseases.
Berberis thunbergi—Japanese barberry	4-6 ft Flowers (yellow) : April Fruit (red) : Sept.–Feb.	Likes full sun in good loam soil. Dense and bushy. Red autumn foliage.	Does not require regular pruning. Remove dead wood in old stock. Clipped hedges should be pruned 2 to 3 times a year. Top of hedges should be narrower than bottom to encourage dense growth.	Barberry aphid
Berberis Julianae—Wintergreen barberry	4-5 ft Flowers (yellow) : Apr.–May Fruit (black) : Sept.–Oct.	Likes full sun in good loam soil. Shiny, prickly foliage. Evergreen.	Does not require regular pruning.	
Berberis verruculosa—Warty barberry	2-3 ft Flowers (yellow) : May–June Fruit (violet black) : October	Likes full sun in protected places. Fruit fragrant. Evergreen.	as above	Asiatic garden beetle
Berberis sinensis—Chinese barberry	4-6 ft Flowers (yellow) : May–June Fruit (purple) : September	Likes full sun in good loam soil.	as above	Barberry worm

TABLE 5.13/CHARACTERISTICS OF SHRUBS (cont.)

Botanical and common name	Description	Conditions and habits of growth	Pruning and other remarks	Insects and diseases
Berberis wilsonae—Wilson barberry	2–3 ft Flowers (golden yellow) : May Fruit (salmon red) : Sept.	as above	as above	Red spiders Eight-spotted forester
Bignonia radicans—Trumpet creeper	30–40 ft Flowers (orange scarlet) : July–Sept.	Likes sun in rich soil. Is a rapid grower and a self clinger.	Requires no specific pruning.	Has no serious pests or diseases
Buxus sempervirens—Common box	4–5 ft Flowers inconspicuous	Likes sun or ½ shade in rich loam soil. Dark green evergreen foliage.	No regular pruning is necessary. Formal hedge treatment requires shearing 2–4 times annually. Trim top of hedge narrower than bottom.	Boxwood leaf miner
Buxus japonica—Japanese box	4–5 ft Flowers inconspicuous	as above	as above	
Buxus sempervirens suffruticosa—True dwarf box	2 ft Flowers inconspicuous	Ditto; English box, slow growth.	as above	Oyster shell scale Spider mites Boxwood psyllid Giant hornet
Calycanthus floridus—Sweetshrub	3–6 ft Flowers (brown) : June–July	Likes good, moist soil in shade. Thick and bushy with a remarkable fragrance.	No regular pruning is necessary.	Has no serious pests or diseases.
Celastrus scandens—American bittersweet	20–25 ft Flowers (greenish white) : June Fruit (yellow and vermillion) : Autumn	Likes good, average soil in sun or ½ shade. Has an irregular and tumbling growth.	Prune only to restrain plant. Makes a good ground cover for rocks and banks.	Two-marked tree-hopper Euonymous scale

Botanical and common name	Description	Conditions and habits of growth	Pruning and other remarks	Insects and diseases
Cercis canadensis—American redbud	15–20 ft Flowers (rosy purple): Apr.	Likes sun or ½ shade in good woods soil. An early bloomer.	Shape plants when young, but prune as little as possible when plant is mature, removing only dead wood.	Two-marked tree-hopper
Cornus florida—Flowering dogwood	20–25 ft Flowers (white): Apr.–May Fruit (red): Aug.–Oct.	Likes sun or ½ shade in good, well-drained soil.	No regular pruning is necessary. Keep dead and diseased parts removed. Excellent fall foliage with red berries which are liked by birds.	Dogwood borer
Cornus florida rubra—Pink dogwood	12–15 ft Flowers (rosy pink): Apr.–May	as above	No regular pruning is necessary. Keep dead and diseased parts removed.	
Cornus alba—Tatarian dogwood	6–8 ft Flowers (cream-white): Apr.–May Fruit (blue-white): Aug. Oct.	Likes sun or shade in moist, good soil. Is upright and bushy with very red twigs and branches.	No regular pruning is necessary. Can be cut back severely without injury when overgrown, or can be cut to the ground in spring for bushy growth.	Dogwood scale Dogwood club-gall midge Flathead borer Leafhoppers
Cornus amomum—Silky dogwood	6–8 ft Flowers (white): May–June Fruit (blue): Aug.–Oct.	Likes sun or shade. Has an upright and bushy growth.	as above	Mulberry white fly Oyster shell scale
Cornus stolonifera—Red-osier dogwood	6–8 ft Flowers (white): May–June Fruit (white): Autumn	Likes sun or shade. Has a bushy, spreading growth with dark red branches.	as above	San Jose scale Cottony maple scale Dogwood bark-borer

TABLE 5.13/CHARACTERISTICS OF SHRUBS (cont.)

Botanical and common name	Description	Conditions and habits of growth	Pruning and other remarks	Insects and diseases
Cornus mas— Cornelian-cherry	10–12 ft Flowers (yellow): March Fruit (red): Fall	Likes sun or shade in moist, good soil. Has a dense upright growth and edible red fruit.	see above	
Cotoneaster horizonalis Rock cotoneaster	6–12 in Flowers (pink): May–June Fruit (bright red): Sept.	Likes full sun in a well-drained soil. Has a creeping habit of growth.	Does not require any specific pruning.	Lace bug Oyster shell scale San Jose scale
Cotoneaster rotundifolia Roundleaf cotoneaster	2–3 ft Flowers (white-pink): May–June Fruit (bright red): Sept.	see above	see above	
Cotoneaster divaricata— Spreading cotoneaster	5–6 ft Flowers (pink): May–June Fruit (bright red): Sept.	Likes full sun in well-drained soil. Has an upright habit of growth with spreading branches.	see above	
Crataegus cordata— Washington thorn	20–25 ft Flowers (white): May Fruit (scarlet): Sept.–Nov.	Likes sun in rich loam. Has abundant scarlet fruit.	Requires only minimum winter pruning to shape plant. Will make an excellent hedge.	Scurfy scale Eastern tent caterpillar
Crataegus oxyacantha— English hawthorn	15–20 ft Flowers (pink): May Fruit (red): Sept.–Nov.	see above	see above	Hawthorn lace bug Thorn-leaf aphid

botanical and common name	Description	Conditions and habits of growth	Pruning and other remarks	Insects and diseases
Crataegus coccinea Thicket hawthorn	20–25 ft Flowers (white): Apr.–May Fruit (large, scarlet): Sept.–Nov.	See Crataegus cordata	See Crataegus cordata	Cottony maple scale San Jose scale Borers Spider mites Wooly aphids Thorn limb-borer
Chaenomeles Lagenaria— Flowering quince	6–8 ft Flowers (red, salmon pinkish, white): Mar.–Apr. Fruit (yellow): Oct.	Likes sun or ½ shade in a well-drained, good soil. Plant is spreading and bushy	Requires only minimum winter pruning to shape plant. If grown as a hedge, it may be cut back when the flowering period is over.	Scurfy scale
Chaenomeles Maulei Lesser— Flowering quince	3–4 ft Flowers (pink and white): Mar.	as above	as above	
Chaenomeles sinensis— Chinese quince	Up to 15 ft Flowers (light pink): May Fruit (dark yellow): Oct.	as above	as above	
Deutzia gracilis— Slender deutzia	3–5 ft Flowers (white): May	Likes sun in a well-drained, good soil, upright, round head.	Should be thinned out well once in 3 years by removing as much of the old wood as possible. The best time for this pruning is in early summer.	Leaf rollers
Deutzia lemoinei— Lemoine's deutzia	4–5 ft Flowers (white): May	as above but is spreading	as above showy large bloom	
Deutzia scabra— Fuzzy deutzia	6–8 ft Flowers (white): June–July	as above but upright	as above many upright branches	
Deutzia scabra candidissima White fuzzy deutzia	6–8 ft Flowers (double white): June	as above	as above	

TABLE 5.13/CHARACTERISTICS OF SHRUBS (cont.)

Botanical and common name	Description	Conditions and habits of growth	Pruning and other remarks	Insects and diseases
Deutzia scabra Pr. of Rochester Pink fuzzy deutzia	8–10 ft Flowers (double pale pink): June	"	"	No serious pests or diseases
Eleagnus pungens— Bronze eleagnus	8–10 ft Flowers (bronze white): Oct.–Dec. Fruit (orange): Winter–Spring	Likes either sun or shade. Evergreen	Does not require regular pruning except to curb straggling habits of growth by shortening the longest shoots during summer. Green-leaved shoots that often appear among the variegated varieties should be removed.	
Euonymus alatus— Winged euonymus	6–8 ft Flowers (yellow): May–June Fruit (purple pods): Sept.–Oct.	Likes sun in good, rich soil. Has a dense, spreading growth.	Does not require any specific pruning	Euonymus scale
Euonymus americanus Brook euonymus	6–8 ft Flowers (purplish green): June Fruit (orange and scarlet): Sept.–Oct.	Likes sun in good, rich soil. Has an upright growth.	as above	San Jose scale
Euonymus europaeus European burning bush	12–15 ft Flowers (yellow–green): May Fruit (scarlet): Sept.–Oct.	as above	as above	Cottony maple scale Lilac leaf miner
Euonymus japonicus— Evergreen burning bush	8–15 ft Fruit (orange): Winter	as above Evergreen	Requires a little shaping when grown as a shrub.	

Botanical and common name	Description	Conditions and habits of growth	Pruning and other remarks	Insects and diseases
Euonymus patens— Spreading euonymus	5–6 ft Flowers (white): June–July Fruit (orange): Oct.–Nov.	"—Evergreen	Does not require any specific pruning	
Euonymus radicans— Wintercreeper	15–20 ft Flowers (greenish-white): June–July Fruit (pale greenish white): Oct.	Likes sun or ½ shade. A ground cover or vine.	When grown as a ground cover under trees or as a border for beds, it should be trimmed or cut over either in spring or summer	
Forsythia intermedia— Border forsythia	6–8 ft Flowers (yellow): Mar.–Apr.	Likes sun or ½ shade in good, rich soil. Has a slender, erect growth.	Special pruning is not necessary, except for thinning out every third year, or they may be clipped moderately each year as soon as the flowering period is over. When grown as a bush, the main branches should be allowed to grow 2–3 ft high and the secondary branches should be cut back to that height each year. This method stimulates the formation of long shoots during the summer which will be in full bloom from end to end the following spring.	No serious pests or diseases.
Forsythia intermedia spectabilis— Showy border forsythia	8–10 ft Flowers (yellow): Mar.–Apr.	Likes sun or ½ shade in good, rich soil. Has an upright. arching, and very showy growth.		

Botanical and common name	Description	Conditions and habits of growth	Pruning and other remarks	Insects and Diseases
Forsythia suspensa—Weeping forsythia	6–8 ft Flowers (bright yellow): Apr.	Likes sun or ½ shade in good, rich soil. Has a pendulous growth.	as above	
Forsythia viridissima Greenstem forsythia	8–10 ft Flowers (bright yellow): Apr.	Likes sun or shade in good, rich soil. Has an erect growth with green stems.	as above	
Hamamelis virginiana—Common witch-hazel	10–15 ft Flowers (yellow): Oct.–Nov.	Likes sun or ½ shade in moist, open soil. Has an upright, bushy growth.	Prune only to shape the plants, particularly when they are young; older plants have no need of further formal pruning.	Witch hazel cone gall
Hedera helix—English ivy	60–80 ft Flowers (greenish): June Fruit (black): Sept.–Oct.	Likes sun in good rich soil. It is a dense, clinging evergreen vine, thriving on the north sides of buildings.	Ivy grown in the form of a bush may require a little shaping each year, merely removing a branch here and there. Old plants may be invigorated by cutting back in spring. If grown against walls, it should be cut back as close as possible to the walls in Feb. or March. At the same time, cut back the upper shoots well below the roof or gutters if the vine is grown on the side of a building. Also examine and cut the vine toward the beginning of July, removing long shoots that are protruding away from the wall.	Cabbage looper Soft scale Oleander scale Red spiders Aphids Long-tailed mealybug Leafhoppers Eight-spotted forester

Botanical and common name	Description	Conditions and habits of growth	Pruning and other remarks	Insects and diseases
Ilex cornuta— Chinese holly	6–8 ft Fruit (bright red): Sept.	Likes ½ shade. Has spreading branches, forming a broad, dense bush.	Do not clip back the shoots since they are naturally stiff and erect; instead, clean out some of the laterals of the shoots thus accentuating them. Holly hedges may be clipped back in the middle or end of summer.	Fall webworm
Ilex cornuta Burfordi— Burford holly	10–20 ft Fruit (large red): Oct.–Dec.	Likes ½ shade. Is a broad, dense tree with showy red berries in winter.	as above	Spider mites
Ilex crenata— Japanese holly	6–7 ft Flowers (white): June Fruit (black): Sept.–Apr.	Likes sun or ½ shade in good, peaty or acid soil.	Minimum pruning before spring growth to shape plant.	Holly scale
Ilex crenata convexa— Shell-leaf Jap. holly	4–6 ft Fruit (black): Sept.–Apr.	as above	Excellent for low compact hedge 1 to 2½ feet. Prune frequently to maintain hedge shape. Keep top of hedge narrower than bottom.	Citrus whitefly
Ilex crenata rotundifolia— Round-leaf Jap. holly	8–10 ft Fruit (black): Sept.–Apr.	as above	Good for medium compact hedge 3 to 4½ feet. Prune frequently to maintain hedge shape. Keep top of hedge narrower than bottom.	Holly leaf miner

Botanical and common name	Description	Conditions and habits of growth	Pruning and other remarks	Insects and diseases
Ilex glabra— Inkberry	5–6 ft Flowers (white) : July Fruit (black) : Sept.	Likes a moist acid soil in ½ shade.	Minimum winter pruning only.	
Ilex verticillata— Black-alder	8–10 ft Fruit (bright red) : Oct.–Dec.	Likes ½ shade. Has spreading branches.	as above	
Ilex vomitoria— Yaupon holly	5–15 ft Fruit (scarlet) : Sept.–Apr.	Likes sun or shade. Can be used as a hedge.	as above	
Jasminum nudiflorum— Winter jasmine	3–4 ft Flowers (yellow) : Feb.	Likes sun in rich loam soil. Has a slender pendulous habit of growth. Has green stems.	The bushy species require occasional thinning but no other formal treatment. They should have the flowering shoots cut back to within 2 buds of the base as soon as the flowers fade, but no further pruning should follow.	Has no serious pests or diseases
Jasminum primulium— Primrose jasmine	6–9 ft Flowers (yellow) : Mar.–Apr.	Likes sun or ½ shade.	as above	
Juniperus chinensis Pfitzeriana— Pfitzer juniper	3–5 ft	Likes sun in well-drained good soils. Has a spreading habit of growth. Has green stems.	Prune only when necessary to restrain plant.	Red-cedar bark beetle

Botanical and common name	Description	Conditions and habits of growth	Pruning and other remarks	Insects and diseases
Juniperus horizontalis— Creeping juniper	2–3 ft Light blue: Sept.	Likes sun in well-drained soils. Procumbent shrub with longitudinal trailing branches	No pruning necessary. Valued as ground cover for sandy and rocky soil.	Twig-blight Juniper webworm Bagworms Juniper scale Aphids Red spider Spruce spider mite
Kalmia latifolia— Mountain laurel	5–6 ft Flowers (white, pink): May–June	Likes partial shade, in a woodsy, loam soil. It is a broad-leaved evergreen.	The species have no need for formal pruning. Prune only to remove dead wood.	Mulberry white fly Leaf spot Leaf blight Lace bug Laurel psyllid
Kerria japonica— Kerria	4–6 ft Flowers (golden yellow): June–Sept.	Likes sun in good, rich soil. It is slender and broad and has very green branches.	Much of the older wood should be removed in order to encourage vigorous young wood. Prune as soon as the flowers fade; the previous year's wood should be slightly shortened after thinning out and the removal of old wood.	No serious pests and diseases

TABLE 5.13/CHARACTERISTICS OF SHRUBS (cont.)

Botanical and common name	Description	Conditions and habits of growth	Pruning and other remarks	Insects and diseases
Kerria japonica Flore-plena Double-flowering kerria	4–6 ft Flowers (golden yellow): June–Sept.	Ditto—Has double flowers	as above	as above
Kolkwitzia amabilis—Beauty-bush	6–8 ft Flowers (shell pink): May–June	Likes sun in good, rich soil. Has a tumbling dense growth and very abundant blooms.	Prune in winter to remove old and dead wood.	as above
Lagerstroemia indica—Crape myrtle	8–10 ft Flowers (white–pink): June–Aug.	Likes sun. Excellent flowering plant.	Minimum winter pruning to shape plant.	Crape myrtle aphid
Leucothoe catesbaei—Drooping leucothoe	2–3 ft Flowers (white): Apr–May	Likes semi-shade in woodsy loam soil. Has a pendulous habit of growth, low branching with purple, bronze, and crimson fall foliage.	Plants treated as shrubs should have their older stems removed and the younger shoots shortened in late February before spring season starts. Shrubs grown for the color effect of their bright green barks should be cut close to the ground in March.	No serious pests or diseases
Lespedeza bicolor—Shrub bush clover	6–8 ft Flowers (purple): July–Oct.	Likes sun in good rich soil. It is slender and graceful with pea-shaped flowers.	To promote good bushy plants cut to the ground each year after they have bloomed.	as above

Botanical and common name	Description	Conditions and habits of growth	Pruning and other remarks	Insects and diseases
Ligustrum amurense— Amur privet	12–15 ft Flowers (white) : June–July Fruit (black) - Sept.–Oct.	Likes sun or ½ shade in average soil. It is a very hardy, upright shrub.	Does not require any formal pruning, except in hedge form.	Privet mite
Ligustrum ibota— Ibota privet	10–12 ft Flowers (white) : June Fruit (black) : Sept.–Oct.	Likes sun or ½ shade in average soil. Has spreading branches, upright, and with pale green foliage.	as above	Japanese scale Olive scale Twig blight
Ligustrum nepalense— Nepal privet	5–7 ft Flowers (white) : May Fruit (black) : Winter	Likes sun or shade in average soil.	as above	White peach scale
Ligustrum ovali- folium— California privet	12–15 ft Flowers (white) : June Fruit (black) : Oct.–Nov.	Ditto—Upright, half ever-green of rather stiff habit of growth.	as above	
Ligustrum sinensis— Chinese privet	7–10 ft Fruit (black) : Sept.–Dec.	Likes sun in average soil.	Ditto—Good plant for inex-pensive massing or hedge.	
Ligustrum lucidum— Glossy privet	6–8 ft Fruit (blue–black) : Aug.–Oct.	Likes sun or ½ shade in average soil. A good ever-green shrub.	as above	Lilac leaf miner Lilac borer Red spider Citrus whitefly

Botanical and common name	Description	Conditions and habits of growth	Pruning and other remarks	Insects and diseases
Lonicera fragrantissima Winter honeysuckle	6–8 ft Flowers (white) : Mar.–Apr. Fruit (scarlet) : May–July	Likes sun or shade in good rich soil. Has a spreading habit of growth and fragrant flowers.	The shrub species should be thinned out every 3–4 years and if overgrown the longer shoots should be cut back. Pruning is done best in summer, but do not prune every year. The climbing species require very little formal pruning if they have room to develop.	Long-tailed mealybug San Jose scale Fall webworm
Lonicera morrowi Morrow honeysuckle	6–8 ft Flowers (white) : May Fruit (red) : May–July	as above	as above	Oblique-banded leaf roller
Lonicera tatarica— Tatarian honeysuckle	8–10 ft Flowers (pink to white) : May–June Fruit (red) : May–July	Likes sun or shade in good rich soil. It is upright and dense with abundant red fruit.	as above	Oyster shell scale Honeysuckle sawfly Flea beetles
Malus floribunda— Japanese flowering crab	15–20 ft Flowers (rose-pink) : Apr.–May Fruit (red) : Fall	Likes sun in moist, rich soil. Has wide-spreading branches. Flowers change from pink to white.	Prune immediately after flowering to shape plant. Keep pruning at a minimum.	Subject to attack by insects and fungi on the common apple
Malus atrosanguinea Carmine crab	15–20 ft Flowers (carmine) : Apr.–May Fruit (dark red) : Fall.	"—Flowers do not fade to white.	as above	

Botanical and common name	Description	Conditions and habits of growth	Pruning and other remarks	Insects and diseases
Malus baccata— Siberian crab	20–40 ft Flowers (white): Apr.–May Fruit (red-yellow): Fall	Likes sun in moist rich soil. A large flowering tree with round head.	as above	
Malus sargenti— Sargent crab	8–10 ft Flowers (pure white): Apr.–May Fruit (dark red): Fall	Likes sun in moist rich soil. A low shrub or tree with horizontally spreading branches. Leaves change to orange and yellow in fall.	as above	
Malus scheideckeri— Scheidecker crab	15–20 ft Flowers (pale pink): May Fruit (yellow): Fall	Likes sun in moist, rich soil.	as above	
Myrica cerifera— Southern wax myrtle	15–25 ft Fruit (gray): Fall	Likes sun in dry good soil.	does not require formal pruning.	Has no serious pests or diseases.
Nandina domestica— Nandina	4–8 ft Flowers (white): May Fruit (red): Fall–Winter	Likes sun or shade in good soil.	Minimum pruning only to remove dead or old wood Plant for fruit effect.	as above
Philadelphus coronarius— Sweet mock-orange	8–10 ft Flowers (white): June	Likes sun in good rich soil. An upright grower with fragrant flowers.	Needs no formal pruning, and in fact is best if left untouched; perhaps thin out a little at intervals of a few years.	as above
Philadelphus lemoinei— Lemoine Mock orange	4–6 ft Flowers (white): June	Likes sun in good rich soil. a spreading grower with fragrant flowers.	as above	as above

TABLE 5.13/CHARACTERISTICS OF SHRUBS (cont.)

Botanical and common name	Description	Conditions and habits of growth	Pruning and other remarks	Insects and diseases
Philadelphus virginalis— Virginal mock orange	6–8 ft Flowers (white) : June	Likes sun in good rich soil. Upright grower with semi-double flowers.	as above	as above
Photinia glabra— Smooth photinia	5–10 ft Flowers (white) : Feb. Fruit (red) : Fall–Winter	Likes sun or shade in good soil. New growth is red.	Minimum pruning only to remove dead or old wood.	No serious pests or diseases
Pyracantha coccinea lalandi— Leland firethorn	8–10 ft Flowers (creamy white) : April Fruit (orange) : Aug.–Oct.	Likes sun or ½ shade in good soil. An upright grower with long shoots covered with orange berries in fall.	Prune in winter to shape plant. It is difficult to transplant, except for small plants.	Subject to scale insects
Pyracantha gibbsia yunnanensis— Yunnan firethorn	5–10 ft Flowers (white) : May Fruit (coral-red) : Fall–Winter	Ditto—except has red berries.	as above	
Rhamnus alnifolia— Alder buckthorn	2–3 ft Flowers (yellow-green) : May–June Fruit (black) : Sept.–Oct.	Likes sun. Low rather compact shrub with bright green foliage.	No special pruning is necessary.	No serious pests or diseases
Rhamnus caroliniana— Carolina buckthorn	15–25 ft Flowers (yellow) : May–June Fruit (red to black) : Sept.	Likes sun. Shrub with handsome leaves, changing to yellow in autumn.	as above	as above

Botanical and common name	Description	Conditions and habits of growth	Pruning and other remarks	Insects and diseases
Rhamnus cathartica— Common buckthorn	8–10 ft Flowers (green) : June Fruit (shiny black) : Sept.	Likes sun in well-drained soil. An open, upright grower.	as above	
Rhamnus frangula— Glossy buckthorn	10–12 ft Flowers (light yellow) : July Fruit (red-black) : Sept.	Like sun in well-drained soil. An open, upright grower with shiny foliage.	as above	
Rhododendron carolinianum— Carolina rhododendron	6–7 ft Flowers (pink) : May	Like shade in woodsy loam. A broad-leaved evergreen. Requires acid soil conditions.	Needs no regular pruning except for the removal of the flower hands as soon as the flower fades. However, young plants should be clipped occasionally to induce a sturdy habit. Overgrown plants that are old may be cut back without serious injury but this should be done in March or April.	Lace bug Giant hornet
Rhododendron catawbiense— Catawba rhododendron	6–8 ft Flowers (red and purple) : May	as above	as above	Pitted ambrosia beetle
Rhododendron maximum— Rosebay rhododendron	8–10 ft Flowers (blush) : June–July	as above	as above	Rhododendron clear wing Azalea stem borer Broad-necked prionus

TABLE 5.13/CHARACTERISTICS OF SHRUBS (cont.)

Botanical and common name	Description	Conditions and habits of growth	Pruning and other remarks	Insects and diseases
Rhus copallina— Shining sumac	5–6 ft Flowers (greenish): July–Aug. Fruit (crimson): Sept.–Oct.	Likes dry, sunny locations. It has a spreading growth with shiny leaves. Planted for its lustrous foliage changing to reddish-purple in fall.	When grown for the large compound leaves and autumn coloration, the young shoots must be cut down to within a few inches of the ground in February or early March. If grown for shrubbery or mass effect, no special pruning, is required.	Has no serious pests or diseases
Rhus canadensis— Fragrant sumac	2–4 ft Flowers (yellow): Mar.–Apr. Fruit (red): Aug.	Likes dry, sunny locations. It is a low, spreading shrub, fragrant with leaves turning orange and scarlet in fall.	as above	
Rhus cotinus— Smoke tree	12–15 ft Flowers (smoky white): July–Aug. Fruit (red): Sept.–Oct.	Likes sun in well-drained soil. It is upright and graceful.	as above	
Rhus glabra— Smooth sumac	10–15 ft Flowers (greenish): July–Aug. Fruit (scarlet): Sept.–Oct.	Likes sun in well-drained soil. Has red autumn foliage and scarlet fruit.	as above	
Rhus typhina— Staghorn sumac	25–30 ft Flowers (greenish): June–July Fruit (crimson): Aug.–Sept.	Likes sun in well-drained soil. Has feathery foliage turning to brilliant scarlet and orange in autumn.	as above	

GROUNDS MAINTENANCE HANDBOOK

Botanical and common name	Description	Conditions and habits of growth	Pruning and other remarks	Insects and diseases
Rosa carolina— Pasture rose	3 ft Flowers (pink): July Fruit (red): Fall	Likes sun or semishade in heavy, rich loam. A low, bushy shrub, spreading by suckers. Well suited for borders of shrubberies.	Ramblers and climbers should have all the old flowering canes removed as soon as the flowers fade. Bush roses should have all the weak wood removed, and vigorous young canes from the root should be encouraged. This general pruning is best done in March.	Rose aphid Rose slugs
Rosa hugonis— Hugonis rose	5–6 ft Flowers (yellow): May Fruit (deep scarlet): July–Aug.	Likes sun or semishade in heavy, rich loam. An upright bushy shrub and very free-flowering.	as above	Eastern tent caterpillar
Rosa multiflora— Japanese rose	8–10 ft Flowers (white): June Fruit (red): Fall	Likes sun or semishade in heavy, rich loam. A tumbling or climbing grower with small, white flowers in numerous heads.	as above	San Jose scale
Rosa rugosa Rugosa rose	5–6 ft Flowers (white-pink): May–Sept. Fruit (brick red): Fall	Likes sun or semishade in heavy, rich loam. It is an upright bush with large red berries. Blooms all summer, foliage turning orange and scarlet in fall.	as above	Fuller's rose beetle Oblique-banded leaf roller
Rosa setigera— Prairie rose	5–6 ft Flowers (deep pink): June–July Fruit (red): Fall	Likes sun in heavy, rich loam. Has a pendulous growth.	as above	Rose midge

TABLE 5.13/CHARACTERISTICS OF SHRUBS (cont.)

Botanical and common name	Description	Conditions and habits of growth	Pruning and other remarks	Insects and diseases
Rosa blanda— Meadow rose	3–4 ft Flowers (pink) : May Fruit (red) : Sept.–Oct.	Likes sun in heavy rich loam.	as above	Black spot
Rosa wichuraiana— Wichuraiana rose	10–12 ft Flowers (white) : June Fruit (red) : Fall	Likes sun or semishade in heavy, rich loam. Has a trailing growth and is fragrant.	as above	Mildew
Rosa spinosissima— Scotch rose	4–5 ft Flowers (yellow-white) : June Fruit (black) : Sept.	Likes sun or semishade in heavy, rich loam. Has an open, spreading growth.	as above	Rose curculio Rose stem-girdler Black-banded leaf roller Flower thrips Rose chafer Rose leaf beetle Leaf hopper Red spider Rose scale Asiatic garden beetle Japanese beetle

Botanical and common name	Description	Conditions and habits of growth	Pruning and other remarks	Insects and diseases
Sambucus canadensis—American elder	6–8 ft Flowers (white): June–July Fruit (black): Aug.–Sept.	Likes shade in moist soil. It is a rapid and open grower.	If grown for colored foliage cut it to the ground in February; otherwise, no regular pruning is necessary.	Cloaked knotty horn
Sambucus nigra—European elder	25–30 ft Flowers (yellow-white): May–June Fruit (black): Aug.–Sept.	Large shrub or tree with deeply furrowed bark. It is a rapid and coarse grower. Likes shade in moist soil.	as above	
Sambucus racemosa—European red elder	10–12 ft Flowers (yellow-white): Apr.–May Fruit (scarlet): June–July	Likes shade in moist soil. A rapid grower with early red fruit.	as above	
Spiraea bumalda—Bumalda spirea	2–3 ft Flowers (pink): July	Likes partial shade and good soil. A low, flat bush.	Requires very little pruning, except to remove dead branches.	Cottony maple scale
Spiraea bumalda, Anthony Waterer—Anthony Waterer spirea	2–3 ft Flowers (crimson): June–July	Likes sun in any good soil. A dense and flat bush.	Remove old flower heads.	Spirea aphid
Spiraea prunifolia—Bridal wreath	8–10 ft Flowers (pure white): Apr.–May	Likes sun in any good soil.	as above	San Jose scale

TABLE 5.13/CHARACTERISTICS OF SHRUBS (cont.)

Botanical and common name	Description	Conditions and habits of growth	Pruning and other remarks	Insects and diseases
Spiraea thunbergi—Thunbergi spirea	4–5 ft Flowers (white): Apr.–May	Likes sun in any good soil. A low, pendulous shrub with feathery bright green foliage turning to orange and scarlet late in autumn.	as above	Oblique-banded leaf-roller Red spiders
Spiraea vanhouttei—Van Houtte spirea	5–6 ft Flowers (white): May–June	Likes sun in any good soil. Has arching, graceful branches with leaves a dark green above and pale bluish-green below.	as above	Oyster shell scale Spirea aphid
Symphoricarpus racemosus—Common snowberry	4–5 ft Flowers (pink): June Fruit (large snow white): Sept.–Nov.	Likes sun in any good soil. Has a pendulous growth.	Does not require any pruning.	Has no serious pests or diseases
Symphoricarpus vulgaris—Coral berry	3–4 ft Flowers (white): May–June Fruit (coral-pink): Oct.–Dec.	as above	as above	
Syringa chinensis—Chinese lilac	10–12 ft Flowers (purple-lilac): May–June	Likes sun in good rich soil. It is an upright, arching shrub, with loose panicles of bloom.	If the plants are flowering freely, no regular pruning is necessary. If the shrubs are not flowering well and growth is weak, thin out the branches removing some of the inside wood and the weak shoots in April. Inspect the shrubs again early in June and remove the weaker shoots. All suckers should be removed from the base of the	Lilac borer Giant hornet Lilac leaf-miner

Botanical and common name	Description	Conditions and habits of growth	Pruning and other remarks	Insects and diseases
Syringa persica— Persian lilac	8–10 ft Flowers (pale lilac) : May–June	as above	as above	Oblique-banded leaf roller Citrus whitefly Cottony maple scale Scurfy scale Euonymus scale White peach scale Promethea moth caterpillar Oyster shell scale Powdery mildew
Syringa vulgaris— Common lilac	12–15 ft Flowers (true lilac or white) : May	as above	as above	
Taxus baccata— English yew	30–40 ft Flowers (inconspicuous) : Mar.–Apr. Fruit (olive-brown) : Sept.–Oct.	Likes sun or partial shade in good, moist soil. A broad roundish head or shrubly. Leaves a lustrous dark green.	Prune only to shape or restrain plant.	Black vine weevil
Taxus brevifolia— Pacific yew	20–25 ft Flowers (inconspicuous) : June Fruit (brown) : Aug.–Oct.	Likes sun or partial shade in good moist soil. Usually with horizontally spreading branches. Leaves dark green, small and clustered.	as above	
Taxus cuspidata— Japanese yew	20–25 ft Flowers (inconspicuous) : Mar.–Apr. Fruit (red) : Oct.–Nov.	Likes sun or partial shade in good, moist soil. Has a rapid, spreading growth.	as above	Oleander scale Red spiders

TABLE 5.13/CHARACTERISTICS OF SHRUBS (cont.)

Botanical and common name	Description	Conditions and habits of growth	Pruning and other remarks	Insects and diseases
Viburnum rhytodiphyllum— Leather-leaf viburnum	8–10 ft Flowers (white): May Fruit (red to black): Sept.–Oct.	Likes partial shade in well drained soil. An evergreen with lustrous dark green foliage.	No special pruning is necessary.	Aphids San Jose scale Oyster shell scale Cottony maple scale Red spiders
Viburnum acerifolium— Maple leaf viburnum	5–6 ft Flowers (yellow-white): May–June Fruit (black): Sept.	Likes shaded dry soil. Has a spreading growth. Good for woodland undergrowth.	as above	Dogwood borer
Viburnum carlesi— Fragrant viburnum	5–6 ft Flowers (pink-white): Apr.–May Fruit (blue-black): Sept.–Oct.	Shrub of broad round habit, very fragrant. Likes sun or partial shade in well-drained soil.	as above	
Viburnum dentatum— Arrowwood	10–15 ft Flowers (white): May–June Fruit (blue-black): Oct.	Likes shade or sun in a good, moist soil. A tall and upright grower.	as above	
Viburnum Lentago— Nannyberry	15–20 ft Flowers (white): May–June Fruit (blue-black): Sept.–Oct.	Likes shade, plenty of moisture in good rich soil. A graceful treelike shrub.	as above	

Botanical and common name	Description	Conditions and habits of growth	Pruning and other remarks	Insects and diseases
Viburnum molle— Kentucky viburnum	8–10 ft Flowers (white): May Fruit (blue-black): Aug.–Sept.	Likes sun or partial shade in good soil. An upright and strong grower.	As above	
Viburnum prunifolium— Blackhaw	12–15 ft Flowers (white): May Fruit (blue-black): Sept.–Oct.	Likes sun or partial shade in good soil. A spreading round-headed shrub.	As above	
Viburnum tomentosum— Double file viburnum	8–10 ft Flowers (white): June Fruit (red to black): Aug.–Sept.	Likes sun or partial shade in good, rich soil. A spreading shrub with unusual flowers.	As above	

Botanical and common name	Description	Pruning and other remarks	Insects and diseases
Abies concolor— White fir	100–120 ft; pyramidal; Leaves bluish-green, soft, approx. 2 in. long, flat; Cylindrical greenish or purplish cones, about 2–5 in. long; Bark smooth, gray, on old trees deeply fissured and scaly, branches yellowish-green.	Should have sun and good soil for good growth. It is a long-lived tree. Do not prune at any time.	Sitka spruce gall
Abies nordmanniana— Nordmann fir	100–150 ft; pyramidal; Leaves lustrous dark green above with two whitish bands beneath, moderately fine; Cylindrical reddish-brown cones, approx. 5 in. long; Flower-none; Bark grayish brown, slightly fissured on old trees, branches gray with scattered short hairs.	as above	Needle and twig blight Leaf-cast Bark beetle Red spider
Cedrus libani— Cedar of Lebanon	100–120 ft; upright and spreading; leaves dark or bright green, fine; ovoid brown cones 3–4 in. long, 1½–2½ in. across; Flower-scales about 2 in. wide; Bark dark gray, smooth on young, fissured and scaly on old trees.	A long-lived tree requiring sunshine and a well-drained soil. No pruning is necessary.	No insects or diseases known.
Ilex aquifolium— English Holly	30–40 ft; short spreading branches, forming a dense pyramidal or oblong head; Leaves dark green and silver, margin wavy with large triangular spiny teeth; clustered red berries, Sept. to March; Flower—white, fragrant, May to June; Bark smooth, dark gray.	A long-lived tree, requiring good soil and plenty of humus. Likes partial shade and responds to watering. No formal pruning necessary.	Tar spot Leaf spot Leaf miner White fly
Ilex opaca— American holly	30–40 ft; spreading branches, forming a narrow pyramidal head; Leaves dull green above, yellow green below with large, remote spiny teeth; usually solitary red berries, Oct. to April; Flower—white, June; Bark smooth, dark gray.	As above	

Botanical and common name	Description	Pruning and other remarks	Insects and diseases
Juniperus virginiana— Red cedar	60–90 ft; upright or spreading branches, forming a narrow or broad pyramidal head; Leaves fine, dark green, spiny pointed; Fruit ovoid bluish and bloomy; Flower—none; Bark reddish-brown, shredding in long strips.	A long-lived tree, in sun and well-drained good soils. Requires no pruning.	See under Juniper shrubs
Picea abies— Norway spruce	120–150 ft; spreading branches with pendent branchlets; Leaves lustrous dark green, short, rarely 2 in. long; Fruit—pendulous light brown cones 4–5 in. long, purple or green before maturity; Flower—none; Bark reddish-brown.	The spruce should never be pruned. Thrives best in moist, sandy, loam soil and will tolerate partial shade.	Eastern spruce gall aphid Spruce spider mite Spruce cone worm
Picea glauca— White spruce	60–90 ft; pyramidal with ascending branches and pendent branchlets; Leaves slightly curved. more or less bluish-green, with disagreeable odor when bruised; Fruit—cylindrical-oblong cones, brown and glossy, green before maturity; Flower—none; Bark grayish. scaly.	As above	Sitka spruce gall Spruce budworm Spruce needle miners Spruce gall aphid Spruce bud scale
Picea engelmanni— Engelmann spruce	120–150 ft; a graceful pyramidal tree with slender, spreading branches; Leaves straight or slightly curved, bluish-green, with disagreeable odor when bruised; Fruit—cylindrical-oblong, light brown cones, green and tinged with red before maturity; Flower—none; Bark brownish-yellow.	As above	Pine sawfly Red headed pine sawfly Abbot's pine sawfly Spruce sawfly Imperial moth Pine tube-moth
Picea pungens— Colorado spruce	70–80 ft; a shapely, vigorous tree, with stout horizontal branches; Leaves rigid, spiny-pointed, incurved, bluish-green, rarely dull green; Fruit—cylindrical-oblong, light brown cones; Flower—none; Bark reddish brown, branchlets, glabrous, bright yellowish-brown.	As above	Pine leaf miner European pine mite

TABLE 5.14/CHARACTERISTICS OF EVERGREEN TREES (cont.)

Botanical and common name	Description	Pruning and other remarks	Insects and diseases
Pinus strobus— White pine	90–150 ft; symmetrical, pyramidal head, in old age usually broad and very picturesque; Leaves slender, soft, serrulate, bluish-green; Fruit— narrow, cylindrical cones, 3–8 in. long, brown; Flower—none; Bark thick, deeply fissured into broad scaly ridges, purplish.	Likes a well-drained soil in sun. It is both an important timber tree and ornamental. Should never require pruning.	False pine webworm Pine pitch borer Pine needle scale Pine bark aphid Bark beetles Spittle bug
Pinus resinosa— Red pine	50–75 ft; a broad pyramidal head, with stout, spreading and sometimes pendulous branches; Leaves (2) flexible, long, coarse, dark green; Fruit—oval, symmetrical cones 1–2 in. long, nut-brown, fall the third year; Flower—none; Bark red-brown, shallowly fissured and scaly.	As above	Scotch pine scale insect Sawyer Ribbed pine borer Blue pine borer European pine-shoot moth
Pinus sylvestris— Scotch pine	50–75 ft; pyramidal when young, round-topped and irregular when old, spreading branches; Leaves (2) rigid, twisted, long, bluish-green; Fruit—short-stalked, conical-oblong cones, dull tawny-yellow, 1–2 in. long; Flower—none; Bark red or red-brown, rather thin and smooth on the upper trunk, darker below.	Likes a well drained soil in sun. Should never require pruning.	White pine weevil White pine blister rust
Pinus nigra— Austrian pine	80–100 ft; pyramidal with spreading branches, old age produces a flat-topped head; Leaves stiff, dark green, approx. 4–10 in. long; Fruit—ovoid cones, 2–3 in. long, yellow-brown; Flower—none; Bark usually light brown.	Likes a well-drained soil in sun. Does not require any pruning.	
Pinus palustris— Longleaf pine	80–100 ft; ascending branches, form an oblong head; Leaves (3), dark green, 8–18 in. long; Fruit—cylindrical dull brown cones, 5–8 in. long; Flower—none; Bark light orange-brown, separating into large, thin scales.	Likes a well-drained soil in sun. An important timber and resin tree. Does not require pruning.	

Botanical and common name	Description	Pruning and other remarks	Insects and diseases
Pinus taeda—Loblolly pine	80–120 ft; spreading branches, upper ones ascending, forming a compact, round-topped head; Leaves (3), slender but stiff, 4–6 in. long, bright green; Fruit—dull, pale reddish-brown cones; Flower—none; Bark bright red-brown, fissured into scaly ridges.	As above	
Pinus echinata—Shortleaf pine	100–120 ft; slender, often pendent branches in regular whorls, broad ovoid head; Leaves (2) slender, 3–6 in. long, dark bluish-green; Fruit—cones, 1–2 in. long, dull brown; Flower—none; Bark light cinnamon-red, broken into large scaly plates.	As above	
Pinus virginiana—Scrub pine	50–90 ft; bushy tree with slender horizontal or pendent branches; Leaves (2) rigid, usually twisted, dark green, 1–3 in. long; Fruit—reddish-brown cones, 1–2 in. long; Flower—none; Bark shallowly fissured into scaly plates, dark brown.	Likes a dry and barren soil in sun. Does not require pruning.	
Pinus rigida—Pitch pine	75–90 ft; open, irregular head with horizontal branches; Leaves (3) rigid, 3–6 in. long, spreading, dark green; Fruit—light brown cones 1–3 in. long; Flower—none; Bark red-brown, deeply fissured into broad, scaly rigdes.	Valuable for planting on dry and rocky soil.	
Tsuga canadensis—Canada hemlock	60–90 ft; broad pyramidal head, long, slender, often pendulous branches; Leaves short and rounded, lustrous dark green, slightly grooved above, with white bands beneath; Fruit—oval, short-stalked cones 1 in. long; Flower—none; Bark yellow-brown.	Likes good, moist soil in either sun or partial shade. Good ornamental tree, also has some value for timber and tanning. Does not require any pruning unless used as a hedge.	Needle rusts Hemlock looper Spotted hemlock borer Red spider Hemlock spanworm Hemlock leaf-miner

TABLE 5.14/CHARACTERISTICS OF EVERGREEN TREES (cont.)

Botanical and common name	Description	Pruning and other remarks	Insects and diseases
Tsuga caroliniana— Carolina hemlock	50–75 ft; compact, pyramidal head with often pendulous branches; Leaves short, lustrous dark green above with white bands beneath; Fruit—short-stalked cones, 1 in. long; Flower—none; Bark orange-red.	A more dense and compact tree than the Canada hemlock. An excellent ornamental. Likes good moist soil in either sun or partial shade. Does not require any pruning unless used as a hedge.	

TABLE 5.15/CHARACTERISTICS, PRUNING, INSECTS, AND DISEASES OF DECIDUOUS TREES

Botanical and common name	Description	Pruning and other remarks	Insects and diseases
Acer platanoides— Norway maple	75–90 ft; Leaves bright green, 5-lobed, 4–6 in. across, slightly toothed with pointed teeth; Flower greenish-yellow, April–May; Fruit—pendulous with nearly horizontal spreading wings, approx. 2 in. long, Sept.–October; Bark gray or grayish-brown.	Likes moisture in good soil. Round form with dense shade. An excellent shade tree. Leaves turn yellow in fall. Prune only to remove dead and dangerous branches and to shape tree. Prune in summer and early fall.	Norway maple aphid Leaf hoppers Cottony maple scale Terrapin scale Bladder gall mite Leopard moth Sugar maple borer Maple and oak twig pruner
Acer saccharum— Sugar maple	90–120 ft; Leaves light green, 3–5 lobed, 3–5½ in. across, sparingly, coarsely, toothed with narrow and deep depressions; Flower—greenish-yellow, April; Fruit—slightly divergent wings, nutlet approx. 1½ in. long, Sept.; Bark gray, furrowed.	Likes good, well-drained soil. Used as a street and shade tree. Dense regular shade tree. Dense regular habit with leaves turning yellow or orange and scarlet in fall. Yields syrup. Prune as above.	Forest tent caterpillar

Botanical and common name	Description	Pruning and other remarks	Insects and diseases
Acer rubrum— Red maple	90–120 ft; Leaves dark green and lustrous above, glaucous beneath, 3–5 lobed, 2–4 in. long, unequal rounded lobes; Flower red, rarely yellowish, March–April; Fruit—wings spread at a narrow angle, 2–4 in. long; nutlet approx. ¾ in. long, usually bright red when young, May–June; Bark gray.	Likes moisture in good soil. Conspicuous in early spring with red flowers and later its red fruit. Leaves turn bright scarlet and yellow in fall. Prune as above.	Bagworm Gypsy moth Brown-tail moth Green striped maple worm Green maple worm Elm span worm Oriental moth caterpillar
Acer saccharinum— Silver maple	90–120 ft; Leaves bright green above, silvery white beneath, deeply 5-lobed, 3–5 in. across; Flower greenish, Feb.–March; Fruit—wings divergent and hooked. 1–2 in. long, nutlet 1½ to 2½ in. long, May–June; Bark gray.	Likes moisture in good soil. A wide spreading tree with slender often pendulous branches. Leaves turn yellow in fall. Prune as above.	Box-elder bug Flat-headed borer Japanese beetle Pitted ambrosia beetle Alder blight aphid Carpenter worm Tussock moth White fly
Acer negundo— Box-elder	50–60 ft; Leaves bright green, lighter green below, pinnate, leaflets 3–5, 2–4 in. long coarsely toothed, terminal leaf 3-lobed; Flower yellowish, green before the leaves, March–April; Fruit—wings at acute angle and incurved, thick nutlet 1 to 1½ in. long, Sept.; Bark gray, branches glabrous.	Likes moisture in good soil. A hardy and drought-resisting maple. Rapid growth when young. Prune as in all other maples.	Maple trumpet Maple leaf-cutter Maple leaf-stem borer Maple nepticula Ocellate maple leaf-gall
Acer palmatum— Japanese maple	15–25 ft; Leaves bright green, deeply 5–9 lobed, 2–4 in. across; Flower purple, June; Fruit—wings spread at an obtuse angle, with nutlet approx. ½ in. long, Sept.; Bark gray, branchlets glabrous and slender.	Likes a rich soil. A shrub or small tree of several forms. Leaves turn bright red in fall. Prune as above.	Fusiform maple gall Bladder maple gall

TABLE 5.15/CHARACTERISTICS OF DECIDUOUS TREES (cont.)

Botanical and common name	Description	Pruning and other remarks	Insects and diseases
Acer ginnala— Amur maple	15–25 ft; Leaves dark green and lustrous above and light green beneath, 3-lobed, 1–3 in. long, 1 to 2½ in. wide; Flower fragrant, yellowish-white, May; Fruit—wings nearly parallel, with nutlet about 1 in. long, Sept.; Bark gray, branchlets glabrous and slender.	Likes a good loam soil. A graceful maple with fruit usually red in summer and the leaves turning bright red in fall. Prune as above.	Norway maple leaf-hopper
Acer pennsylvanicum— Striped maple	20–40 ft; Leaves large, bright green, 3-lobed, 5–7 in. long; Flower yellow, May–June; Fruit—wings spreading at a wide angle with nutlet about 1 in. long, Sept. Bark branches green, smooth, conspicuously striped with white lines.	A small tree with large bright green leaves turning clear yellow in autumn. The striped branches are conspicuous in winter. Prune as above.	Maple phenacoccus Gloomy scale Japanese scale insect Callous borer Ambrosia beetle Wilt Bleeding canker Leaf spots—purple eye spots Bull's-eye spot Tar spot Leaf blisters
Aesculus glabra— Ohio Buckeye	25–30 ft; Leaves—5 leaflets, finely toothed, 3–5 in. long. Flower pale greenish-yellow, May; Fruit prickly, 1–2 in. long.	A handsome small tree with leaves turning yellow in autumn. Likes moisture in good soil. Prune after blooming period. Keep inside of tree cleaned out.	Leaf blotch Bagworm Oyster shell scale English walnut scale Japanese beetle
Aesculus hippocastanus— Horsechestnut	60–75 ft; Leaves—5–7 leaflets, double toothed, 4–8 in. long, green beneath; Flower white, tinged with red, May–June; Fruit—prickly, about 2 in. across; Bark—smooth branches.	A showy flowering tree, used for shade and street tree plantings. Likes deep, good soil. Prune same as above.	Tussock moth Scurfy scale

Botanical and common name	Description	Pruning and other remarks	Insects and diseases
Betula lutea— Yellow birch	60–90 ft; Leaves ovate, 3–5 in. long, with long pale hairs on the veins above and below; Flower yellow, April; Fruit—short-stalked cones, approx. 1 in. long by ¾ in. thick; Bark yellowish or silvery-gray, separating into thin flakes, reddish-brown on old trunks, young bark aromatic and somewhat bitter.	Likes damp, good soil. An ornamental tree, attractive in spring with its long and slender pendulous catkins. Prune only to shape tree and to remove injured, diseased or dead branches. Prune in summer after the leaves have developed or in early autumn.	Leaf spots Leaf blisters Canker Die-back Case bearer Leaf miner Leaf skeletonizer Bronze birch borer
Betula nigra— River birch	60–90 ft; Leaves dark green above, whitish below, doubly toothed, 1–3 in. long; Flower yellow, April; Fruit—oblong cones, 1 to 1½ in. long, wing ½ or nearly as broad as nutlet; Bark reddish-brown or silvery-gray on younger branches, torn and ragged.	Likes a moist, sandy soil. A graceful tree with an oval head and slender branches. Has a torn and ragged bark. Prune as above.	
Betula papyrifera— Canoe birch	60–90 ft; Leaves smooth green, 1½ to 4 in. long, coarsely toothed; Flower yellow, April; Fruit—cylindrical cones, 1–2 in. long, pendulous; Bark white, torn and ragged.	Likes moisture in good soil. Has gleaming white paper bark. Prune as above.	
Carpinus betulus— European hornbeam	40–60 ft; Leaves double-toothed, rounded at base, dark green, approx. 4 in. long; Flower inconspicuous; Fruit—a ribbed nutlet hanging from a 3-lobed bract, fall; Bark gray, branches slender.	Likes good soil. It holds its leaves late into the winter. No pruning necessary.	No serious pests or diseases.
Carpinus caroliniana— American hornbeam	Ht.—30–40 ft; Flower—inconspicuous; Leaves sharply and doubly toothed, 2–4 in. long, dark green; Fruit—same as above; Bark gray, branches slightly pendulous.	A small bushy tree. Leaves turn scarlet and orange in fall. Likes good soil. No pruning necessary.	

TABLE 5.15/CHARACTERISTICS OF DECIDUOUS TREES (cont.)

Botanical and common name	Description	Pruning and other remarks	Insects and diseases
Celtis occidentalis— Hackberry	Ht.—50–75 ft; Leaves bright green, smooth and lustrous above, paler below, 2–4½ in. long; Flower—inconspicuous; Fruit—small, orange-red to dark purple, stone-pitted, fall; Bark gray, smooth.	Has a straight trunk and spreading, rigid or sometimes pendulous branches forming a round topped head. Bright green foliage turns light yellow in fall. Fruit interesting to birds. No pruning necessary.	Mourning cloak caterpillar Caterpillars Hackberry nipple gall Cottony maple scale Witches broom Bud gall
Cladrastis lutea— Yellow-wood	Ht.—30–40 ft; Leaves—7–9 bright green leaflets 2–4 in. long; Flower—white, fragrant, June; Fruit—pod, 2–3 in. long, Aug.–Sept.; Bark—smooth bark and yellow wood.	An ornamental tree with fragrant white flowers. Leaves turn yellow in fall. Woodsy loam soil. No pruning necessary.	No serious pests or diseases.
Fagus americana— American beech	Ht.—80–100 ft; Leaves dark bluish-green above and light green and smooth below, 2–5 in. long; Flower inconspicuous; Fruit—oval nuts in fall; Bark light gray.	Likes a well-drained soil. Has orange fall foliage. No pruning necessary except to remove dead or diseased branches.	Leaf mottle Beech blight aphid Woolly beech aphid Brown wood borer Leaf tier
Fagus sylvatica— European beech	Ht.—80–100 ft; Leaves lustrous, dark green above, light green beneath, 2–4 in. long; Flower inconspicuous; Fruit —nuts in clusters with upright prickles about 4 in. long; Bark dark gray.	Same as above.	Beech scale Two-lined chestnut borer Datana caterpillar Antlered maple caterpillars Gypsy moth
Fraxinus americana— White ash	Ht.—80–100 ft; Leaves dark green above and yellowish-green beneath, leaflets 5–9 usually 7, 2–6 in. long; Flower red, March; Fruit—1–2 in. long, cylindrical, 1-seeded nutlet; Bark dark green or brownish, smooth and shiny.	Likes good soil. A vigorous tree with the leaves turning deep purple or yellow in fall. No pruning necessary.	Leaf spots Sawfly Fall canker-worm Plant mite Ash timber beetle Ash borer

Botanical and common name	Description	Pruning and other remarks	Insects and diseases
Fraxinus excelsior—European ash	Ht.—80–100 ft; Leaves dark green above and lighter green beneath, 7–11 leaflets, 2–5 in. long; Flower inconspicuous; Fruit—1–2 in. long, narrow-oblong, 1 seeded nutlet; Bark—winter buds black, branches smooth.	Likes good soil. No pruning necessary except to remove dead or diseased branches.	Banded ash borer Lilac borer Carpenter borer Fall webworm Oyster shell scale Scurfy scale
Ginkgo biloba—Maidenhair tree	Ht.—80–100 ft; Leaves bright green, clusters of 3–5, 2–3 in. across, fan-shaped, golden-yellow in fall; Flower—inconspicuous; Fruit—an oval angular nut covered by a pulpy, ill-smelling, and acrid outer coat, about 1 in. long, yellow, kernel sweet, edible; Bark dark brown.	Likes a well-drained rich soil. Varies in shape from a tight pyramid to wide-spread irregularity. No pruning necessary.	No serious pests or diseases.
Gleditsia triacanthos—Honey-locust	Ht.—100–125 ft; Leaves bright green, 5½–8 in. long with 20–30 leaflets 1–1½ in. long; Flower—white, June; Fruit—pod, 12–18 in. long, Oct.–Dec.; Bark gray with spines 2–4 in. long on trunk and branches.	Used as an ornamental tree. The large, branched thorns make the tree conspicuous in winter. No pruning necessary except to keep diseased and dead branches removed.	Locust borer Locust leaf beetle Locust gall maker Bagworm Carpenter worm
Gleditsia triacanthos inermis—Thornless honey-locust	Same as above except thornless.	Prune as above.	
Juglans nigra—Black walnut	Ht.—100–150 ft; Leaves dark green, 15–23 leaflets, 2–4 in. long; Flower—inconspicuous; Fruit—nut broader than high, strongly and irregularly ridged, 1–1½ in. across and covered with an outer pulpy covering; Bark deeply furrowed and brown.	A tall tree with round head and dark green foliage. Nuts are edible. A valuable timber tree. No pruning necessary except to keep diseased and dead branches removed.	European canker Die-back Leaf spots Trunk decays Black walnut curculio Butternut curculio Codlin moth Walnut husk-maggot Walnut aphid Walnut datana Walnut scale

DISEASE AND INSECT CONTROL

TABLE 5.15/CHARACTERISTICS OF DECIDUOUS TREES (cont.)

Botanical and common name	Description	Pruning and other remarks	Insects and diseases
Larix europaea—European larch	Ht.—80–100 ft; Leaves soft, bright green, approx. 1 in. long, deciduous; Flower—inconspicuous; Fruit—oval cones, 1–1½ in. long, violet-purple at maturity changing to grayish-brown; Bark dark grayish-brown, branches slender and yellowish.	Likes a moist, well-drained soil. Tree has a pyramidal, later irregular head. Looks like an evergreen but loses its leaves in fall. No pruning necessary.	
Larix leptolepis—Japanese larch	Ht.—60–80 ft; Leaves flattened, rather broad, light or bluish-green with white bands below, each with five rows of openings; Flower—inconspicuous; Fruit—same as above; Bark scales off in narrow strips leaving red scars; branches yellowish.	Likes a moist well-drained soil. Has short horizontal branches. A very rapid grower. No pruning necessary.	Leaf cast Larch case bearer Gypsy moth Sawfly Woolly larch aphid
Larix americana—American larch	Ht.—50–60 ft; Leaves light, bluish-green, 1–1½ in. long; Flower inconspicuous; Fruit—same as above but smaller; Bark reddish-brown; branches reddish-yellow.	Likes a moist, loamy soil in full sunlight. Has short horizontal branches forming a narrow pyramidal head. No pruning necessary.	
Liriodendron tulipifera—Tulip-tree	Ht.—120–150 ft; Leaves saddle-shaped, 3–5 in. long and about as wide, pale green; Flower tulip-shaped, 1½–2 in. long, greenish-white with a broad orange band near base, May–June; Fruit—cone-like, brown, 2½–3 in. long; Bark—brown.	A straight, pyramidal tree with smooth trunk. Leaves turn clear yellow in fall. Likes a moist, rich soil. Prune only to remove diseased and dead branches.	Tulip scale Promethea moth Tulip spot—gall Willow scurfy scale
Liquidambar styraciflua—Sweet gum	Ht.—100–125 ft; Leaves dark green and shiny above, paler beneath, 4–6 in. wide and long, 5–7 lobed; Flower inconspicuous; Fruit—lustrous, brown capsules about 1 in. long, surrounded at base by short scales, Oct, persisting during the winter; Bark red-brown, often with corky ridges or thick wings, deeply furrowed.	A pyramidal and symmetrical tree. Leaves turn deep crimson in fall. Likes a moist, rich soil. Prune only to remove diseased and dead branches.	Leaf tier Bagworm Fall webworm Forest tent caterpillar

Botanical and common name	Description	Pruning and other remarks	Insects and diseases
Magnolia acuminata— Cucumber tree	Ht.—70–90 ft; Leaves—4–9 in. long, light green beneath; Flower greenish-yellow, 2–3 in. high, May; Fruit cone-like, red, 2–3 in. long, Aug.–Sept.; Bark—branches red-brown, shiny; trunk, soft silvery gray.	Likes a good, porous soil. A pyramidal tree with rather short branches, upright at first, later spreading. Prune as soon as flowers drop. Remove dead or diseased branches and clean out inside of tree.	Die-back Magnolia scale
Magnolia glauca— Sweet bay	Ht.—30–40 ft; Leaves shiny green, 3–5 in. long; Flower white, fragrant, June–July; Fruit conelike, dark red, 1½–2 in. long, Aug.–Sept.; Bark soft gray; branches slender smooth.	Likes a moist, rich soil. Almost evergreen in the South. Prune as above.	
Magnolia macrophylla— Bigleaf magnolia	Ht.—30–40 ft; Leaves large, 10–30 in. long, shiny dark green; Flower cup-shaped, approx. 10 in. across, fragrant, creamy-white, May–June; Fruit conelike, rose-colored, 2–3 in. long, Aug.–Sept.; Bark silvery gray.	A round headed tree with heavy branches. Likes a moist, rich soil. Prune as above.	
Magnolia tripetala— Umbrella magnolia	Ht. 30–40 ft; Leaves pale green beneath, 10–24 in. long; Flower white with a heavy odor, 7–10 in. across, May–June; Fruit conelike, rose-colored, 3–4 in. long, Aug.–Sept.; Bark silvery gray, smooth.	Tree with wide-spreading branches forming an open head. Likes a moist, rich soil. Prune as above.	
Magnolia soulangeana— Saucer magnolia	Ht.—20–25 ft; Leaves—shiny green, more or less hairy beneath; Flower purplish, nearly white, May; Fruit conelike, Aug.–Sept.; Bark gray, smooth.	Likes a moist, rich soil. Small tree or large shrub. Prune as above.	
Nyssa sylvatica— Sour gum	Ht.—80–100 ft; Leaves green. 2–4½ in. long, shiny above, turning bright scarlet in fall; Flower white, May–June; Fruit oval, blue-black, with thin acrid flesh, stone slightly ribbed; Bark gray.	Tree with slender spreading branches, forming a flat-topped cylindrical or sometimes broad head. Likes a moist rich soil. No pruning necessary.	No serious pests or diseases.

DISEASE AND INSECT CONTROL

279

TABLE 5.15/CHARACTERISTICS OF DECIDUOUS TREES (cont.)

Botanical and common name	Description	Pruning and other remarks	Insects and diseases
Oxydendron arboreum— Sorrel tree	Ht.—50-60 ft; Leaves shining green, 3-8 in. long; Flower white, July-Aug.; Fruit—light gray tassels, Sept.-Oct.; Bark deeply fissured, gray.	A summer flowering tree with large shiny leaves, turning scarlet in fall, but remaining pale beneath. Likes a well-drained woodsy loam. Prune only to remove dead or diseased branches.	No serious pests or diseases.
Paulownia tomentosa— Empress tree	Ht.—40-60 ft; Leaves 10-20 in. long, 3-lobed, dark green; Flower pale violet, Apr.-May; Fruit—seeds, Sept.-Nov.; Bark gray.	A round-headed tree with heavy branches. Likes a light, deep loam. Very large leaves.	Has no serious pests or diseases.
Platanus occidentalis— American plane tree	Ht.—100-120 ft; Leaves 4-8 in. wide, 3-and sometimes 5-lobed; Flower inconspicuous; Fruit—heads smooth, consisting of several nutlets, about 1 in. across, Sept.-Oct. Bark almost creamy white, peeling in small plates, dark brown and fissured at base of older trunks.	A tall tree with round and oval head. Likes a moist rich soil. Often used for street trees. Prune during summer and fall. Remove diseased and dead branches and shape tree.	Lace bug Bagworm White fly Blight White-marked tussock moth Canker
Platanus orientalis— European plane tree	Ht.—80-100 ft; Leaves 4-8 in. wide, 5-7 lobed; Flower inconspicuous; Fruit—2-6 fruit heads, 1 in. thick and bristly; Bark peeling in large flakes, dull gray or greenish.	A broad, round head and short, thick trunk, often divided near base into several stems. Prune as above. Likes a well-drained average soil.	

Botanical and common name	Description	Pruning and other remarks	Insects and diseases
Populus alba—White poplar	Ht., 90–100 ft; Leaves 3–5 lobed, with triangular, coarsely-toothed lobes, 2–4 in. long, dark green above, white beneath; Flower pendulous catkins before leaves, approx. 2 in. long; Fruit oval, brown, 2–4 valved seeds, ripening before leaves are fully grown; Bark whitish-gray, smooth; rough at base of old trunks.	Large, irregular tree. Prune only to remove dead or diseased branches. Likes a moist, average soil.	Red-humped caterpillar Tent maker Poplar borer Willow leaf beetle Bronze birch borer Cottonwood borer Poplar sawfly
Populus tremuloides—Quaking aspen	Ht., 90–100 ft; Leaves—1½–2½ in. long, thin, smooth and shiny beneath; Flower—cottony catkins, April; Fruit—same as above except smaller; Bark smooth, reddish-brown.	Same as above. Leaves move in the slightest breeze.	Satin moth Forest tent caterpillar Spiny elm caterpillar
Populus nigra—Black poplar	Ht.,—90–100 ft; Leaves light green beneath, rounded at base, smooth 2–3 in. long; Flower—catkins, approx. 2 in. long, April; Fruit—2-valved seeds on fruiting catkins 4–5 in. long; Bark deeply furrowed, often with large burs, branches smooth, orange, changing to ashy gray the second year.	A wide spreading tree. Prune only to remove dead and diseased branches.	Gypsy moth Cottonwood leaf beetle Oyster shell scale
Populus balsamifera—Cottonwood	Ht.,—90–100 ft; Leaves smooth, bright green below, 3–4 in. long and as wide; Flower—catkins 3–4 in. long, April; Fruit—fruiting catkins 6–8 in. long, seeds 3–4 valved; Bark brown and smooth.	Upright spreading branches with an open broad head. Prune as above.	Poplar curculio Fall webworm Leaf blister Leaf spots
Quercus alba—White oak	Ht.,—100–120 ft; Leaves 4–8 in. long, bright green above, narrow at base with 5–9 oblong entire lobes; Flower—greenish-yellow catkins, late spring; Fruit—brown acorn about 1 in long ¼ enclosed by a cup-shaped cap; Bark smooth, light reddish-brown.	Heavy, spreading branches, forming a broad, open head. Bright green foliage changing to deep red or violet purple in autumn. A	Datana caterpillar Saddle-backed caterpillar White blotch oak leaf miner

TABLE 5.15/CHARACTERISTICS OF DECIDUOUS TREES (cont.)

Botanical and common name	Description	Pruning and other remarks	Insects and diseases
quercus alba (cont.)		long-lived tree. Prune only to remove dead and diseased branches.	Obscure scale Lecanium scale Kermes scale Golden oak scale Two-lined chestnut borer Brown tail moth Orange striped oak worm Spiny oak worm Buck or maia moth
Quercus coccinea—Scarlet oak	Ht.—60–80 ft; Leaves bright green and smooth beneath, 3–6 in. long with 7 oblong lobes; Flower same as above: Fruit—oval acorn about ¾ in. long, ⅓ to ½ enclosed by a cup; Bark gray, with inner bark reddish; buds dark reddish brown.	Gradually spreading branches, forming a round-topped, rather open head. Bright green foliage turning brilliant scarlet in autumn. Likes a gravelly soil. Prune as above.	Forest tent-caterpillar California oak moth Hag moth caterpillar Saddle-backed caterpillar Oak mite Cecropia moth Carpenter worm
Quercus macrocarpa—Mossy-cup oak	Ht.—60–80 ft; Leaves dark green and shiny above, grayish or whitish beneath, 4–8 in. long; Flower same as above; Fruit—broad oval acorn about ¾–1½ in. long, ½ enclosed by a large cup;. Bark light brown, deeply furrowed and scaly.	A tall trunk and spreading branches, forming a broad head, pyramidal while young. Corky branches conspicuous in winter. Likes a rich soil. Prune as above.	Leopard moth Twig pruner Ribbed bud-gall Pacific oak twig girdler Flat-headed apple tree borer Ivory-dotted long horn Northern brenthian Twig blister Leaf blister

Botanical and common name	Description	Pruning and other remarks	Insects and diseases
Quercus palustris— Pin oak	Ht.—60–80 ft; Leaves bright green above, lighter green, shiny and smooth beneath, about 3–4½ in. long, with 5–7 oblong lobes; Flower same as above; Fruit—acorn ½–¾ in. across, ⅓ enclosed by a thin saucer-shaped cup; Bark—branches dark red-brown or orange, buds chestnut brown.	Slender branches, usually pendulous at the ends, forming a symmetrical pyramidal head while young, irregular and oblong in older trees. A rapid grower in rich soil. Prune as above.	Io moth Fall canker worm Spring canker worm Gypsy moth
Quercus phellos— Willow oak	Ht.—40–60 ft; Leaves light green, shiny above, 2–4 in. long; Flower same as above; Fruit—half round acorn about ½ in. high, enclosed only at base by a saucer shaped cup; Bark reddish-brown.	A conical round-topped head and willow-like leaves, turning pale yellow in autumn. Likes moist, clay soil. Prune as above.	
Quercus rubra— Red oak	Ht.—60–80 ft; Leaves dull green above, gray or white or sometimes pale yellow-green beneath, 4½–8½ in. long, with 7–11 lobes halfway to the middle; Flower same as above; Fruit—oval acorn, 1 in. high, ⅓ enclosed with half cup; Bark gray with branches becoming dark red.	Stout spreading branches form a broad round-topped head. Foliage turns dark red in autumn. Rapid grower in moist, rich soil. Prune as above.	
Quercus stellata— Post oak	Ht.—60–80 ft; Leaves dark green and rough above, grayish or brownish beneath, 4–8 in. long with 2–3 pairs of broad lobes; Flower same as above; Fruit—oval acorns ½–1 in. high, ⅓ or ½ enclosed by cup; Bark reddish-brown, deeply fissured and scaly.	A dense, round head with large dark green leaves. Prune as above.	

TABLE 5.15/CHARACTERISTICS OF DECIDUOUS TREES (cont.)

Botanical and common name	Description	Pruning and other remarks	Insects and diseases
Quercus velutina— Black oak	Ht.—80–100 ft; Leaves shiny dark green above, brown beneath, 4–8½ in. long with 7–9 broad lobes; Flower same as above; Fruit—oval acorn ½–⅜ in. high, ½ enclosed by cup; Bark dark brown, inner bark orange.	Large tree of rapid growth with slender branches and open narrow head. Foliage turns dull red or orange-brown in autumn. Will stand dry soil. Prune as above.	
Salix nigra— Black willow	Ht.—30–40 ft; Leaves 2–4 in. long, pale green, wedge-shaped, tapered to a point and finely toothed on the edge; Flower inconspicuous; Fruit—none; Bark dark brown, rough and scaly, branches yellowish.	Slender spreading branches, graceful. Likes a moist, rich soil. No regular pruning necessary.	Bagworm Carpenter worm Willow-leaf beetle Red-humped caterpillar
Salix babylonica— Weeping willow	Ht.—30–40 ft; Leaves 3–6 in. long, dark green above, grayish-green beneath, wedge-shaped, tapered to a point and finely toothed on the edge; Flower inconspicuous; Fruit—none; Bark smooth, brown.	Long, pendulous, swaying branches. Likes a moist, rich soil. No pruning is necessary.	Scurfy scale Cottonwood leaf beetle Yellow-spotted willow slug Elm sawfly
Salix discolor— Pussy willow	Ht.—15–20 ft; Leaves 2–4 in. long, dark green; Flower silver-gray, Mar.; Fruit—none; Bark smooth, gray.	Likes a moist, rich soil. Its bloom marks the beginning of spring. No regular pruning is necessary.	Spiny elm caterpillar Gypsy moth Satin moth Japanese beetle Fall webworm Powdery mildew Poplar borer Cone gall Willow shoot sawfly Willow scale

Botanical and common name	Description	Pruning and other remarks	Insects and diseases
Tilia americana— American linden	Ht.—80–100 ft; Leaves light green beneath, coarsely toothed with long pointed teeth, 4–8 in. long; Flower yellow, July; Fruit—nutlike, thick shelled without ribs; Bark smooth, green.	Likes a moist, rich soil, with fragrant rapid growth. No regular pruning is necessary.	Oyster shell scale Japanese beetle Leaf beetle Cecropia moth Linden borer
Tilia vulgaris— Common linden	Ht.—80–100 ft; Leaves dark green and smooth above, bright green beneath, 2–4 in. long, sharply toothed; Flower yellow-white, June; Fruit nutlike, thick-shelled, faintly ribbed; Bark smooth.	Likes a moist, rich soil, produces heavy shade and is much used as a street tree. No regular pruning is necessary.	Tussock moth Twig girdler Spring cankerworm Fall cankerworm Leaf blotch Leaf spot
Tilia cordata Littleleaf European linden	Ht.—60–80 ft; Leaves dark green, smooth, shiny above, 1½–2½ in. long, sometimes broader than long; Flower yellow-white, fragrant, July; Fruit nutlike, thin-shelled, slightly or not ribbed; Bark smooth or slightly hairy.	Likes a moist, rich soil. Has a fragrant dense foliage. No regular pruning is necessary.	
Tilia tomentosa— Silver linden	Ht.—60–80 ft; Leaves dark green above, whitish beneath, sharply and doubly toothed, 2–4 in. long; Flower yellow-white, June; Fruit nutlike, oval, minutely warty and slightly 5-angled; Bark hairy.	A broad, pyramidal tree, forming a dense shade, in moist rich soil. No regular pruning necessary.	
Ulmus americana— American elm	Ht.—100–120 ft; Leaves dark green, 3–6 in. long, unequal at base, doubly toothed, rough above and smooth beneath; Flower reddish-brown, April; Fruit—oval nut about ½ in. long, deeply notched at end, with short hairs; Bark light gray, scaly, and deeply fissured.	Likes moist, rich soil. A tall tree with limbs usually spreading outwards and forming a wide spreading head. A very graceful tree. Requires very little pruning.	Carpenter worm Fall webworm Leopard moth Scurfy scale Twig girdler Spring cankerworm Fall cankerworm Tussock moth Leaf beetle Spiny elm caterpillar Elm case bearer Cockscomb gall European elm scale Brown-tail moth

TABLE 5.15/CHARACTERISTICS OF DECIDUOUS TREES (cont.)

Botanical and common name	Description	Pruning and other remarks	Insects and diseases
Ulmus campestris—English elm	Ht.—120–150 ft; Leaves dark green and rough above, soft and downy below, 2–4 in. long, doubly toothed with about 12 pairs of veins; Flower inconspicuous; Fruit—small nut about ½ in. across, with a small closed notch at end; Bark light gray, deeply fissured.	Tall tree with straight stem and spreading or ascending branches. forming an oval or oblong head. Likes a moist, rich soil. Requires very little pruning.	Bagworm Japanese beetle Elm sawfly Elm leaf miner Elm leaf aphid Oyster shell scale Gypsy moth European bark beetle
Ulmus parvifolia—Chinese elm	Ht.—25–40 ft; Leaves 1–2 in. long, shiny green and smooth above; Flower inconspicuous; Fruit about ½ in. long, notched at end, seed in middle; Bark smooth.	A fast growing tree with slender and somewhat brittle branches, forming a broad round head with small leaves. Likes moist, rich soil. Requires very little pruning.	Elm borer Dutch elm disease Leaf spots
Ulmus fulva—Slippery Elm	Ht.—40–60 ft; Leaves dark green, very rough above, densely hairy beneath, 4–8 in. long; Flower pinkish, April; Fruit about ½ in. long, slightly notched; Bark red-brown, rough and downy.	Tree with spreading branches, usually forming a broad open head, with large foliage turning dull yellow in autumn.	

CHAPTER SIX

WEEDS

AND THEIR

ERADICATION

Weeds are objectionable plants, or plants that are undesirable in cultivated land, and like other plants they have their botanical classifications. For the purpose of weed control under a maintenance program, however, both the botanical system and a more practical system are used.

BOTANICAL CLASSIFICATION OF WEEDS

Botanists have based their classification of weeds on the natural differences in growth habits of plants, and the time each requires to complete a life cycle. Plants fall botanically under the headings of annuals, biennials, and perennials.

Annuals are plants which complete their life cycle in one year. From a seed, the plant grows, matures, and produces seed, after which the plant dies. The two types of annuals are *summer annuals*, which germinate in the spring, grow during the summer, and die in the fall; and *winter annuals*, which germinate in the fall, grow slightly during the winter, blossom in the spring, and die about midsummer.

Biennials require two years for completion of the life cycle. The first year the roots and leaves are developed; the second year the flowers and seeds and produced and the plant dies.

Perennials, the largest class of plants, live three or more years. They pro-duce seeds abundantly, and may spread also from underground parts. The three types of perennials are *simple perennials,* which have a fibrous or fleshy root and reproduce only by seeds; *creeping perennials,* which are propagated by creeping rootstocks as well as seeds; and *bulbous perennials,* which reproduce by bulbs, bulblets, and seeds.

PRACTICAL CLASSIFICATION OF WEEDS

A more practical and easier way to classify weeds is in four groups: common weeds, noxious weeds, lawn weeds, and poisonous weeds.

Common weeds are those most commonly found in fields under ordinary tillage and forage conditions.

Noxious weeds are those found to be unusually troublesome and detri-mental when once established. They cause great damage in fields and crops, and a loss in crop value.

Lawn weeds are those most commonly found on lawns, courts, and walk-ways.

Poisonous weeds are those which produce toxic effects in either human beings or animals.

WEED CONTROL

Good weed control can be secured if several important practices are fol-lowed: proper management and fertilization of the soil; proper seedbed preparation; sowing of clean seed. Control of some of the more persistent weeds, however, depends upon special tools and methods.

Tools

The tools used for weed control may be simple hand implements or more or less complicated machines.

Hand tools: The common hoe and spade are used over small areas to cut weeds at the surface and to dig out deep roots.

Field tillage implements: The common plow is used for deep and shallow plowing to turn under weeds. The disk harrow will cut and turn weeds under, and is adapted to killing small weeds which spring up on plowed or fallow ground. Weeders and rotary hoes are also effective.

Sprayers: Power or hand sprayers of any kind may be used to apply chemical weed killers.

Automatic liquid guns: These are used to a limited extent for the destruction of individual weeds.

Weed torches: Torches burning gasoline or kerosene are used in the eradication of weeds by burning.

Seed cleaners: Fanning mills and other types of seed cleaners are effective in blowing out light weed seeds and sifting the small, heavier seeds.

Methods

Mowing: Close mowing prevents many weeds from reseeding, thereby eliminating them.

Pasturing: Pasturing an infested area is often effective, since some weeds are palatable to cattle.

Smothering crops: A number of quick-growing farm crops, such as alfalfa, soybeans, sorghums, Sudan grass, and the millets, if thickly sown, are useful in smothering weed plants.

Mulching: Straw or mulch paper and other materials, if properly placed to shade weed plants, will finally cause the plants to die.

Chemical weed destroyers

There are numerous chemicals which can be used advantageously, provided there is sufficient knowledge of the type of chemical and its action on plants other than weeds. The most common chemical formulas used today are 2,4-D and 2,4,5-T. A further discussion of the use of these will follow.

Selective weed chemicals, such as Sodar, Weedone L-850, Artox, Di-Met, Crab-E-Rad, Crag Herbicide I, and others are being used more and more frequently for weed control in turf and in shrub beds. They are especially effective against crabgrass and chickweed.

The chemicals most commonly used in weed control are the following:

1. Chlorates: Calcium, Sodium
2. Sodium chloride (or common salt)
3. Acids: Carbolic (or Phenol), Hydrochloric, Nitric, Sulfuric
4. Sulfates: Iron, Copper
5. Petroleum oils: Crude, Kerosene
6. Sodium arsenite
7. Ammonium sulfocyanate
8. 2,4-D (a combination of some of the above)

Chlorates

The chlorates have been used as weed killers in both liquid and dry form. They have the ability to kill tops, and at the same time, they work down into the roots and destroy them. Sodium chlorate has been used the longest, but an objection to it is that it may create a dangerous fire hazard.

Sodium chlorate: Sodium chlorate, if applied as a spray, is made by dissolving 1–2 lb of the chemical in 1 gal water, and sprayed at the rate of 100 gal per acre. The foliage should be thoroughly covered, and within a few days the leaves will start to die and turn brown. It will work more efficiently on damp days or toward evening. Sodium chlorate can also be used as a dust and applied directly to the foliage of weeds. The application should be 100–200 lb to the acre. If applied in sufficient quantities to destroy weeds completely, sodium chlorate will render the ground sterile for six to eighteen months. The period of sterility can be lessened by the addition of small quantities of lime. The best time for application is in the latter part of October and November.

Calcium chlorate: Although like sodium chlorate, calcium chlorate is preferred for two reasons: (1) It is not flammable, and (2) It does not render the soil sterile.

Sodium chloride

Common salt is an old and tried remedy for weed destruction. It kills all vegetation with which it comes in contact, by absorbing and withdrawing the water from the roots. It should therefore be applied on a hot, dry day. It is especially effective in driveways and walkways. It will, however, make the soil sterile for a prolonged period.

Salt may be applied either dry or in the form of a brine. If applied dry, 2–10 tons per acre will be required. If a solution is to be used, dissolve 3 or 4 lb in 1 gal of water and apply 100 to 400 gal per acre.

Acids

There is limited use for acids, but they must be used with extreme care because they will burn clothing and flesh. They must never be used in spray form, must always be stored and carried in glass containers. They are most useful for destroying plants with permanent crowns, such as dandelions, plantains, and some of the mustards.

Sulfates

Both iron and copper sulfate have been widely used.

Iron sulfate: Used dry or as a spray, iron sulfate should be applied on a bright, clear day. It is used to advantage in grain fields, since grains seem to be resistant to the chemical. The rate of mixture is 100 lb to 1 bbl (or 52 gal) of water.

Copper sulfate: Most active on young tender growth, copper sulfate should be sprayed in a fine mist on clear days when there is no likelihood of rain for some hours. Rate of mixture is 10–15 lb to 1 bbl of water.

The rate of application of these sulfates is 60 gal to the acre. Both of them act upon foliage and flowers, and should be utilized when these are at their height.

Petroleum oils

Acting upon all vegetation alike, petroleum oils kill all plants in the area treated. The recommended rate is 300–400 gal per acre, applied in the form of a fine spray. Precautions should be taken against fire.

Sodium arsenite

Sodium arsenite is very poisonous, and the greatest care should be taken when it is used around human beings and livestock. It acts upon the foliage of weeds and causes the starvation of the root system. For the usual succulent weeds, 1 lb of arsenite dissolved in 25 gal of water is sufficient, but the chemical must be mixed when strictly fresh; otherwise it will harden. For the hardier plants with heavy leaves and a perennial root system, 2–5 lb of the chemical should be used to 25 gal of water.

Ammonium sulfocyanate

A 20 per cent solution of ammonium sulfocyanate is useful for the destruction of weeds in walks, driveways, and on walls.

THE USE OF 2,4-D

The well known 2,4-D is available in several commercial forms and varying strengths. The manufacturer's specifications usually are adequate in describing the use. Not only the leaves and tops of most kinds of weeds are killed, but also the roots. It does not injure most of the grasses common to lawns and pastures.

The full name of this compound is 2,4-dichlorphenoxyacetic, an organic acid. It is a synthetic coal tar derivative, and the active ingredient in all weed killers of this type. Commercial weed killers based on 2,4-D are marketed in three different forms: sodium salt, amine salt and ester.

Perennial weeds are difficult to control with 2,4-D. Best results have been obtained by treating during the active growing stage—the bud stage, generally. One application of 2,4-D seldom gives complete eradication; repetitions are necessary. It is generally agreed that where eradication is the objective, higher rates of 2,4-D have given the best results. Where long-time control under cropping conditions is the objective, the rate of application should be governed by the maximum amount the crop will tolerate.

Many annual weeds can be controlled with 2,4-D, although some are resistant. They are more susceptible in the seedling and early stages of development, and when conditions are such as to promote vigorous growth. Some weeds which are resistant at later stages are readily killed when young and actively growing. In some areas ester formulations have been much more effective in control of annual weeds than either amine or sodium salt. Apparently 2,4,5-T is no more effective than 2,4-D. Some weeds may be controlled with dosages as low as ⅛ lb of 2,4-D per acre.[1] Established stands of most perennial grasses are so tolerant of 2,4-D that dosages used may be those necessary to control susceptible or semitolerant weeds. An exception should be made in the case of bent grasses and buffalo grass. These grasses may be susceptible under some conditions.

Seedling grasses may be injured by 2,4-D applied immediately following emergence, but after reaching the four-to-six-leaf stage seedlings may be treated with ¼ or ½ lb acid per acre. As the seedlings grow dosages may be increased and after they are well established and have 12 or more leaves, they may be treated much as full-grown plants, and will tolerate dosages adequate to control broad-leaved weeds. It is not advisable to use 2,4-D for control of broad-leaved weeds in grass seedlings if the land is heavily infested with seeds of weedy annual grasses. Such treatment often encourages increased competition by the undesirable grasses, which cannot be controlled with 2,4-D.[1]

Precautions in Using 2,4-D

The following is an extract from Farmer's Bulletin No. 2005, United States Department of Agriculture, November 1948:

2,4-D is a chemical that will work for you or against you, depending on how you use it. It will kill or damage most broad-leaved plants—valuable crops as well as weeds.

Do not dust from an airplane. 2,4-D dusted from an airplane may drift for miles, killing or damaging susceptible crops.

Use no more than the minimum need. 2,4-D is not a cure-all. Study label on the container. Study manufacturer's directions. Measure quantities accurately.

Check equipment carefully. Be sure your equipment is right and that it does not leak. Proper nozzles, accurately adjusted, are the key to safe, thorough spraying.

Safeguard sensitive plants. Flowers, vegetables, clovers, cotton, tomatoes, and other crops are extremely sensitive. Beware of wind's drifting spray to nearby plants. Fumes of some types (esters) of 2,4-D also may do damage.

Apply at the right time. 2,4-D is most effective when plants are in active growth. Do not apply diluted spray solutions when the vegetation is wet with rain or dew. Avoid windy days for spraying. Use separate sprayer for 2,4-D. Minute quantities of 2,4-D left in a sprayer later used for insecticides will damage sensitive plants. It is safer, more convenient, and more practical to have a separate sprayer.

[1] Statements taken from the 1948 Report of the Policy Committee on Herbicides of the North Central Weed Control Conference.

Weeds and crops classified as to their response to 2,4-D

The weeds and crops believed to be "susceptible," "intermediate," and "resistant" to 2,4-D are given below. The terms refer to the reaction of the plants when sprayed while in an active growth. Many "susceptible" weeds are intermediate or resistant when mature.

Annual and winter annual weeds

Group 1. Susceptible
Plants readily killed by 2,4-D, at least at early stages.

Beggar-ticks
Black medic, yellow trefoil
Bitter wintercress
Blue bur
Butterprint, Indian mallow or
  velvetleaf
Cocklebur
False flax
Fanweed, Frenchweed, stinkweed,
  pennycress
Flower-of-an-hour
Galinsoga
Hemp
Hemp-nettle
Henbit, dead-nettle
Indigo
Jewelweed
Jimsonweed
Orache
Pepper grass, annual

Pigweeds—rough, prostrate
  tumbling, etc.
Pineapple weed, wild marigold
Puncture vine
Radish, wild
Ragweed, com.
Redweed
Rough cinquefoil
Saltbush
Sow thistle, annual
Sunflower
Vervain
Kochia
Marsh elder
Mexican weed
Morning glory, an.
Mustard, wild
Vetches
Wild cucumber
Wormwood
Yellow star thistle

Group 2. Intermediate
Plants less readily killed by 2,4-D than those in Group 1, but controlled by 2,4-D under favorable conditions or with high concentrations. Plants often recover after treatment.

Bedstraw
Buckwheat, wild
Carpetweed
Dodders
Fleabane, daisy, and others

Goosefoot, oak-leaved, and others
Knotweed, doorweed
Lamb's quarters
Lettuce, prickly
Mallow, round-leaved

Chickweed, com.
Coreopsis
Curly indigo
Marestail, Canada fleabane
Russian thistle

Shepherds purse
Smartweeds
Speedwells
Spurge, mat
Spurge, spotted

Group 3. Resistant
Nearly uninjured by 2,4-D. Control by 2,4-D probably not possible.

Black night shade
Buffalo bur
Catchflys
Corn cockle

Cow cockle
Grasses
Purslane
Wood sorrel

Perennial and Biennial Weeds

Group 1. Susceptible
Tops readily killed by 2,4-D at some stage, roots frequently killed by one application.

Artichoke, Jerusalem
Austrian field cress
Bindweed, hedge
Buckhorn
Bull thistle
Burdock
Catnip
Chicory
Cinquefoils, fivefingers
Coneflowers
Dandelion
Dragon head
Evening primrose
False sunflower
Fiddleneck
Figwort
Four-o'clock
Ground ivy
Gumweed
Heal-all
Hedge nettle
Hoary alyssum

Horsetail
Lawn pennywort
Licorice, wild
Loco weed
Moonseed
Mouse-ear chickweed
Nettle, stinging
Plantains
Poppy mallow
Rosin weed
Skeleton weed
Slender rush
Sweetclovers
Thistle, biennial
Vervains
Vetch, crown
Vetch, bird or tufted
Water hemlock
Water hyacinth
Western ragweed
Wild parsnip
Wild sweet potato, man-of-the-earth

Group 2. Intermediate

Top partly or completely killed by 2,4-D at early or rapid growth stages; control by 2,4-D probably possible under favorable conditions and/or with repeated treatments.

Alligator weed
Arrowhead
Bindweed, field
Blueweed
Bouncing Bet
Bur ragweed
Buttercups
Canada thistle
Carrot, wild
Cattail
Docks
Dogbane
Goatsbeard
Goldenrods

Gourd, wild
Houndstongue
Lettuce, blue perennial
Pokeweed
Poverty weed
Silverleaf poverty weed
Sorrel, red or sheep
Spurge, leafy
Teasel
Texas blueweed
Tule
Wild garlic
Wild onion
Yarrow

Group 3. Resistant

Tops and roots slightly or not at all injured by 2,4-D. Control by 2,4-D probably not feasible.

Alkali mallow
Beardtongue
Bittersweet, climbing nightshade
Bracken
Cactus, prickly pear
Climbing milkweed
Ferns, many kinds
Goutweed
Grasses—all species
Ground cherry
Horse nettle
Milkweeds
Strawberry, wild
Tick-trefoil

Toadflax
Violets
Vervain
Mullein, com.
Night-blooming catchfly
Ox-eye daisy
Ragwort
Russian knapweed
Smartweed, swamp, tanweed
Spurge, cypress
Spurge, snow-on-the mountain
White cockle
Wood sorrel
White horse nettle

Woody plants

Group 1. Susceptible

Leaves and current year's growth readily killed. Entire root system often readily killed by repeated treatments of 2,4-D.

Alder	Lead plant
Aspen	Locust, black
Birch, black	Plum, wild
Boxelder	Rose, cherokee
Cherry, wild	Sumac, poison
Elderberry	Sumac
Grape, wild and cultivated	Tamarisk
Hazel	Virginia creeper
Honeysuckle	Walnut, black

Group 2. Intermediate

Leaves and current year's growth killed under favorable conditions or with high concentrations of the esters of 2,4-D or 2,4,5-T, or with mixtures of same. Eventual kill may be possible with several to many foliage or cut surface treatments using the above materials.

Blackberry, wild	Osage orange
Buckbrush	Tree of heaven
Chestnut	Poison ivy
Cottonwood	Raspberry
Elm, American	Tuliptree
Hawthorn	Willows

Group 3. Resistant

Reactions with esters of 2,4-D and 2,4,5-T uncertain and erratic. No consistent kills reported by experimenters. Subject to revision as experimental work continues.

Ash	Juniper
Basswood	Laurel
Beech	Maple
Dewberry	Mesquite
Dogwood	Oak
Hemlock	Persimmon
Hickory	Snowberry

Woody plants readily controlled by 2,4-D[1]

Alder	Box elder
Aspen	Catalpa
Birch	Cherokee rose
Black willow	Chinaberry

[1] Information obtained from the Dow Chemical Company, Midland, Michigan.

Chokeberry
Cottonwood
Dogwood
Elderberry
Elm
Grape
Hackberry
Hazel
Japanese honeysuckle
Juneberry
Mountain ash
Poison ivy

Poison oak
Poison sumac
Sassafras
Shadbush
Staghorn sumac
Sycamore
Virginia creeper
Walnut
Wild cherry
Wild plum
Willow

Woody plants where control may be erratic

Black gum
Hawthorn
Mesquite
Oak
Persimmon

Poison ivy (in shade)
Sweet fern
Hickory
Locust
Rhododendron

Woody plants that resist 2,4-D

Ash
Maple

Pines
Sweet gum

BRUSH CONTROL

Increased emphasis has been placed on chemical control of brush and weeds during the past few years, mainly because of the need to find cheaper and faster ways of accomplishing the work previously done by hand.

Best results (including a greater degree of root kill) are obtained if brush is chemically treated while still comparatively young. Less spray volume is required, and therefore the cost of application is reduced. Tall brush is best treated by first cutting it and then treating the suckers or sprouts when they are 3–6 ft tall. When brush has reached 15 ft or more, only a thorough wetting of the leaves and stems can kill it.

The most important consideration is timing. Good results have been obtained during the period from the first full leaf stage until two or three weeks before frost.

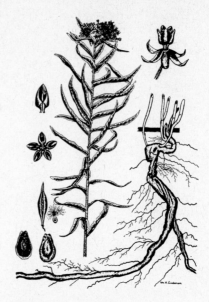

Fig. 6.1   Bracken fern   Fig. 6.2   Butterfly weed

Fig. 6.1   Bracken fern (*Pteris aquilina*)

This fernlike plant is rather widespread in pastures and meadows, and is poisonous to horses and cattle. The plant varies in height, depending upon the location, but it may grow as high as 6 ft. It has a creeping black rootstock extending for many feet along the surface and penetrating 2 or 3 ft into the soil. Hay should not be cut from places where this fern grows. Two or three years of clean cultivation will destroy the deep-lying rootstocks by starving them out. Other chemical control: Ammate.

Fig. 6.2   Butterfly weed (*Asclepias tuberosa*)

A mildly poisonous weed, tall, erect, and sturdy in habit, confined to sunny, dry open places along roadsides and in pastures. It comes from a thick tough perennial root, with many stems from the crown forming a bushy clump. It has many dark green leaves, clasping the stem at their base. The flowers are orange and very showy, and are followed by the characteristic milkweed pod with silky, flying seeds. Control by repeated spudding out below the crown followed by an application of common salt to the cut root surfaces.

Fig. 6.3   Buckhorn (*Plantago lanceolata*)

A very persistent perennial, reproduced by seeds in large numbers. Seed matures from May to November. Leaves are long, narrow, ribbed, and hairy. Flowers are small and form a collar around a short spike. Stem is 6 to 15 in. tall. Seeds are brown and boat-shaped, with a waxy coat.

The most effective method of control is to prevent weeds from producing seeds. Small infestations may be dug out, or heavier infestations may be effectively sprayed with 2,4-D.

Other chemical control: Weedar MCP; Na salt at rate of 2 lb per acre.

Fig. 6.4 Canada thistle (*Cirsium arvense*)

A perennial spreading by seed and rootstock. The long white underground roots lie deep in the ground and sometimes attain a length of 15 to 20 ft. They send up new plants at intervals, and stems reach 1 to 4 ft high. It has an erect, sturdy growth, with a bristly appearance. Leaves are cut and curled, spined, and with blooms much smaller than other thistles. Blooms are white to lavender. This weed forms dense patches to the exclusion of other plants. It is offensive to most grazing animals, and reduces feeding value as well as market value of hay.

The Canada thistle is very hard to control because of its spreading underground roots. Spray with a solution of calcium chlorate (½ lb per gal of water) just before the bloom stage. Apply enough spray for a thorough wetting of all the above ground vegetation, and repeat when new growth begins. Two or three applications are usually required.

Other chemical controls are: 2,4-D; Sodium salt of 2,4-D (effective in spring and early summer); Ester of 2,4-D foliage spray; 2,4-D postemergence spray (at 1 lb per acre); Eastern Brush Killer; Weedar MCP.

Fig. 6.5 Clover dodder (*Cuscuta arvensis*)

An annual weed of parasitic habit, spreading by seeds. This is a weak golden, leafless vine, subsisting by suckers which penetrate into the host plant, thereby reducing food supplies and retarding the development of clover. Once established, it rambles and twines rapidly, forming large patches in a field. Small rough coated seeds are formed in large numbers from July to October. There are several control measures which may be taken; the most effective is to burn the infested plants with a weed burner. This method also will kill dodder seeds on the ground. Infested plants may also be sprayed with oil, kerosene, sulfuric acid, ammonium thiocyanate (1 lb in 2 gal water) or sodium chlorate (1.5 lb in 1 gal water) and burned when dry. 2,4-D has also proved effective.

Fig. 6.3 Buckhorn

Fig. 6.4 Canada thistle

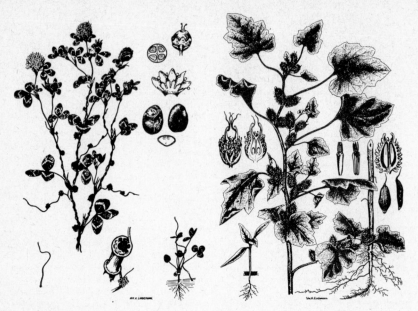

Fig. 6.5　Clover dodder　　　　　　　Fig. 6.6　Cockle bur

Fig. 6.6　Cockle-bur (*Xanthium canadense*)

A tough, hardy annual, 1 to 3 ft high, with rough-surfaced, alternate leaves. It reproduces by seeds. It is poisonous to swine feeding on the seedlings, and does internal damage to other animals if found in hay. Keep animals away from infested spots. Hand-pull, pile, and burn the plants while young. Chemical control may be achieved by spraying with 2,4-D.

Fig. 6.7　Common Chickweed (*Stellaria media*)

An annual, spreading by seeds and by rooting at the nodes of the stem. In sheltered spots it may bloom all year, producing seed in abundance. It is prostrate to upright in growth; the leaves are small and opposite, with small white flowers. It forms dense clumps or patches, choking out grass. For control, spray with iron sulfate and repeat if necessary. Small patches, however, should be removed by digging, especially in autumn, since this weed is capable of vigorous winter growth.

Chemical control may be obtained as follows: 2,4-D (high concentration as dust in soil) ; Weedar MCP; Dinitrol; Dow General Weed Killer (in oil emulsion) ; DN Dry Mix No. 1 or DN 111.

Fig. 6.8　Crabgrass (*Digitaria sanguinale*)

An annual, sometimes called finger grass, spreading by seed and by rooting at the lower joints. Seed matures from August to October. Seed head contains three to six, and sometimes as many as 10 fingers, several inches long and generally purplish or reddish-brown, arranged in a whorl like the fingers of the hand. Seed will remain alive in the ground for many years. Crabgrass is very difficult to eradicate or control. Preventing formation of seed heads by constant mowing or pulling will help to check its spread. Several chemicals have been used to control this weed, with varying degrees of success. Chemical solutions containing phenyl mecuric acetate will kill crabgrass, but it will also either kill other grasses or turn the grass brown for several weeks. Probably the most selective and best chemical to use is potassium cyanate. This is a nonpoisonous chemical and can safely be used where pets and children play.

Caution: Do not confuse potassium *cyanate* with potassium *cyanide*, which is a deadly poison. Potassium cyanate is sold under several brand names, and full instructions for

Fig. 6.7   Common chickweed

use are furnished. Briefly, these instructions are as follows:

1. Use a pump-up pressure garden sprayer in order to get a misty spray.

2. Apply when grass is green and lush. The chemical does not work well on dry ground. Wait for a good rain, or give grass a good watering before spraying.

3. Spray early for best results, with the first application in early July to catch the first crop and the second in mid-August to kill crabgrass germinating later.

Note: (1) Crabgrass cannot be killed in one season because there will be seed from preceding years in the ground, and (2) you will need to fertilize, water, and cut the lawn properly for best results.

Fig. 6.8   Crabgrass

WEEDS AND THEIR ERADICATION

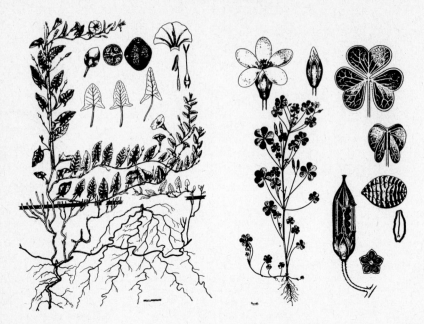

Fig. 6.9   Field bindweed

Fig. 6.10   Field sorrel

Fig. 6.9   Field bindweed (*Convolvulus arvensis*)

A perennial, spreading by seed and root stocks. The root system is extensive and penetrates to great depths. Growth is prostrate, forming dense mats which choke and crowd out other plans. Leaves are usually shovel-shaped; flower usually white or pink, funnel-formed and single on the stems. An inch or two below the flower are two small leaflike appendages which distinguish it from the hedge type of bindweed, which carries two leafy bracts close to the flower. Spraying with 2,4-D will give adequate control.

Fig. 6.10   Field sorrel (*Oxalis stricta*)

This plant likes a moist acid soil and frequently invades lawns. Leaves are similar to clover; the flowers are yellow, and the plant is prostrate to erect; sometimes creeping and spreading. Seeds are borne in a tight, erect-parted capsule. Control by preventing seed production.

Chemical control can be obtained by using 2,4-D, or (on the seedlings only) Weedar MCP.

Fig. 6.11   Glaucus-leaved anticlea (*Zyadenus chloranthus*)

A poisonous perennial coming from an onion-like bulb. All parts of the plant are poisonous, but the bulb is most poisonous of all. The plant reproduces by seeds. It is grasslike with long, narrow leaves surrounding an erect flower stem which bears numerous small yellowish flowers in a loose cluster. All animals should be kept away from infested areas, and they should also be kept well salted to prevent their forming an appetite for this weed. During the flowering period, grub out, pile, dry, and burn all plants.

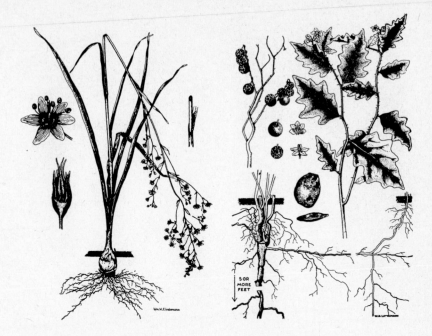

Fig. 6.11   Glaucus-leaved anticlea   Fig. 6.12   Horse nettle

Fig. 6.12   Horse nettle (*Solanum carolinense*)

A rugged perennial, hairy and prickly. The leaves are large, and similar to oak leaves. The flowers are like those of the potato, and the berries resemble small tomatoes, each of which may produce 40 to 60 seeds. The root system is deep, spreading, and tough. Seeds are oval, flattened and yellowish. Horse nettle spreads vegetatively by means of creeping horizontal rhizomes up to 3 ft long and usually 6 to 10 in. below the surface. Vertical taproots extend as deep as 8 ft.

A good sod of bluegrass will smother this weed out, as will regular cultivation. There are several chemicals which will give control: (1) salt applied at the rate of 1 psf after the shoots are cut in full bloom; (2) waste crankcase oil diluted with kerosene and applied as a drench when the first flower buds open; (3) sodium chlorate applied as a foliage spray in July, and again in September. Apply at rate of 1 to 1.5 lb chemical per gallon of water; (4) spraying with 2,4,5-T.

Fig. 6.13   Heal-all (*Prunella arelgaris*)

A slendar, leggy plant with pale violet flowers in moist, shaded situations. In open fields or on grassy roadside banks it is shorter and more compact, with darker colored flowers. In lawns, where it is cut back severely and regularly it develops horizontally and may form prostrate patches of considerable extent. The leaves vary from oblong to ovate, and the flowers range from purple to flesh color, or even white. An application of a strong (8 per cent) solution of iron sulfate will eliminate the weed without causing injury to other grasses. It may have to be treated at intervals of several weeks until all the plants disappear. Spraying with a high concentration of 2,4-D will also give control.

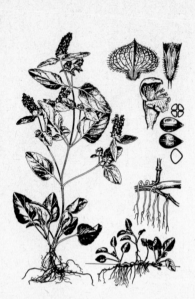

Fig. 6.13   Heal-all   Fig. 6.14   Hemp

Fig. 6.14   Hemp (*Cannabis sativa*)

An annual with palmately compound leaves composed of from five to seven narrow-tapering, coarsely-toothed leaflets. It has small greenish flowers, with the two sexes developed on separate plants. This plant produces a drug known as marihuana, a powerful narcotic. It can easily be controlled by pulling or cutting close to the ground.

Fig. 6.15   Horsetail (*Equisetum arvense*)

A poisonous perennial commonly found growing in gravelly soil, especially where there is ample water in the subsoil. There are two kinds of shoots, fertile and sterile, the fertile shoots appearing first, being unbranched, nearly naked stems, sheathed at the joints. The sterile shoots appear later and are branched and taller. Drain and cultivate areas infested with this weed. Keep animals away. Spray with a high concentration of 2,4-D.

Fig. 6.16   Jimson weed (*Datura stramonium*)

An annual with poisonous properties occurring most frequently on dumps, waste ground, and poor pastures. The plant has oaklike leaves and stems and foliage give off an unpleasant scent when broken and bruised. The plant is coarse and ill-scented, with spiny pods. It is a source of atropine, and its long tabular flowers have a kind of exotic beauty. Hand pulling is an easy matter and should be done before the pods have matured.

Chemical control can be obtained as follows: 2,4-D or 2,4-D postemergence spray (at 1 lb per acre); Weedar MCP (Sodium salt at 1 lb per acre).

Fig. 6.17   Knotweed (*Polygonum aviculare*)

An annual with greenish-white flowers, ranging from a low, prostrate form to trailing and climbing forms. The most distinguishing feature is the somewhat cylindrical sheath at the base of each leaf, just where the petiole joins the stem. Many species are thickened at the nodes, giving them a jointed or "kneed" look. It may be controlled by hoeing and pulling, or—when it occurs in driveways, paths, or tennis courts—by the application of chlorate sprays or by salting.

Other chemical controls are: 2,4-D or 2,4-D postemergence spray (at 1 lb per acre); Sodium TCA 90%.

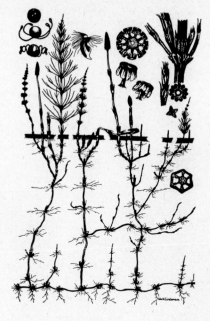

Fig. 6.15   Horsetail

Fig. 6.16   Jimson

Fig. 6.17   Knotweed

Fig. 6.18 Fanweed frenchweed (*Thalspi arvense*)

Sometimes called "stinkweed." An erect, close-growing plant, sparingly leaved except near the soil; mustard-colored, with the entire top full of greenish yellow bloom. Mature seed pods are like small winged capsules, with oval reddish-brown seeds marked by concentric ridges. It is an annual, appearing early and prolifically. Odor and taste are offensive. Spraying with 2,4-D as a post-emergence spray at ½ lb per acre, or as a solium salt, will give control.

Other chemicals that may be used are Dinitrol and Weedar MCP.

Fig. 6.19　Leafy spurge

Fig. 6.19　Leafy spurge (*Euphorbia esula*)

A perennial with deep, tough, woody roots, spreading both vegetatively and from matured seeds. It is an erect, branching plant having many buds at base of the crown, and forms tufts or dense clumps and patches. The entire plant is a yellowish green, leafy, and resembles a willow shoot. The flowers are small and surrounded by a group of leafy bracts resembling a flower head. Milky, poisonous sap causes blisters on skin. Seeds are mottled and smooth. Some roots have been found at depths slightly over 15 ft, and are relatively numerous at 8 to 12 ft.

Leafy spurge is very difficult to eradicate or control. 2,4-D has no effect, and since horses and cattle do not relish it, grazing is ineffective. Grazing by sheep, however, has been known to give some control. An application of from 2.5 to 4 gal per rod of the following solution has given some control: 1 lb sodium chlorate, 4 g[1] animal glue, 3 cc sulfuric acid, and 1 gal water. Apply when plants come into bloom and again just before first frost. Use of borax has given some control.

[1] 4 grams = 0.14 oz.

WEEDS AND THEIR ERADICATION

Fig. 6.20   Low or common mallow

Fig. 6.21   Marsh shield fern

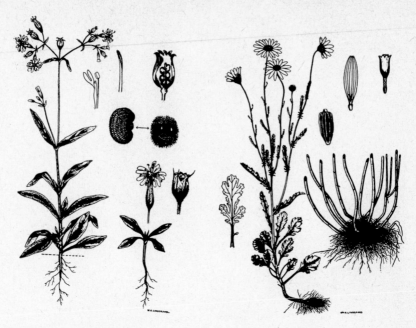

Fig. 6.22   Night-flowering catchfly   Fig. 6.23   Ox-eye daisy

Fig. 6.20   Low or common mallow (*Malva rotundifolia*)

A biennial or perennial plant producing vigorous, leafy stems from deeply embedded and extensive roots. Stems trail along the ground and cover a considerable area. The rounded, shallowly lobed and prominently veined leaves are borne on long petioles, from the axils of which arise the pale pink five-petaled flowers. The small flattened circular fruit suggests miniature cheeses. May be controlled by high concentrations of 2,4-D, when plants are young and in active growth, or with Weedar MCP, sodium salt, at 2 lb per acre.

Fig. 6.21   Marsh shield fern (*Dryopteris thelypteris*)

A fern found in wet marshes and woods, rarely in dry soil. It comes from creeping, blackish rootstocks. The leaves are compound, divided into many distinct leaflets. It is poisonous to livestock, and if marsh hay is used, care should be taken in mowing. Control by grubbing out all rootstocks or by draining to prevent conditions suitable for growth of this plant.

Fig. 6.22   Night-flowering catchfly (*Silone noctiflora*)

A tall, branched plant developing from a thick fleshy root. The stems are hairy and somewhat sticky; and leaves are opposite and lance-shaped. The flowers are perfect, with three styles. Stamens and carpels occur in the same flower, and petals are white. This weed can be controlled by spraying with 2,4-D.

Fig. 6.23   Ox-Eye Daisy (*Chrysanthemum leucanthemum*)

A perennial, spreading by seeds and by rootstocks from the thick, tufted crown. It is an early bloomer, with seeds maturing rapidly even after they are cut from the stalk. The flowers are single at end of stalk, and white with yellow center. Leaves are crinkled and cut. The plant blooms from May to October and seeds from June to November. Control by preventing plants from going to seed, and by working land in cultivated crops for several years.

Chemical control may be obtained as follows: 2,4-D (at high concentrations); Weedar MCP (at high concentrations on young plants).

WEEDS AND THEIR ERADICATION

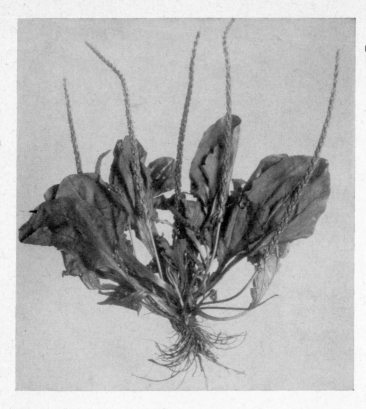

Fig. 6.24
Plantain

Fig. 6.24   Plantain (*Plantago major*)
A perennial with a thickened crown and fibrous wiry roots. The leaves are smooth, broad, thick-veined; often red or purplish along the main stem. The flowers are small, borne on a long spike, and produce many small, black, irregular shaped seeds.

Chemical control may be obtained as follows: 2,4-D; Dow General Weed Killer or Chipman General in oil emulsion; Weedar MCP (a sodium salt at rate of 2 lb per acre); DN Dry Mix No. 1 or DN 111 in oil emulsion.

Fig. 6.25   Perennial pepper grass (*Lepidium draba*)
A perennial which is reproduced by seeds and rootstock; forms large dense patches which choke and crowd out other vegetation. It is a rapid grower, blooming early and maturing many seeds. The leaves are hairy, clasping stem at base, and are numerous at the crown and sparser above. The plant is much branched, carrying heavy flower stems with small white flowers. Seeds are oval, chocolate brown, and two in a pod.

A postemergence spray of 2,4-D at 0.5 lb per acre will control.

Fig. 6.26   Poison ivy (*Rhus toxicodendron*)
A widespread poisonous vine or shrub, climbing vine, or erect bush. The leaf is composed of three leaflets. Flowers are small and greenish, borne in drooping clusters, and are followed by whitish, waxy-coated berries that remain after the leaves fall. All parts of the plant are poisonous at any time of year.

Chemical control may be obtained as follows: 2,4-D (several applications will completely eradicate); 2,4-D (as an ester or as an aqueous foliage spray); 2,4,5-T (foliage spray, esters or aqueous); Ammate (1.5 lb dry per sq yd, or as aqueous foliage spray); Borax; 2,4-D and 2,4,5-T (mixed esters, foliage spray); Esteron brush killer.

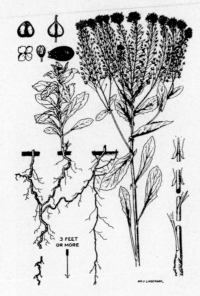

Fig. 6.25   Perennial pepper grass

3 FEET
OR MORE

Fig. 6.26   Poison ivy

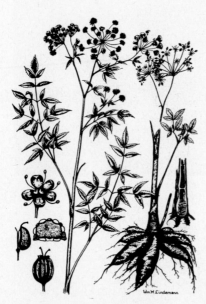

Fig. 6.27   Poison hemlock

Fig. 6.27   Poison hemlock (*Circuta maculata*)

A very poisonous perennial plant confined to low, wet pastures, creek banks, and ditches. The plant grows to a height of 2 to 6 ft, with swollen, hollow, dahlialike roots. The stems are stout and streaked with purple spots. The leaves are pale green, lacy, and much divided. The flowers are small, greenish white, and borne at the top of the branches forming flat clusters; in each cluster there may be from 15 to 30 small flowers. Grub out the root clusters, pile, dry, and burn.

Chemical control may be obtained as follows: 2,4-D; 2,4-D (high concentration or sodium salt) ; 2,4-D and 2,4,5-T (mixed esters) ; Esteron brush killer; Weedar MCP.

Fig. 6.28

Fig. 6.28   Quack grass (*Agropyron repens*)

A perennial grass spreading by creeping root stock and by seed. It forms a dense sod, crowding out more valuable plants. It is erect, smooth, and dark green, with the seed borne on a spike, similar to two-rowed barley.

This grass can be reduced if not eradicated by shallow plowing (4–6 in. deep) or digging infested areas during hot, dry summer weather. It can also be effectively crowded out with desirable grasses or white clover, or by close mowing or grazing. A spray of 1.5 lb of calcium chlorate per gal water just before the bloom stage is also fairly effective. Two or three applications are usually required.

Other chemicals which have given control are: 2,4-D; MH; Sodium TCA 90 per cent.

Fig. 6.29 (a) Common ragweed   Fig. 6.29 (b) Giant ragweed

Fig. 6.29a   Common ragweed (*Ambrosia elatior*)

Common ragweed has leaves which are pinnately twice-divided. Its seedlings somewhat suggest the marigold, but lack the rank odor. The female flowers are borne in small clusters in the axils of the leaves, while the male or staminate heads are crowded into racemes at the top of the plant and the ends of the upper branches. If sprayed at the appropriate time 2,4-D will give effective control at the rate of 2 lb per acre.

Fig. 6.29b   Giant Ragweed (*Ambrosia trifida*)

An annual, growing to a height of 12 or 15 ft with numerous branches. The leaves are palmately divided into three or occasionally five lobes. The plant likes a moist, rich soil. Spraying with 2,4-D in the early stages of growth gives good control. Use at the rate of 1.25 lb in 100 gal water per acre, or 0.5 lb per acre, postemergence spray. Ammate will also give control.

Fig. 6.30   Sow thistle   Fig. 6.31   Shepherd's purse

Fig. 6.30   Sow thistle (*Sonchus arvensis*)
A persistent perennial spreading by seeds and rootstocks. It grows erect, forming dense patches to the exclusion of other plants. Leaves are dark green with edges spined and recurving toward the base; upper leaves are usually uncut but spined, clasping stem at base. Roots are yellowish and brittle. Plant is filled with a milky sap; flowers are similar to those of the dandelion. Cultural methods are the most practical means of control or eradication. One year of shallow cultivation will entirely eradicate perennial sow thistle.

1. In middle of June (or just before the plants begin to blossom) plow to a depth not greater than 3 or 4 in.; harrow or disk immediately to close the furrows.

2. During the following twelve weeks, keep the soil entirely free of top growth, employing a disk, duckfoot cultivator, or rod or wire weeder.

Chemical control may be obtained as follows:

2,4-D: high concentration applied to cut stem; 1 lb per acre, post emergence spray; Na salt—high concentration; butyl ester, 1 lb per acre.

Weedar MCP: Na salt, 1 lb per acre; high concentration.

Fig. 6.31   Shepherd's purse (*Capsella bursa-pastoris*)
The lower or rosette leaves are deeply toothed or lobed with long, tapering bases, while its stem leaves are arrow-shaped with entire or wavy margins and clasping bases. The most characteristic feature is the heart-shaped, flattened seed-pod, which liberates innumerable small seeds. The plant may behave as a winter annual. It may be controlled by high concentrations of 2,4-D when plants are young and in active growth, and by Dinitrol sodium salt, Dow General Weed Killer, or Chipman General and Weedar MCP.

Fig. 6.32   Sheep sorrel   Fig. 6.33   Snow on the mountain

Fig. 6.32   Sheep Sorrel (*Rumex acetosella*)

A low, creeping perennial, producing a large number of small seeds. It has numerous creeping roots in the upper 8 in. of soil, parts of which may extend to a depth of 5 or 6 ft. Since sheep sorrel tolerates an acid condition, its presence may indicate an acid soil. However, it thrives best on rich well-drained soils containing lime.

Acid soils infested with sheep sorrel may be improved by treatment with ground limestone, 2 tons per acre, hydrated lime, 1.5 tons per acre, or quicklime, 1 ton per acre. Lime has no harmful effects on sheep sorrel, but creates soil conditions that enable crop plants to compete with the weed. Selective sprays, such as iron sulphate, dilute sulphuric acid, and sinox, will kill sheep sorrel and will not permanently harm pasture grasses except clover.

Other means of chemical control are as follows:

2,4-D: Na and Amine salts; Ammonium salt, high concentration.

Dow General Weed Killer, Chipman General, DN Dry Mix No. 1, or DN 111 in oil emulsion.

Weedar MCP—Na salt as dust.

Fig. 6.33   Snow on the mountain (*Euphorbia marginata*)

This plant is used as an ornamental annual in some regions, but it has properties that are poisonous to some people. It is a tall, branching, strong-growing plant; pale green, and leafy at the top with leaf margins edged in white. Flowers are small, in loose clusters among the closely crowded leaves. It reproduces by seeds, and thereby often escapes cultivation and becomes a weed. It can be readily controlled by hand pulling before it flowers.

Fig. 6.34   Silvery or hoary cinquefoil
(Potentilla argentea)

A perennial silvery gray weed of creeping spreading habit. The leaves are finely cut, five-parted. The flowers are yellow, opening from May to September, and seeds are developed from June to November. Control by frequent control may be obtained as follows: Weedar MCP (Na salt, 4 lb per acre) ; 2,4-D (foliage spray) ; 2,4-D and 2,4,5-T (mixed esters, foliage spray).

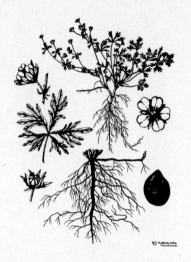

Fig. 6.34   Silvery or hoary cinquefoil

Fig. 6.35   White snakeroot

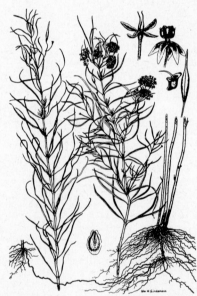

Fig. 6.36   Whorled milkweed

Fig. 6.37   Wild lupine

Fig. 6.38   Wild carrot

Fig. 6.35   White snakeroot (*Eupatorium urticaefolium*)

A shade-loving perennial plant which causes milk sickness or milk fever in cattle and among humans. It is erect, 2–3 ft high, and leaves are opposite, dark green, and strongly three-veined on the back. The flowers are borne at ends of branches in flat clusters; very small, white, and close bunched. The roots are blackish, stringy, and tough, forming a thick crown or cluster, not deep or running in character. Hand pull, pile, and burn all plants found.

Chemical control may be obtained by using mixed esters of 2,4-D and 2,4,5-T.

Fig. 6.36   Whorled milkweed (*Asclepias verticillata*)

A perennial weed, poisonous to livestock, especially horses and sheep. The plant comes from a running rootstock or seed. It is pale green, with numerous small narrow leaves, almost like the blades of grass arranged in clusters around the stem. The flowers are small, greenish white, and borne at ends of branches in a compact cluster. They are followed by a long green pod filled with cottony seeds which are dispersed by the wind. The average height is about 2 ft. A system of clean cultivation and crop rotation will control this weed.

Chemical control may be obtained as follows: 2,4,5-T (35% solution); 2,4-D and 2,4,5-T (mixed esters) stem painting.

Fig. 6.37   Wild lupine (*Lupinus perennis*)

Plant is strong, erect, rather fleshy, and slightly hairy. The leaflets are usually in groups of seven to eleven, attached to a central stem. Flowers are pea-shaped and blue to white. The root is strong, penetrating the soil for several feet. This perennial is considered poisonous to livestock. Control by spading off below the crown several times during the season.

Fig. 6.39   Witch grass

Fig. 6.40   Yarrow

Fig. 6.38   Wild carrot (*Daucus carota*)
A biennial coming from a thick boring tap root, similar to the common garden carrot. The leaves are lacy and fernlike, mostly at the crown, with the stem sparingly leaved and much branched. The flowers are small, white, and close bunched, forming a flat cluster. As the seeds form, the flower stems turn inward, so that when ripened the entire flower head resembles a bird's nest. Seeds are ridged and spined so that they adhere.

Fig. 6.39   Witch Grass (*Panicum capillare*)
An annual, recognized by the small one-flowered spikelets with their very unequal glumes, the outer of which is much shorter than the inner. Fall panicum is a smooth leaved, much-branching species. It may appear as a sprawling, prostrate specimen or as a vigorous, robust specimen up to 5 or 6 ft in height. It varies in color from bright green to blood red. It should be pulled out or cut back before flowers have a chance to form. Seeds are scattered by winds.
    Chemical control may be obtained as follows:
        2,4-D: 1.5 lb per acre, butyl ester, pre-emergence Na salt.

Fig. 6.40   Yarrow (*Achillea millefolium*)
The flowers are aggregated into a head surrounded by a series of bracts. They may be of two kinds: (a) tubular disk flowers, which when present constitute the central part of the head, and (b) flattened ray flowers, which usually surround the disk. Yarrow is a resolute and obstinate weed which flourishes in a wide variety of habitats. Its tough root-stocks make it particularly undersirable in lawn or garden, and it should be either cut out or repeatedly cut back.
    Chemical control can be obtained with 2,4-D at high concentration or as a sodium salt in spring or early summer.

318

Actually, careful research has shown that the movement of 2,4-D from the leaves to the stem of the plant takes place most readily when the plant is translocating carbohydrates in the same direction. In the stem the 2,4-D moves both upward and downward. Obviously, large acreages cannot be treated economically within a short period, so spraying operations must spread over a major part of the growing season. Both 2,4-D and 2,4,5-T have been found effective against a wide variety of woody species. Some species are easy to kill; others show more resistance. Certain ones are apparently more susceptible to 2,4,5-T than 2,4-D, including: sweet gum, osage orange, some oaks, poison ivy, elm, maple, blackberry, raspberry, hickory, ash, rose, ribes, basswood, meadowsweet, and others.[1]

Brush control methods

To control brush generally, use 1½–2 qt per 100 gal of water of an emulsifiable 2,4-D ester formulation (Esteron Ten-Ten) containing 4 lb acid equivalent per gal, or an emulsifiable 2,4,5-T ester formulation (Esteron 245) containing 4 lb acid equivalent per gal. A combination of these two (Esteron Brush Killer) can be used at the rate of 3 to 4 qt in 100 gal of water.

Apply the spray in sufficient quantity to wet the foliage and stems thoroughly. In order to get the best kill, it is necessary to have a lot of growth substance absorbed and translocated within the plant. It will require as much as 100 to 250 gal of spray per acre to accomplish this. If the sprays are applied properly, a 75 per cent or more reduction in regrowth usually may be expected. Do not expect 100 per cent kill. Apply one spray treatment the first season and a second the next season. Third and fourth year applications will usually be limited to spot treatment. For the purpose of determining cost of treatment, the program should be planned on a five-year basis.

Brush control equipment

The type of equipment to use will vary with the kind of job to be done. Power wagons equipped with 150–200 gal spray tanks and the orchard type of spray gun are best for large acreages. Such equipment should be capable of maintaining 150–400 psi spray pressures. The spray guns should be adjustable in order to cover foliage both close by and at some distance away. In areas where the terrain will not permit use of mobile equipment an additional quantity of hose (1,000 to 1,500 ft) should be carried.

The problem of drift must be considered at all times. Adjoining property must be protected, since many crops, flowers, and ornamentals are very susceptible to 2,4-D or 2,4,5-T sprays. Such drift is minimized when a dilute spray is properly applied with spray guns. Also, drift may be avoided to some extent by reducing the spray pressure. If there is any serious question about spray drift, the best decision is not to spray.

[1] Larry Southwick, Dow Chemical Co., Midland, Mich.

There are many areas where it is impossible for power operated equipment to reach all portions to be sprayed. Here 2–5 gal knapsack sprayers can be used. The same amount of 2,4-D and 2,4,5-T should be applied by this method as with the power equipment. Both water and oil have been used as carriers, and satisfactory results have been obtained. Uniform coverage is of utmost importance, but complete wetting will of course not be possible. The total volume of spray required will depend upon the density and height of vegetation. Under many conditions 13–15 gal of spray per acre will give satisfactory coverage, provided this volume is applied uniformly to the foliage and the solution contains sufficient amounts of the chemicals.

Stump treatment

For general stump treatment use 4 gal of an emulsifiable 2,4,5-T ester in 96 gal of oil, or 6 gal of a combination of 2,4-D and 2,4,5-T in 94 gal of oil. For smaller quantities, use 1½ pt of the combination spray in 3 gal of fuel or diesel oil, or 1 pt Esteron 245 in 3 gal of fuel or diesel oil.

The use of 2,4–D and 2,4,5–T for stump treatment during winter, fall, and early spring months adds tremendously to the versatility of the chemical control of woody vegetation. One man, using a knapsack sprayer, can spray all stumps and stubs that a good sized crew can cut on an average right of way. There is but little hand labor in treating stumps by this method, and the per-acre cost of chemicals is low. In areas where cotton and other susceptible crops are grown near the areas to be sprayed, stump treatment is less hazardous than foliage spraying. . . .

A knapsack sprayer equipped with oil-resistant check valves, pump leathers, and hose, is standard equipment for this job. Pressures of 15–25 psi are sufficient. The fan type of spray nozzle is held close to the stumps or stubs, or close to the ground when spraying, in order to minimize spray drift. It is suggested that the spray be applied within two or three days after cutting, if possible. Various methods have been used for marking stumps that have been treated, and several organic oil-soluble dyes have been tested. . . .

Substations and pole yards

A serious fire hazard is created if vegetation is left to grow unchecked in pole storage yards and substations. In addition to removing weeds, brambles, and woody vegetation from these areas, controlling grass is also desirable. This problem has usually been handled by means of hand or machine cutting, and by contact herbicides such as oils, pentachlorophenol, dinitrophenols, and others. These contact sprays kill the above-ground vegetation, but do not affect the roots of perennial grasses to any extent.

An effective weed killer is sodium trichloroacetate, known commercially as "Sodium TCA 90%." The herbicidal action of "Sodium TCA" appears to be principally through roots, and is most effective when there is an abundance of soil moisture. When excessive rainfall occurs shortly after application, the "Sodium TCA" may be subject to leaching, particularly on light-textured soils. This is one reason why an application does not cause prolonged soil sterility. "Sodium TCA 90%" may retard or kill the following grasses: Johnson, Bermuda, para, quack, Kentucky blue, Canada blue, redtop, orchard, timothy, buffalo, and smooth brome. In addition, a number of winter annual grasses have been found to respond, often at lower dosages than required for established perennials. Relatively small amounts applied to the soil often prevent the emergence of grass seedlings. Prickly pear cactus and palmetto have been controlled with "Sodium TCA."

Soil sterility from "Sodium TCA" is usually of relatively short duration—that is, one to three months. Its toxicity is about the same as that of table salt, and it is compatible with 2,4-D and 2,4,5-T formulations in water sprays. In addition, it can be used with contact weed killers such as emulsifiable pentachlorophenol and dinitrophenol formulations. Its action is relatively slow when used alone. For established stands of perennial grasses, the use of 100–200 lb of "Sodium TCA 90%" per acre is suggested. . . .

Highways

Chemical weed control along highways is rapidly becoming a firmly established and economically sound practice. Better knowledge of application methods and more efficient products now make chemical maintenance a wise choice for most highway weed control problems. Where woody plants are desirable, herbaceous perennials are the chief problem, and combination sprays using 2,4-D and 2,4,5-T esters can be utilized. 2,4-D liquid amine salt sprays have proved very effective against most herbaceous weeds and some of the less resistant woody species. They are somewhat safer to use in areas bordering crop land ornamentals than the "Esterons," although spray drift is always a factor no matter what 2,4-D or 2,4,5-T formulation is used.

In most areas, especially where vegetation is dense, application with an orchard type of spray gun will prove efficient. There are many areas where vegetation should be controlled some distance from the road, such as at grade crossings and intersections, where brush or high weeds form a hazard in terms of obstructed vision. Several equipment manufacturers offer rigs with spray booms designed for, or readily adaptable to, highway work. Boom application is most satisfactory where high pressure and high voltage are not required. A boom should be rigged to extend to the depth of the area to be sprayed, insofar as possible, and from the right side of the applying vehicle. It should be rigged so that it may be raised or lowered by the operator to conform with the slope of the shoulder, or to avoid obstacles. Such a rig may have a jointed boom so that the outward section may be lowered or raised independently of the first section.

The volume and pressure required may vary directly with the density of the weed growth to be controlled. For example, to control dandelion, plantain, thistle, and similar weeds in the attractive turf bordering our better highways, low pressure (40 psi), low dosage rate (15–30 gal per acre), and nozzles giving a coarse spray are suggested. Here 2,4–D amine salt may be used at 1½– 2 lb acid equivalent per acre in 20 or more gal of water. On the other hand, where weed growth is vigorous, tall, and dense, 2 lb acid equivalent per 100 gal water may be used in sufficient spray volume to give adequate coverage, which means rather complete wetting of foliage. This may require up to 300 gal of spray per acre. 2,4-D esters may also be used; they will be more effective if certain types of brush predominate. It should be stressed again that coarse, low-pressure sprays do not present the drift hazard of fine, high pressure sprays. . . .[1]

Aerial brush control

The airplane has been used for a long time for spraying large areas with insecticides, but only during the past few years has it been used successfully for controlling weeds. Aerial spraying for weeds is being done in farm crops and undesirable brush and trees, for range improvement purposes, and for the maintenance of transmission line rights of way.

The main advantage of aerial spraying with herbicides is its speed and relatively low cost. Aerial spraying is also ideal in remote areas which cannot be reached by mobile equipment, and in areas which cannot be sprayed from the ground because the brush is either too tall or too dense.

The principal disadvantage is the problem of drift. Aerial spraying must of necessity be restricted to nearly windless weather, and to areas where there is no chance of injuring desirable stands of trees or crops on adjacent land. Minimum weather conditions for aerial spraying should be as follows:

Wind velocity: Maximum 6 mph

Height of flight: 50–60 ft (lower levels desirable)

Time of day: Early morning (3 A.M.) or late afternoon, when air movement is at a minimum.

Costs of aerial spraying will vary with the type of control. For range improvement purposes the costs vary from $1.00 to $2.00 per acre. For transmission line control work the costs are relatively higher, averaging $5.00 to $10.00 per acre. Costs for ground hydraulic spraying vary from $50.00 to $80.00 per acre, depending upon the terrain.

SPECIFICATIONS FOR CHEMICAL TREATMENT OF BRUSH

Foliage spray method

A low-volatile ester brush-killer composed of equal parts of 2,4-D and 2,4,5-T should be used as the active ingredient. The mixture should contain 2 lb of 2,4-D acid equivalent and 2 lb of 2,4,5-T acid equivalent to 1 gal of

[1] Larry Southwick, Dow Chemical Co., Midland, Mich.

concentrate. Mix the active ingredients with water at the rate of 1 gal of concentrate to 100 gal of water. Spray only after the plants have acquired full leaf growth. The sprayer tank must be equipped with an agitator, and the spray solution must be thoroughly mixed before spraying is started. The spray solution must not be discharged into any stream. Any water, provided it is clean, may be used in preparing the spray solution. Provide sufficient hose to spray a maximum distance of 1500 ft from the pumping equipment in areas which are inaccessible to mobile equipment. Isolated areas which cannot be reached by hose may be treated by the basal spray method. Use an orchard type of spray gun to apply the spray solution. Vary the gun setting from a fine mist to a semisolid stream to secure full coverage of the plants sprayed. Keep the spray gun within 25 ft of the plants being sprayed. The normal nozzle pressure should be between 150 psi and 200 psi. Maximum nozzle pressure should be 250 psi.

All woody plants, including briers, should be thoroughly wet with the spray solution. Wet the entire leaf surface of the plants so that the solution just begins to drip from the leaves. Any portion of the area which has been sprayed less than one hour before a heavy rain should be sprayed again, but at least one hour must elapse after the end of a rain before spraying is started. No spraying should be done when the air temperature is below 60° F.

Basal spray method

This method utilizes a low-volatile ester brush-killer composed of 2 lb of 2,4-D acid equivalent and 2 lb of 2,4,5-T acid equivalent to 1 gal of concentrate. This active ingredient should be mixed with No. 2 fuel oil, kerosene, or equivalent at the rate of 4 gal of concentrate to 96 gal of oil. Spraying may be done at any time when the lower 14 in. of the plant stems are accessible so that the spray mixture can run down to the root crown. Apply the spray mixture in sufficient quantity to wet the entire circumference of the stem thoroughly and to allow the solution to flow down as described.

TABLE 6.1/CHEMICAL CONTROL OF WEEDS, GRASS, AND BRUSH

For Weed, grass and brush control	Recommended weed killers	Amount to use	When to use	Remarks
Weed control in pastures, and along highways, ditch banks, and fence rows	Esteron 4C or 2, 4-D weed killer, Formula 40	2-3 qt in 100 gal of water	When plants are in full leaf and actively growing	Wet thoroughly for control of broad-leaved annual and perennial weeds. If woody vegetation is a problem, use Esteron Brush Killer.
Chemical mowing	Dow general weed killer (Dinitro)	2-3 pt in 10-20 gal of oil make up to 100 gal with water	While vegetation is young. Respray as growth warrants	Thorough wetting of vegetation is essential. Established plants such as perennial grasses will recover. Seedling plants will be killed if sprayed when young. The higher amounts of oil will give better results where grasses are the primary problem.
Woody plants and brush, including brambles and poison ivy (foliage-application)	Esteron Brush Killer Esteron 245	3-4 qt in 100 gal of water 2-3 qt in 100 gal of water	When plants are in full leaf, but not later than 2 weeks before normal frost date	Wet thoroughly all foliage, stems, and bark, using hand or power sprayer. Esteron Brush Killer contains both 2,4-D and 2,4,5-T to give best control of brush. This product will control most species normally found in pastures, fence rows, rights of way, and other such areas. Esteron 245 contains only 2,4,5-T and may be used effectively against solid stands of 2,4-D resistant species such as osage orange, brambles, poison ivy, and horse nettle.
Tree stumps	Esteron 245 Esteron Brush Killer	1 pt in 3 gal of fuel or diesel oil 1½ pt in 3 gal of fuel or diesel oil	Spray stumps soon after cutting. Wet thoroughly, including all exposed bark	Good results can be obtained with applications made during dormant or growing season. Wet entire stump thoroughly to the ground. This means spraying until run-off is noticeable. Best results will be obtained on stumps 1 in. in diameter or larger.

Basal bark treatment in the dormant or growing season to control brush and small trees	Esteron 245	1 pt in 3 gal of fuel or diesel oil	Apply at any time including the winter months. Particularly good results have been obtained from late winter and early spring applications	Apply spray to the stems from the ground line up to 12–18 inches above the ground. Wet this area *thoroughly* on all sides. This means spraying until run-off is noticeable. Do not allow spray drift to touch desirable trees, ornamentals or crop plants. Low spray pressures are desirable.
	Esteron Brush Killer	1½ pt in 3 gal of fuel or diesel oil		
Grass control	Sodium TCA 90%	50–100 lb per acre for Bermuda and quack grass. 100–150 lb per acre for Johnson grass. 75–125 lb per acre for para grass	Apply under conditions of favorable soil moisture since the effect of TCA is largely through the roots.*	Sodium TCA 90% should be mixed with sufficient water to ensure solubility and uniform spray application. One pound will readily dissolve in one gal. of water.

* For quack grass, best results are obtained with applications immediately following plowing and cultivation and the lower rate of 50 lb per acre may be used. For Johnson grass, late fall applications of 50–75 lb appears promising. Allow 60 days or longer after application before planting most crops.

Note: For mixing small quantities of spray, one tablespoonful in 1½ gal of water is about equivalent to one qt in 100 gal of water. One-quarter lb of Sodium TCA 90% per 100 sq ft is about equal to 100 lb per acre.

Warning: Weed killer formulations will kill or seriously injure many desirable forms of vegetation. Do not use when there is any hazard from drifting spray mists. Always consult container label for application directions and precautions. Certain weed killer formulations are toxic and present health hazards when swallowed, allowed to contact the skin, or breathed in the form of vapors or spray mists.

TABLE 6.2/ATLACIDE CONTROL CHART

Kind of Weed	When to Treat for Best Results	Spray Application			Dry Application
		Dilution per Gal of Water	Approx. Amount Sol. per Sq Rod	Approx. Amount Sol. per 100 Sq Ft	Approx. Amount per Sq Rod
Bindweed Canada thistle Horse nettle Russian knapweed	Early fall treatment is usually preferable, but best time varies in different areas.	1½ lb	3-3½ gal	1-1½ gal	5-8 lb
Nut grass	When plants are fully developed. Make re-treatment as needed.	1½ lb	1-2 gal	⅓-⅔ gal	Spray
Johnson grass	Midsummer or late fall. Early fall treatment is usually	1-1½ lb	3-8 gal	1-3 gal	Spraying recommended
Bermuda grass Quack grass			3-4 gal	1-1½ gal	
Willows Brush Choke cherry	Abundant foliage, heavy vigorous growth. Full foliage, but growth moderate, or second growth after cutting.	1-1½ lb	As required for coverage	As required for coverage	Spraying recommended
Poison ivy	When plants are in full foliage.	¾-1 lb	as above	as above	Spray
St. Johnswort	When plants are in full foliage	1½ lb	1-2 gal	⅔ gal	2 lb
Sow thistle	At the leaf cluster state, as stems are beginning to form.	1½ lb	2 gal	⅔ gal	Spray
Honeysuckle	During the growing season.	1 lb	3 gal	1 gal	Spray
Leafy spurge	Before blooming. Repeat.	1-1½ lb	3-4 gal	1-1½ gal	Spray
Blackberry and other brambles	When in full foliage—follow up treatment in fall.	1½ lb	As required for coverage	As required for coverage	Spraying recommended
Puncture vine and other annual weeds	Before seed forms.	1 lb	2 gal	⅔ gal	Spraying recommended

CHAPTER SEVEN

SOIL EROSION

The control of soil erosion is a major problem in many areas. Many maintenance problems stem from the original poor construction of roads and the inadequate attention given to slopes and drainage areas.

GENERAL PRINCIPLES OF EROSION CONTROL

Methods to correct these deficiencies are available and known, but are too often ignored. Briefly, these methods are as follows:

1. It is possible on most soils to establish good vegetative cover without the use of topsoil. This may seem a controversial point, but it has been done for several years in the TVA area, and the New York State Department of Public Works has reported similar success in its final report on "Roadside Vegetative Cover."

When topsoil is used, most grading operators try to finish a slope by leaving it as smooth as possible, instead of leaving it rough, with ridges along the contour to slow and catch the runoff water.

Again, topsoil is usually dumped along the top of the slope and spread with a bulldozer. This leaves the heaviest deposit of topsoil at the top of the slope, and only a thin layer of soil at the bottom.

Combine these two situations—a smooth surface and an unbalanced layer of topsoil—with a heavy rainfall, and no amount of mulch, seeding, brush, or grass will keep all that soil from sliding to the bottom.

2. Practically all soils can be made to support a vegetative cover by initial fertilization and liming, and an adequate schedule of refertilization.

3. Rock outcropping should not be blasted away, but should be left to appear as natural as possible.

4. Deep gullies should first be checked with adequate dams, or heavy brush or rock.

5. Diversion ditches should be dug at the top to minimize the amount of runoff across the face of the slope.

6. Soil should be analyzed, to ascertain the kind of grass it will support, and the amount of fertilizer and lime needed.

7. On poor soils it may be necessary to add organic matter, such as straw or sawdust. Although costly as an initial expense, this operation is essential, and will pay dividends in the long run.

8. Unless the steepness of a slope requires a fast-germinating seed such as Italian ryegrass, it is a good idea to limit the varieties of grasses to one or two good ones.

9. If topsoil or other soils are added to a slope, the minimum uniform depth should be 2 in. This layer should be compacted into the existing soil by means of a sheepsfoot roller, and before compaction the slope should be fertilized, limed, and mulched with hay or straw. Not more than two tons of mulch should be used per acre. At the same time that it compacts the topsoil into the slope, the sheepsfoot roller will mix the fertilizer and lime into the soil and anchor the straw in place. After rolling, the slope can be seeded.

10. A very economical method of stabilizing slopes is the use of a seeding and mulching machine, which performs these operations in two steps. The machine will first blow the seed and fertilizer mix onto the slope, or, using an improved method, incorporate water into the mixture and force it onto the slope hydraulically. In the second step, the mulch is blown onto the slope from the mulching machine, and kept in place with asphalt sprayed onto the straw as it comes from the blower. As it settles on the slope, each piece of straw adheres to its neighbor. The effectiveness of this mat has been demonstrated many times. Labor and material costs have been reduced as much as 75 per cent by use of this machine.

11. A mulch is essential to controlling or stabilizing slopes. Sometimes the mulch alone is sufficient, but some protection must be given seeds, and water in the slope must be conserved.

12. Mowing should be done as needed, but the slope should never be cut closer than 2 in. and preferably 3 in.

KINDS OF SOIL EROSION

The two common forms of soil erosion are sheet erosion and gullying.

Sheet erosion

In sheet erosion—or "sheet washing"—heavy rainfall loosens the soil on bare slopes and moves it down the slope by the flow of excess water. As the soil moves, its volume and velocity are increased, and it may appear to be moving in one continuous sheet. Such erosion is often not readily discernible, since it progresses slowly, removing the most fertile topsoil over a period of years. Sometimes it can be detected only by the gradual change in the color of the soil and by the appearance of "galled" spots in the field. Sheet-eroded areas can be treated by plowing, seeding, and mulching. If soil and moisture conditions are poor, fertilization and mulching are advisable. By disking the fertilizer and mulch into the soil before seeding, soil conditions can be greatly improved.

On long, easy slopes, contour furrows may allow greater absorption of water and also provide a planting site for trees. On long, steep slopes where terraces or diversion terraces are impractical, brush placed in strips along the contour of the slope and wired down will slow the flow of water. (See detailed control specifications at the close of this chapter.)

Gully erosion

Gullies are continuous trenches cut through the surface structure of the soil, normally by continuous heavy sheet washing. The first indication of gullying is frequently a concentration of rills in the natural depressions of the slope, or a uniform spreading of rills over the slope.

Major gullies occur when erosion breaks through the surface soil and into the subsoil. Such gullies will increase in size and depth until bedrock or a nonerodable channel has been reached.

In order to plan successful control treatment of major gullies, the following steps are necessary:

1. A study of the drainage area
2. A computation of runoff into each gully
3. Diversion of runoff
4. Construction of channel control works

To control a major gully successfully, it is first necessary to stop the cutting in at the bottom and at the head of the gully. The control measures needed to accomplish this will depend upon the volume and velocity of water draining into the gully.

Sometimes minor changes in the drainage area will permit a simpler method of control in the gully. Such measures might include planting or seeding barren areas above the gully, protecting the area from grazing, or constructing terraces or contour furrows. If it is possible to divert all the drainage from the gully, control measures may be limited to sloping the banks and seeding or planting, or stabilizing the flow line of the channel with brush.

METHODS OF EROSION CONTROL WITH PERMANENT STRUCTURES

Soil-saving dams

Soil-saving dams are used chiefly in large gullies or narrow draws. In order to justify their cost, a large basin should be created on the upstream side to catch and hold a substantial quantity of soil. A drainage area in excess of 50 acres should have a dam designed with a greater factor of safety than is usually needed for erosion control measures.

Excavation

All sod, stumps, roots, and large stones must be removed from the foundation of the dam before the fill is started, and the surface of the foundation should be scarified. If the dam is to impound water to a depth of more than 5 ft, or if the foundation of fill material contains a large proportion of sand or gravel, a trench 2 to 4 ft wide should be cut to a depth of 1 to 2 ft along the axis of the dam to prevent seepage and allow for construction of a core. The trench should be cut with vertical side walls to break the seam between the natural ground and the fill.

Construction

The dam should be not less than 2 ft wide at the top, with the side slopes constructed on a minimum slope of 2:1. The fill for the dam should be made of earth that is free from roots, large stones, stumps, and debris. It should be applied in well-compacted, 6-in. layers. If the nature of the soil or the height of the dam requires the construction of a core, the core should be of impervious clay, tamped lightly in 6-in. layers. It should be kept slightly higher than the main body of the dam until the full height of the dam has been reached. Approximately 20 per cent should be allowed for shrinkage in the fill, and the downstream face of the dam should be sodded or seeded as soon as possible. The upstream face of the dam should be riprapped.

Construction of spillway

Spillways, whether concrete or masonry, should be installed before the earth fill, and as the fill progresses, impervious clay should be packed tightly against the wing walls of the structure. Emergency spillways may be provided by the construction of a diversion channel leading from the upper side of the dam to a stabilized outlet in a heavily sodded or wooded area.

GROUNDS MAINTENANCE HANDBOOK

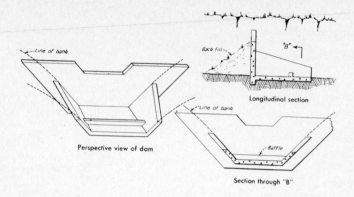

Line of bank

Back Fill

'B'

Longitudinal section

Perspective view of dam

Line of bank

Baffle

Section through "B"

Fig. 7.1   Concrete dam

Concrete dams

Concrete and masonry check dams are used in channels where watershed conditions do not permit the establishment of controlling vegetation. When properly located and constructed, permanent check dams provide an effective control of channels carrying a large volume of water. Such dams may be constructed to a height not exceeding 4 ft, measured from the top of the apron to the bottom of the spillway notch, without the use of reinforcing.

A 1:1 slope should be established along the gully banks for the entire length of the dam and apron, and the sloping extended to the full height of the dam. The apron sloping should extend 2 ft up the banks at the dam, tapering to a minimum of 1 ft at the lip of the apron. The excavation for the dam should be 1 to 2 ft deep, and should extend into the banks 2 to 4 ft. The thickness of the dam at the base should be equal to or greater than the thickness at the top (minimum 6 in.). The apron excavation should permit the top of the finished apron floor to be flush with, or slightly below, the normal gully floor. See Fig. 7.1.

Construction

Forms for concrete dams should be built of smooth plank, well braced, and anchored to prevent spreading or sliding. The concrete, using a 1:2:4 mix, should be poured evenly and well tamped or "spaded" on both faces of the dam to eliminate voids. After the forms are removed, the surface of the concrete should be covered with moist straw, soil, or burlap for at least seven days.

The upstream face and wings of the dam should be backfilled at a minimum slope of 2:1 immediately after the forms are removed. This backfill should be thoroughly tamped to prevent seepage.

If no reinforcing is used, the dam must be poured as a unit, and no part should be allowed to "set" before the next section is poured. The length of the apron should be at least one and one-half times the height of the dam, measured from the top of the spillway notch, and should be at least as wide at the lip as at the base of the dam.

The side walls of the apron should be set below the surface of the gully banks on a slope of not less than 1:1. They should be at least 2 ft high at the dam, and may taper to a minimum of 1 ft at the lip. A stilling basin not less than 6 in. deep should be constructed across the apron. The baffle should be built as a part of the apron, at a distance from the dam equal to two-thirds the length of the apron. The entire apron, including the baffle, should be poured as a unit, and the finished concrete should be protected for not less than seven days by a covering of moist straw, earth, or burlap.

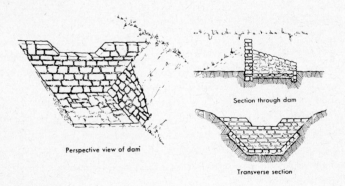

Section through dam

Perspective view of dam

Transverse section

Fig. 7.2 Masonry dam

Masonry dams

Masonry dams require the same excavation as described for concrete dams, except that the minimum thickness at the top of the dam should be 12 in. See Fig. 7.2.

Construction

The bottom of the excavation should be covered with a layer of mortar (1:3 mix) 1 in. to 2 in. thick. Masonry work is begun on the top of this layer of mortar and continued until top of dam is reached. As soon as the dam is completed, it should be covered with moist straw, earth, or burlap for not less than seven days. Upstream face and wings should be backfilled as required for concrete dams.

The apron should be at least one and one-half times the height of the dam, measured from the top of the spillway to the normal gully floor. A toe wall should be set at the lip of the apron, extending 6 in. into the ground below the floor of the apron, and into the banks not less than 1 ft beyond the width of the spillway of the dam. The top of the finished toe wall should be flush with or slightly below the normal floor of the channel. The apron floor should be at least 1 ft wider than the bottom of the spillway notch, and should be at least as wide at the lip as at the base of the dam.

The side walls of the apron should be set below the surface of the gully banks on a slope of not less than 1:1, at least 2 ft high at the dam, and tapering to a minimum of 1 ft at the lip. A stilling basin not less than 6 in. deep should be built by excavating sufficiently between the toe wall and the base of the dam to permit the floor of the apron to be 6 in. below the top of the toe wall, or by constructing a 6-in. baffle across the apron.

Concrete and masonry checks

Checks are usually constructed of concrete and masonry from 6 to 8 in. thick and 12 to 18 in. high. They should be spaced so that the top of one check is slightly higher than the bottom of the one next above, thus eliminating the need for apron construction. Checks are useful in controlling broad, shallow gullies, highway ditches, and terrace outfall ditches of low gradient. They are seldom feasible for grades exceeding 6 per cent.

METHODS OF EROSION CONTROL WITH SEMIPERMANENT STRUCTURES

Check dams constructed of loose rock may be classed as semipermanent structures, and are frequently used as substitutes for check dams of less durable materials. These dams are not recommended for use on areas that are to be restored to agricultural use, since they may interfere with the use of agricultural implements. The average loose-rock dam is about 3 ft high and 8 ft long. See Fig. 7.3.

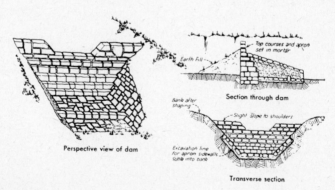

Perspective view of dam

Section through dam

Transverse section

Fig. 7.3 Combination masonry and loose-rock dam

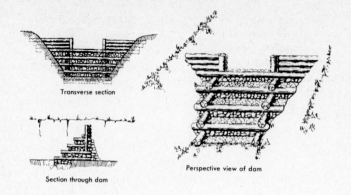

Transverse section

Section through dam

Perspective view of dam

Fig. 7.4　Rock-filled log crib dam

Crib dams

Logs and fieldstone can be used to construct semipermanent structures called crib dams. These are generally used in controlling large gullies carrying a heavy runoff. The logs are used to hold the stones in place until they become settled and sealed into stable position by the collection of silt. An average rock-filled log crib is 8 ft high and 20 ft long, and contains 400 cu ft of rock and 250 lin ft of logs not less than 8 in. in diameter. See Fig. 7.4.

All loose rock, soil, and debris should be cleaned out of the gully bottom at the site of the dam. Dig a trench of sufficient size and depth to hold two logs, laid one upon the other, across the gully at the toe of the dam. The top log should be flush with the normal gully floor. Extend the trench and logs at least 3 ft into the gully banks. Excavation for the first layer of straw and rock should be made for a distance of 3 ft behind the top log.

Building of the dam should be started from the front or toe. Place two logs, one on top of the other, in the excavation across the gully. Bedrock in straw behind the logs to the level of the top log. Secure two tie logs parallel to the gully to the top toe log. Place these tie logs against the gully bank. The space between tie logs should never be less than the width of the spillway. Place the first cross log back of the toe log at a distance equal to the diameter of the tie logs. This will produce a 1:1 slope on the face of the dam. Fill the space behind this log with rock, bedded in straw. Place the larger rocks in the face of the dam so that water action will not force them out between the logs.

Repeat this performance until the desired height of the dam is reached. Set upright posts in the rock base of the dam to a minimum depth of 4 ft in order to hold the logs of the spillway section. Attach logs for the spillway to the uprights and extend into the gully banks 2 to 4 ft, measured at right angles to the slope.

Do not place any backfill behind the dam, but rather allow the water to filter through the layers of rock and straw, filling the voids with silt.

Concrete or rock paving

Erosion may be controlled in gullies carrying runoff at high speeds by lining the channel with concrete or rock. Such construction is especially useful in highway or terrace outfall ditches on steep grades and from high embankments. Loose rock paving without grouting may be used where the runoff does not reach a high speed, or where the grade does not exceed 15 per cent.

METHODS OF EROSION CONTROL WITH TEMPORARY STRUCTURES

Temporary structures are used primarily to establish vegetation in gullied areas. Their effective life must be consistent with the time required for the growth of vegetation on the site.

Log or plank check dams

Log or plank dams are used in gullies which have large volumes of runoff but which may be stabilized by certain types of vegetation. Since vegetation eventually attains control, the spacing and height of these structures must be such that "breaks" will not occur in the gully bottom after the structure has decayed. A desirable height is 2 ft, measured from the top of the apron to bottom of the spillway notch. The maximum height should be 3 ft. See Fig. 7.5 and 7.6.

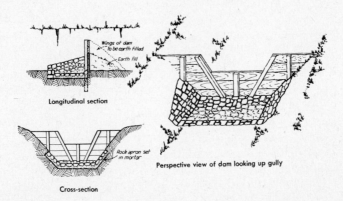

Longitudinal section

Cross-section

Perspective view of dam looking up gully

Fig. 7.5   Plank dam with rock apron

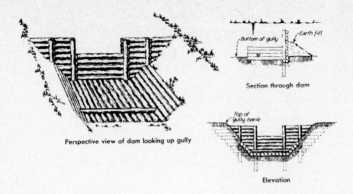

Perspective view of dam looking up gully

Bottom of gully

Earth fill

Section through dam

Top of gully bank

Elevation

Fig. 7.6   Log dam with log apron

Excavation

Slope the gully banks to a 1:1 slope for the entire length of the dam and apron. Sloping should extend up the sides of the gully to the full height of the dam, tapering down to a minimum of 1 ft at the lip of the apron. The excavation for the dam should be 1 to 2 ft deep, and should extend into the banks 2 to 4 ft, measured at right angles to the slope.

Construction

Set two upright posts to a minimum depth of 2 ft in the downstream edge of the excavation, in order to form the sides of the spillway notch of the dam. Set an additional post in the center, if the width of the spillway notch exceeds 6 ft. Set additional posts, at intervals not exceeding 6 ft, between the spillway posts and the points where the top cross logs or planks enter the gully banks. Place a 2-in. layer of straw, grass, or leaves in the bottom of the excavation to prevent leakage under the dam. Place horizontal logs or planks of sufficient length to span the entire width of the gully on the up-stream side of the posts. Short top logs or planks extending into the gully banks and fastened to the central upright posts form the spillway notch. If logs are used, the space between the logs should not exceed 0.5 in., and should be chinked tightly with straw or grass. Backfill, on a 2:1 slope, the upstream face and wings of the dam.

The length of the apron should be at least one and one-half times the height of the dam, measured from the top of the spillway to the normal gully floor, and should be at least 1 ft wider than the bottom of the spillway notch and at least as wide at the lip as at the base of the dam.

A toe log or wall should be set at the lip of the apron, and extend into the ground 6 in. below the floor of the apron, and into the bank not less than 1 ft beyond the width of the spillway of the dam. The top of the finished toe log should be flush with, or slightly below, the normal floor of the channel. The side walls should be set below the surface of the gully banks on a slope of not less than 1:1. They should be at least 2 ft high at the dam, and may taper to 1 ft at the lip of the apron.

Construct a stilling basin of not less than 6 in. deep, by excavating between the toe wall and the base of the dam sufficiently to permit the floor of the apron to be 6 in. below the top of the toe log or wall, or by a 6-in. baffle across the apron. Build the baffle at a distance from the dam equal to two-thirds of the length of the apron.

Brush or wire check dams

The most general and effective use of brush or wire check dams is to collect and hold silt and moisture in gully bottoms, thereby providing favorable growing conditions for vegetation. The effective height should be held to approximately 18 in., with ample over-fall protection provided. Height should never exceed 2 ft. See Fig. 7.7.

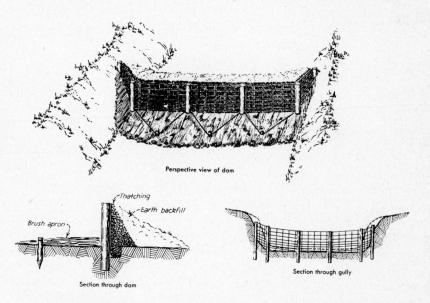

Fig. 7.7 Wire dam

Failures of brush or wire dams are usually due to one of three causes: (1) improper packing of brush or backfill, which produces leakage through the dam; (2) insufficient spillway space, which produces end-cutting, or (3) excessive height, which produces undercutting.

SOIL EROSION

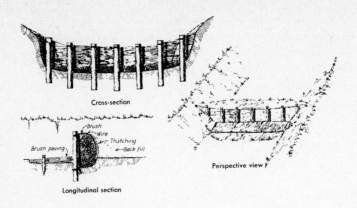

Cross-section

Brush
Wire
Thatching
Back Fill
Brush paving

Perspective view

Longitudinal section

Fig. 7.8   Single-post brush dam

Single-post brush dams

Slope the gully banks for the entire length of the dam and apron on a 1:1 slope, and extend sloping up the sides of the gully to the full height of the dam. See Fig. 7.8.

The base of the dam should usually be excavated 12 to 18 in. wide, and never less than 6 in. The excavation should extend into the gully banks from 6 to 18 in. at right angles to the slope. The bottom of the excavation should be rounded to the curve desired in the finished dam, so that the finished structure will have a minimum weir depth of 9 in.

Construction

Space posts 2.5 ft apart, and 18 to 24 in. deep, in the downstream face of the excavation. A single wire should be fastened to each post near the base before it is set in the ground. This wire will be used in tightening brush. Cover the bottom of the excavation with a layer of straw, grass, or leaves 2 or 3 in. thick. Place the brush lengthwise in the excavation, placing the smaller branches near the bottom. Keep the brush at a uniform height for the full length of the dam, tamping each layer for compactness. After all the brush is in place, draw the wires attached to the base of the posts across the top of the dam as tightly as possible, and secure near the top of each post. Set or cut the posts so that they will not extend above the top of the dam.

For apron construction, excavate the gully bottom to the approximate shape of the dam. Extend the excavation up on the banks to the full height of the dam. The excavation should equal in length one and one-half times the height of the dam.

Construct the apron by placing a layer of brush 4 to 6 in. thick in the excavation below the dam. Lay the brush parallel to the gully, with the butt

GROUNDS MAINTENANCE HANDBOOK

ends extending into the base of the dam. Secure the brush by means of a wire to stakes set 12 to 18 in. apart in rows across the apron. Set the stakes and drive them part way in before the wire is attached. After the wire is fastened and the brush is in place, the stakes can be driven all the way, drawing the wire tightly across the brush.

Double-post brush dams

Double-post brush dams require the same excavation as single-post brush dams, with a minimum weir depth of 9 in. See Fig 7.9.

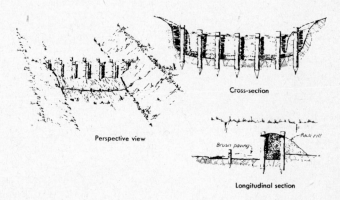

Perspective view

Cross-section

Longitudinal section

Fig. 7.9   Double-post brush dam

Construction

Place a layer of hay, straw, or leaves, 2 to 3 in. thick, in the trench. Drive stakes along the bottom of the trench at intervals of 2 or 3 in. Drive stakes at intervals of 2 ft, set opposite each other, for the entire length of the dam. Place brush as for single-post dams. After all the brush is in place, fasten a wire securely to the top of the stakes and drive them to their final depth. Backfill as for single-post brush dams.

Wire check dams

Slope the gully bank for the entire length of the dam and apron on a 1:1 slope, and extend sloping up the sides of the gully to the full height of the dam. Dig a trench 6 to 12 in. deep and 12 in. wide across the bottom of the gully. The wing trenches may be made upstream into the banks of the gully at a 45 degree angle to the cross trench, with a minimum depth equal to the height of the finished dam.

SOIL EROSION

Construction

Set posts 2.5 ft apart in the downstream edge of the excavation to a depth of 18 to 24 in. The wing or anchor posts should be set to a depth of 2.5 to 3 ft in the gully banks. Allow a minimum weir depth of 12 in. in the center of the dam. Fasten the wire to the upstream face of the posts, and thatch with straw, grass, fine brush, or burlap, or place a well-compacted layer of brush 12 to 18 in. thick on the upstream side of the dam. Backfill on a slope of 2:1 with clay or topsoil.

For apron construction, see single-post brush dams.

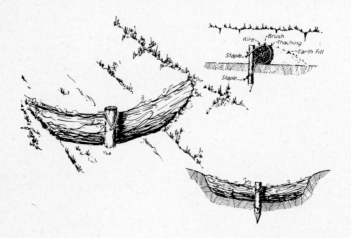

Fig. 7.10   Bundled brush check

Brush checks

In gullies carrying a very small amount of runoff, brush checks can be used. It is seldom necessary to do any excavation, and the checks serve as planting sites. The principal features of brush check construction are: maximum height of construction, 1 ft; little or no excavation in the gully bottom; simple devices for holding brush in place. All brush checks should be backfilled with clay or topsoil well compacted. See Fig. 7.10.

Brush paving

Brush paving is used largely in stabilizing gully channels to permit the growth of vegetation, and is especially good for use on steep slopes in gullies carrying a considerable runoff. The effective life of brush paving is about one to three years, and vegetation must be established quickly. See Fig. 7.12.

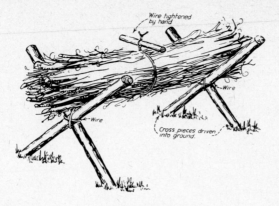

Fig. 7.11   Brush bundler

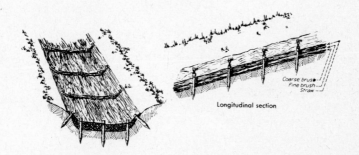

Fig. 7.12   Brush paving

The gully bottom should be rounded or flattened, and the gully banks sloped to a minimum of 1:1 above the expected height of the water in the channel during storm periods. All loose earth in the channel should be removed or well compacted by tamping.

The materials for brush paving are: green cedar or pine brush; or hardwood, if cedar or pine is not available. Use only branches of 1-in. diameter or less; stakes 18 to 24 in. long of durable wood; straw, grass, or leaves; and 9–14 gage wire.

Construction

A 1-in. layer of straw, grass, or leaves should be placed in the gully for the full width of the paving. The brush should be laid with the butt ends downstream, using the small branches in the bottom layer. Brush should be placed to provide a finished thickness of 1.5 to 2 in., after the paving has been wired down. The stakes should be set at intervals of 18 to 24 in., and partially driven. Wire should be fastened securely around each stake and the stakes driven in, to draw the wire down tightly across the brush.

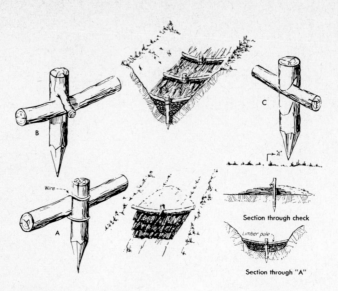

Fig. 7.13 Flow-line staking and brush checks

Flowline staking

This is a variation of brush paving which can be used in gullies carrying less than 5 cu ft per second of runoff. See Fig. 7.13.

Gullies adaptable to this method of control seldom require excavation.

Green cedar, pine, or hardwood brush; timber poles 1 to 2 in. in diameter; 18- to 24-in. stakes of durable wood; and 9- to 14-gage wire are the materials used.

Construction

Cover the bottom of the gully with fine brush and larger brush, placed in the same manner as for brush paving. Hold the brush down by timber poles laid crosswise of the gully and drawn down tightly to a single stake set in the center of the channel, or stake and wire brush as in brush paving at intervals of 4 to 6 ft. If hardwood brush is used, the branches should be laid crosswise in the channel.

Strip matting

Strip matting may be used on steep, sheet-eroded hillsides, to check runoff and to provide a protected area for planting. Construction procedure is to place layers of brush 1.5 to 2 in. thick and 4 to 6 ft wide at intervals along the contour, depending upon the length and steepness of the slope. The strip is formed by placing a 3- to 4-in. layer of brush with butt ends downhill. If a straw mulching is used, a 1-in. layer of brush is sufficient. The strip is then staked and wired at intervals of approximately 4 ft.

Diversion ditches

Diversion ditches are used primarily for the reduction and control of run-off, and as an aid to vegetative control. They are used to advantage in diverting runoff from major gullies or from critical gully heads and sheet-eroded areas, thereby permitting a simpler form of control. They should not be used unless they can be emptied into a safe and stabilized outlet.

Construction

The grade should not exceed 1 per cent. A fall of 4 to 6 in. per 100 ft is usually satisfactory. Where active gullies carrying a large volume of water enter the diversion ditch, the grade should be increased for a distance of several feet above the entrance of the ditch in order to prevent the piling up of silt at the intersection point. The increase in grade should not exceed 1 per cent.

The ditch should be at least 2 ft wide, with sides sloped as much as possible. They should be constructed to carry one and one-half times the computed runoff. The additional capacity will allow for silting in the channel.

Contour furrows

Contour furrows create a series of basins to catch and hold water. The water thus caught reduces the runoff and permits a greater absorption of moisture for the use of vegetation. The furrows also serve as ground preparation for planting trees or sod. Their most practical use is in pasture or grass land which has a minimum of 60 per cent ground cover.

The effectiveness of contour furrows may be protected by raising the plow at intervals of 20 to 50 ft, or by the construction of dams across the furrow at specified intervals. The advantage in so dividing the furrow is that, should a break occur in any weak sector, the entire furrow will not be drained to flood the furrow below.

Contour furrows are constructed with an ordinary turning plow or hillside plow. The furrow will function more efficiently if all the soil is turned downhill. Contour lines should be run with a level and stakes set at intervals of 25 to 50 ft, depending upon the slope.

Plowing and mulching

In gullies which average less than 4 ft in depth the most effective method for quick control is to plow in the sides and fill the gully. The loose soil, when covered with a layer of protective straw, hay, or brush, makes an excellent planting or seedbed site.

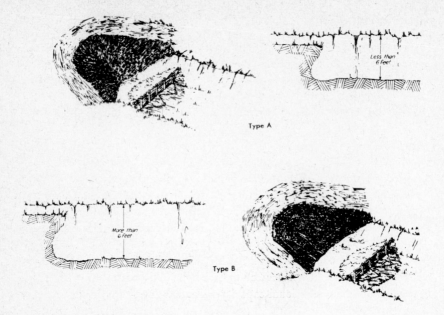

Fig. 7.14 Gully head treatment for less than half acre drainage

GULLY HEAD TREATMENTS

There are four classifications of gully heads, according to drainage area and depth of gully at the head. See Fig. 7.14 and 7.15.

1. Type A: Gully heads less than 6 ft high and draining less than one-half acre. The head should be sloped to a 1.5:1 slope. Ground should be broken to a minimum depth of 6 in. for 5 ft back from the head, and completely encircling it. The head should then be mulched with straw with a light covering of cedar brush; with straw with a light covering of hardwood brush; or with hardwood brush alone. The 5-ft flat should be mulched with straw alone; with finely chopped cedar brush alone; or with finely chopped hardwood brush alone.

2. Type B: Gully heads more than 6 ft high and draining less than one-half acre. The head should be sloped to a 1.5:1 slope, with the ground broken to a minimum depth of 6 in. for 8 ft back from the head, and completely encircling it. The head should then be matted with straw with a covering of cedar brush; with straw with a covering of hardwood brush; with cedar brush alone; or with hardwood brush alone. This matting should be tied down by driving into it stakes 5 ft apart in rows 5 ft apart, with wires fastened to the stakes, the wires running both vertically and horizontally so that 5-ft squares are formed. The stakes should be long enough to reach into the ground.

GROUNDS MAINTENANCE HANDBOOK

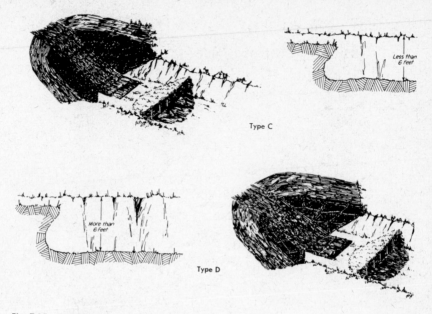

Type C

Type D

Fig. 7.15 Gully head treatment for more than half acre drainage

The mulching on the 8-ft flat above the head need not be fastened down. Mulching materials may be straw alone; finely-chopped cedar brush alone; or finely-chopped hardwood brush alone.

3. Type C: Gully heads less than 6 ft high draining more than one-half acre. The treatment is the same as in Item 1 above, except for a flume constructed down the flow line, as follows:

Excavation for flume should be made on a 2:1 slope, with the sides on a 1.5:1 slope. Excavation should be in hard soil. The bottom of the excavation is then broken to a depth of 2 to 3 in. and mulch and fertilizer are mixed with loose earth. Treat the sides in the same manner, and sod sides and bottom with Bermuda. Hold sod in place with woven wire or brush. A wire or brush dam should be placed 6 ft from the bottom of the flume to form a 6-ft stilling basin 1 ft deep.

4. Type D: Gully heads more than 6 ft high draining more than one-half acre. The treatment is the same as in Item 2 above, except that a flume of the same specifications as shown under Item 3 is constructed.

EROSION CONTROL FOR HIGHWAY SLOPES

The maintenance of road slopes is an expensive item in general highway maintenance. Soil eroded from a cut slope is usually deposited in a position blocking drainage ditches, filling culverts and underground drains, or di-

SOIL EROSION

Fig. 7.16 Board-faced, undrained terraces on 1:1 cut slopes are subject to undermining.

rectly on the roadway, where it causes considerable damage to the pavement and creates serious traffic hazards. The cost of cleaning up this sloughed material is a considerable item in all road maintenance budgets. In addition, an eroded cut slope is undesirable because it is unattractive. See Fig. 7.16.

Many methods of control have been tried, and some have proved successful. The most common methods are described below:

Diversion and intercepting ditches

The most common method of reducing the amount of runoff water pouring over a cut slope is to construct an intercepting ditch at the top of each cut slope. This restricts the amount of runoff water which could cause erosion on the slope, and limits soil loss to the amount falling directly on the face. These ditches lose their value, however, if they are not kept clean to allow the free flow of water. See Fig. 7.17 and 7.18.

GROUNDS MAINTENANCE HANDBOOK

Fig. 7.17 An unattractive intercepting ditch. Culverts may be clogged with eroded material when this type of soil loss occurs

Fig. 7.18 A broad, flattened intercepting ditch. Vegetation may be easily established here, and a large volume of water is carried without damage.

Low cuts are not subject to serious or rapid soil loss. Runoff water accumulating on low cuts does not attain the volume or velocity to move much soil, although the process of soil loss, while slow, is sure. If high cuts were therefore broken up into a series of low banks or terraces, the same soil loss characteristics would exist. The terraces must be so constructed that they will intercept runoff water and lead the water to one side, where it can be carried to the bottom of the cut in paved ditches or pipes.

SOIL EROSION

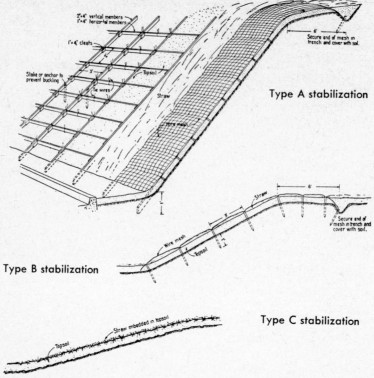

Type A stabilization

Type B stabilization

Type C stabilization

Fig. 7.19   Slope stabilization

Type A stabilization, for 1:1 or flatter slopes
1. Lay soil retaining frames on slope and nail securely. On slopes over 15 ft high (slope distance) anchor frames to slope to prevent buckling.
2. Attach 14-gage galvanized tie wires for anchoring wire mesh.
3. Fill frames with moist topsoil and compact the soil.
4. Spread straw about 6 in. deep over the slope.
5. Cover straw with 14-gage 4-in. mesh galvanized reinforcing wire. Secure mesh tightly to frames with tie wires.
6. Secure wire mesh at least 6 ft back of top of slope.
7. Plant ground cover plants through straw into topsoil.

Type B stabilization, for 1.5:1 or flatter slopes
1. Cover slope with moist topsoil and compact to about 6-in. thickness.
2. Spread straw about 6 in. deep over slope.
3. Cover straw with 2-in. mesh galvanized poultry netting or 4-in. mesh galvanized reinforcing wire.
4. Anchor wire mesh to 2 by 2 18 in. stakes spaced 3 ft apart in staggered rows with tie wires. Tying is preferred to nailing the stakes.
5. Plant ground cover through straw into topsoil.
6. If slope is to be seeded, sow seed before placing straw.

Type C stabilization, for 1.5:1 or flatter slopes
1. Roughen cut slopes on a rough contour with a scarifier or cultivator type of implement, in a series of longitudinal grooves or corrugations.
2. Cover cut slopes with about 3 to 6 in. of topsoil. If topsoil is not available, cultivate slope 4 to 6 in. deep and apply fertilizer. Fill slopes will not ordinarily require topsoil or cultivation unless very sterile or compacted.
3. Cover slope with straw at the rate of about 4 tons per acre. Embed straw into loose soil with a sheepsfoot roller.
4. Plant ground cover through straw into topsoil.
5. If slope is to be seeded, sow seed before placing straw.

The terrace method works very well, provided the terraces are kept clean so that they drain at all times. The chief objection to this method is that the cost of construction is high, for any but exceptional slopes.

Protecting slopes by hydro seeding and asphalt mulching

New equipment is constantly being introduced on the market. In the past few years, methods of seeding, fertilizing, and mulching steep slopes and large areas have undergone radical changes. For instance, the old methods of applying straw and hay mulches by hand and then staking and tying the mulch down became so expensive that it was rapidly becoming necessary either to stop mulching altogether or to devise more economical ways of getting the job done. As a result, new machines were invented that did the job quickly and economically. See Fig. 7.19. These methods are described in detail in Chapter 2, page 44.

Use of board wattles on 1:1 slope

This method has been common in the past, but for the most part has been unsuccessful. Its main purpose was to establish favorable conditions for ground cover plants. A ditch was dug in the slope, and faced with a length of 1- by 4-in. lumber held in place by stakes, and the space between boards was backfilled with topsoil and planted. Runoff water over-topping the board facings dropped to the slope below, eroding the steep slope between terraces. Such action caused the undermining of the board facings and subsequent loss of topsoil. In general, 1:1 slopes cannot be successfully protected without extremely high construction costs. See Fig. 7.19.

Establishment of vegetative cover

The most natural and attractive method of controlling erosion on cut slopes is to establish a solid vegetative cover. Since the angle of repose of loose soil is about 1.5:1, it first becomes necessary to flatten all slopes to a minimum of 1.5:1. The flatter the slope the more successful erosion control methods will be. Details are given on Fig. 7.20.

A combination of 1.5:1 slope or a flatter, well-roughened cut face, and a relatively thin blanket of topsoil, seeded with good grass seed, properly mulched, and with mulch secured to prevent blowing away, will give adequate protection under normal conditions. However, if a heavy and prolonged rainfall occurs (2 to 4 in. in 24 hours) before the grass is established, some slippage and erosion may occur.

Fig. 7.20   Well-roughened cut slope ready to be topsoiled

Fig. 7.21   Spreading and smoothing topsoil on a roughened slope

Control of highly erosive soil types

On soils which have erosive tendencies, the above treatment is not sufficient. To solve this problem successfully, straw should be added on the topsoil before seeding, and a sheepsfoot roller should be used to compact the
straw into the topsoil, thereby increasing its water-holding capacity. The
former procedure of driving stakes through the topsoil layer into the subsoil,

in an attempt to anchor the soil and straw in place, has produced the opposite effect of increasing the tendency toward saturation and consequent slippage of the topsoil. The method described above has given satisfactory control during periods of normal rainfall, and even when rainfall exceeds 3 to 4 in. in one storm it has been successful in reducing slippage to a minimum. Detailed specifications for the most successful methods of slope erosion control are discussed at the end of this chapter, beginning on page 356.

Types of seed and ground cover planting

There are several kinds of grass and ground cover plants which have been used successfully to control erosion on highway slopes. These may be classified as annual grasses, perennial grasses, and ground cover plants.

Annual grasses

There are two annual grasses in general use—Italian ryegrass and Korean lespdeza—which provide a quick cover under practically any condition. They are usually effective during the first year, but do not provide permanent cover. They are useful as nurse crops for more permanent grasses or ground covers, and in preventing soil erosion during periods when it is impossible to establish a permanent cover.

Perennial grasses

The most common sod-producing grasses which can be used on highways are Bermuda grass, Lespedeza sericea, the fescues, Kentucky bluegrass and clover. These are fully described in Chapter 2.

Ground cover plants

Where they are practical, various ground cover plants have been used on slopes with varied success. Generally, planting road slopes to ground covers is confined to reservation roads, park roads, and freeways. The following is a list of plants which do not require routine mowing or cutting back, and which have been used with success for this purpose.

Honeysuckle, common Japanese (*lonicera japonica*)
Honeysuckle, Hall's Japanese (*lonicera japonica halliana*)
Ivy, English (*Hedera helix*)
Jasmine, winter (*Jasimum nudiflorum*)
Kudzu (*Kudzu*)
Periwinkle, bigleaf (*Vinca major*)
Periwinkle, common (*Vinca minor*)
Rockspray (*Cotoneaster horizontalis*)
Rose, prairie (*Rosa setigera*)
Rose, wichurian (*Rosa wichuriana*)

English ivy should be used only under good soil conditions, and in areas where the surrounding grounds are well landscaped. Rockspray is a good ground cover where there is a preponderance of rock outcropping. It is uneconomical to use except where landscape work is a feature.

Kudzu, while a rapid grower, a good soil builder, and an effective erosion control agent, should be used only under conditions where its growth can be controlled. It becomes a pest when allowed to spread into adjacent woods or farm lands.

EROSION CONTROL ON FILL SLOPES

Erosion on fill slopes generally goes on unnoticed until it reaches major proportions and begins to endanger the highway. By that time, extensive repairs are necessary in order to save the highway. Many methods have been tried, some successfully and others unsuccessfully. The following methods are the most common and have proved successful under certain conditions.

Control of raw fill slopes

Many fill slopes which are not highly erosive or very infertile can be stabilized very cheaply and effectively by seeding the fill before rain has compacted the soil. Timing is all important in this procedure, and unfortunately it cannot usually be attained. To counteract this element of time, straw mulches and fertilizer can be used to protect the slope until the grass is well established. Old fill slopes which have been consolidated and gullied by rainfall before being seeded generally produce poor results under the above treatment, until the gullies are filled up and straw or other humus worked into the gullies to prevent them from redeveloping before the seeds germinate.

Control of highly erosive soils on fill slopes

Where fills are made of highly erosive soils, more elaborate measures of control must be taken. These are described in detail later, but in general they are as follows:

Straw and sheepsfoot roller method

After the degree of slope has been established, a straw covering is put in place. A sheepsfoot roller is then run over the completed slope in order to compact the soil and to incorporate the straw into the top layer of soil. The roller will leave a few inches of loose, uncompacted soil on the surface, but this loose soil is mixed with the straw, forming a food seedbed. Under normal

GROUNDS MAINTENANCE HANDBOOK

Fig. 7.22   Rolling straw-covered 1½:1 slope with sheepsfoot roller

Fig. 7.23   Rolling 10-ft strip of fill slope after application of straw

conditions, a relative compaction of 89.4 per cent is obtained below the top 4 in. This degree of compaction reduces the water-holding capacity of the soil, and the tendency of the soil to liquefy is substantially reduced. If the soil is poor in fertility, fertilizer should be added before either the straw or the rolling process is done. The same procedure is followed whether the slope is topsoiled or the existing fill is treated. See Fig. 7.22 and 7.23.

SOIL EROSION

Wire mesh or brush mat method

On deep-fill slopes composed of highly erosive material, an additional anchoring effect is needed. This is usually attained by the use of wire-reinforced brush mats, straw or wire mesh mats, or brush layers, installed on the contour during fill construction. These mats and layers act as screens or filters in the event the surface straw protection breaks down. If gullies start to form, the mats or layers are exposed, and, by filtering the water and decreasing its velocity, will tend to reduce the damage. The outer edge of the mat should be left flush with the surface of the fill slope to permit use of a sheepsfoot roller in compacting the loose surface material and embedding the straw in the soil.

It is important that the brush layers should not protrude beyond the slope face. Where brush is allowed to protrude 12 in. or more from the slope, the filtering action of the brush will cause terraces to build out to the point where runoff water, overtopping the terrace, will drop straight down and strike the slope below with considerable force, gouging out the slope below the layer.

EROSION CONTROL ON HIGHWAY SHOULDERS

On highway shoulders, erosion control is limited, depending upon the type of soil and grade. It is seldom a serious problem, and generally occurs during the first year after construction and before the shoulder has become stabilized. Damage to road pavements caused by shoulder erosion may amount to a considerable sum, if allowed to go unchecked. Asphalt or bituminous surfaces have a tendency to fray or deteriorate on the edges, unless an adequate shoulder is maintained.

There are several ways by which erosion on highway shoulders may be controlled. The two most effective methods are (1) surface the shoulders with 2 to 3 in. of gravel, and (2) mulch and seed the shoulder in order to establish a turf. The latter method is effective only in climates where there is adequate rainfall during the summer months. If rills develop, a thin coating of straw should be spread over the shoulder at the rate of approximately three tons per acre, run over by a sheepsfoot roller, and then seeded. This will stabilize the shoulder in a relatively short time. Korean lespedeza or fescues are best suited for this purpose.

Expensive treatments, such as topsoiling and planting of elaborate turfs, are not necessary except under extreme conditions or in highly developed public-use areas.

EROSION CONTROL IN DRAINAGE DITCHES

Erosion in intercepting and drainage ditches is potentially dangerous to highways, and becomes very ugly. In the past, little attention has been paid to the proper construction of these ditches, and as result major erosion problems occur. Equipment is still being used that cuts a V-shaped ditch into the subsoil—an open invitation to erosion. Methods of control and construction are very simple and inexpensive, as follows:

1. The grade of drainage and intercepting ditches should never be steeper than 2 per cent. The steeper the grade, the greater the velocity of the water and the greater the soil loss from the ditch.

2. Never cut a ditch in the V-shape. Such ditches usually cut deeply into the subsoil, where it is difficult for vegetation to become established. As a result, each storm or rainfall cuts the ditch deeper and deeper, making control more and more difficult and expensive.

3. Wherever possible, form the ditch in a broad U-shape. Such ditches do not cut deeply into the subsoil and reduce to a minimum the amount of water carried in a single channel. The bottom of the ditch should be cultivated, fertilized, and seeded with a quick-growing annual grain so that protection is provided the first year after construction. Native wind-blown seeds will be caught by the grain and will quickly establish a permanent cover.

4. Wherever it is impossible to construct a broad U-shaped ditch, an alternate method can be used. Scrape a thin layer of topsoil from the slope immediately above the top of the slope face, and form it into a low, rounded berm merging into the rounded brow of the cut. A motor grader can be used for this job. Cultivate the disturbed area, and then seed both the berm and the disturbed area. Again, the fescues and Korean lespedeza are satisfactory for seeding. If the soil conditions are such that topsoil is not available, use the existing soil and add fertilizer and mulch.

5. The construction of contour ditches at the ends of cut slopes will take runoff water into dispersal areas without any soil loss.

6. Where erosion has occurred in roadside ditches, the following control measures can be taken:

a. Pack cut brush, supplemented with straw, into the ditch in order to filter the soil and slow up the runoff water to a point where it reduces the cutting action to a minimum.

b. In deep erosion ditches, construct check dams placed in such a manner that the grade from the foot of one to the top of the next does not exceed 2 per cent. Such dams may be made of concrete, stone, logs, or other available material.

c. Where right of way widths permit, and the eroded ditches are not too deep, regrade into U-shape and treat as described in Item 4 above.

MAINTENANCE OF HIGHWAY SLOPES

Too often, maintenance crews will forget or ignore highway slopes after the initial slope stabilization treatment has taken hold. Unfortunately most slopes cannot be ignored for several years. A good maintenance program of fertilization is necessary until the slopes are completely stabilized. If rills and small gullies are caught in time, they can be prevented from developing into large gullies and causing subsequent damage, not only to the slope, but also the roadbed. Weak spots should be re-treated with seed, fertilizer, and straw as they occur, and any damage caused by animals or fire should be repaired as soon as possible.

It is necessary to maintain constant vigilance in order to prevent streams of runoff water from running down over the slope face. Clogged culverts, or broken, clogged, or inadequate berms and intercepting ditches may allow a concentrated stream of water to pour down over the slope, forming large gullies very rapidly. Under such conditions, surface protection of the slope is of no value.

Sloughed material removed from gutters and shoulders should be disposed of in places where it will not cause damage to existing slopes. If such material is dumped on stabilized slopes, the entire stabilization treatment is wasted. It is usually possible to find some gully which needs filling within a reasonable hauling distance.

Since any form of slope stabilization treatment represents a sizable investment, sound economic practice justifies the expenditure of a proportionate amount to protect that investment.

DETAILED SLOPE STABILIZATION METHODS

Type A stabilization—for 1:1 or flatter slopes: The most elaborate and expensive method for stabilizing steep slopes (1:1) is the wooden grid system. This method, however, has been successful wherever tried, and is useful in slope stabilization in highly developed urban areas where a wider right of way, to allow for flatter slopes, is either impossible or too expensive to obtain. Such slopes are too steep for economical mowing and should be planted to a ground cover instead of grass.

Type B stabilization—for 1.5:1 or flatter slopes: This type of stabilization is very effective where erosion must be controlled to prevent damage to the adjacent urban property, or where a slope is constructed at the top of a retaining wall. This method is expensive, costing approximately $1.50 to $2.00 per sq yd, but gives effective protection. A thick layer of straw on top of a compacted topsoil layer, secured by anchored strips of wire mesh, effectively prevents the two types of soil movement—surface loss and slippage. Ground cover plants can be planted through this layer and soon will provide a permanent cover.

Type C stabilization—for 1.5:1 or flatter slopes: Probably the most economical method of slope stabilization is that for Type C (Fig. 7.19). On cut slopes the surface should first be roughened with a scarifier or cultivator type of machine. This roughened slope should show corrugations on a rough contour, which, when the soil becomes saturated, will tend to break up the smooth slippage plane which forms between the layer of topsoil and the subsoil. The topsoil blanket should be restricted to a thickness of 2 or 3 in. Thicker coverage will tend to become saturated and slip, and 2 or 3 in. will produce as dense a growth as a thicker layer. Over the topsoil blanket, a layer of straw is spread at the rate of 4 tons per acre. The slope is then compacted by rolling with a sheepsfoot roller. Several methods for rolling slopes with such a roller have been developed:

1. A single roller equipped with a yoke can be connected by wire cable to a power-operated drum unit on the back of a caterpillar tractor. The roller is lightened of ballast to the point where it will roll down the slope when the cable is slack, but will not cause an excessive load on the power unit when it is being pulled back to the top of the slope. The tractor is positioned at the top of the slope, broadside to the slope face. The roller is let down—the speed of descent being controlled by the power unit brake—and then pulled back. The tractor is then moved a distance equal to the width of the roller, and the process is repeated.

2. A truck crane has been used to roll low fill slopes lengthwise. Two cables are attached to the roller, one to control the position of the roller on the slope, and the other to pull it. Care must be taken to keep the axis of the roller at right angles to the direction of the pull, because a skewed roller has a tendency to pick up straw from the surface of the slope.

3. High fill slopes can be rolled with a heavily-weighted two-section sheepsfoot roller, provided a cable winch of sufficient power and braking capacity is available. A truck crane will roll slopes as much as 300 ft long. The roller, connected directly by cable to the winch, is stationed at the top of the slope, the crane boom cable is hooked to an eye attached to the roller frame, the roller is hoisted free of the slope, the truck is moved forward a distance equal to the width of the roller, the boom cable is unhooked, and the rolling is resumed.

4. When straw is spread on the completed portion of a fill slope at stages during the construction of the fill, a long-arched extension tongue has been used to connect a standard two-section sheepsfoot roller directly to the tractor drawbar. The tractor is backed to the top of the slope, and the roller is let down over the edge. The required number of round trips is made by moving the tractor forward away from the top of the slope and back for a distance equal to the length of the tongue.

SOIL EROSION

After the slope has been compacted, spread fertilzer and lime in accordance with soil tests. In fact, it is better to spread the fertilizer and lime before rolling operations begin, in order that these materials may be mixed into the soil. Seed the slope to the desired grass, depending upon local conditions.

The approximate cost of slope preparation, roughing, straw, rolling, fertilizer, and seed, but exclusive of topsoil, is $.75 per yard.

Type D stabilization—for 1.5:1 or flatter slopes, where topsoil is not available: Many of the clay soils will, if properly prepared, support certain types of grass. Where such soils exist, it is not necessary to topsoil the slope before seeding. The same procedure of roughening the slope, spreading straw, and rolling with a sheepsfoot roller can be followed, with these exceptions:

1. The roughening of cut slopes should be more thorough and deeper, in order to insure a fairly loose seedbed 2 to 3 in. deep.

2. Fertilize and lime the slope heavily. A soil test will determine the quantities and kind of fertilizer to use.

3. Increase the amount of straw from 4 tons to 6 tons per acre.

4. Roll by any of the methods previously described.

Brush layer method for stabilizing fill slopes

The brush layer method is used in stabilizing fill slopes composed of highly erosive soils. Its principal function is to minimize the formation of gullies should the surface protection fail. Installation of brush layers or mats differs from Type C methods in that a heavier application of straw and additional rolling with a sheepsfoot roller are specified. The complete stabilization treatment should be given fill slopes at stages during fill construction, so that no extensive area of unprotected slope will be exposed to damage. Each portion of the slope should be thoroughly rolled in order to obtain the maximum compaction. When brush is not readily available, the following alternates are possible:

1. Straw mat: Lay 1-in. mesh galvanized netting or fencing on the prepared fill bench surface. The mesh should extend into the fill about 5 ft. Spread straw on the mesh to such depth that after compaction the finished mat will be approximately 4 in. thick. Proceed as for brush layer.

2. Wire mesh mat: Lay 60-in. wide, 4-in. mesh, galvanized fencing on the prepared fill bench surface. On top of this lay several courses of small-mesh poultry netting. Proceed as for brush layer.

3. Wire reinforced brush mat: Lay 60-in. wide, 2- to 4-in. mesh galvanized fencing on the prepared fill bench surface. Place brush on wire, leafy ends outward, to such depth that after compaction the finished mat will be

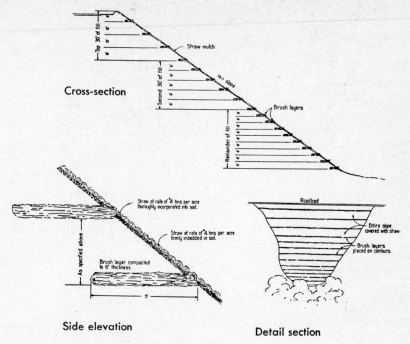

Cross-section

Side elevation

Detail section

Fig. 7.24 Brush layer method

1. At required fill elevation, smooth edge of fill bench on contour to width of mat.
2. Lay brush, leafy ends outward, flush with edge of fill to such depth that after compaction the finished mat will be approximately 6 in. thick.
3. Place additional fill material on top of brush and compact as for remainder of fill.
4. At convenient stages of fill construction, spread straw evenly over slope at rate of 4 tons per acre. Roll with a sheepsfoot roller operated vertically to the plane of the slope until straw is thoroughly incorporated into the soil. At least four round trips of the roller will be required.
5. Sow evenly over the slope a mixture of 50 per cent barley, 45 per cent rye grain, and 5 per cent alfalfa seed by weight at rate of 200 lb per acre.
6. Spread second application at rate of 4 tons per acre. Repeat rolling operation until straw is firmly embedded in soil.
7. Plant live cuttings of bacceris and willow, or cuttings and seed of hardy varieties of plants indigenous to the locality, between mats for permanent vegetative protection.
The total quality of straw applied per acre will vary according to the character of fill material. Loose, granular, disintegrated granite soil usually requires more straw per acre for an adequate cover (6 to 10 tons per acre) than does soil of a loamy character (4 to 8 tons per acre).

from 4 to 6 in. thick. Lay wire mesh on top of brush and tie edges together at 1-ft intervals, with 16-gage galvanized wire. Tie along center and at quarter points, at 3-ft intervals. Proceed as for brush layer.

On low embankments and the upper portions of high slopes, every fourth brush layer is replaced by a wire-reinforced brush mat, and as the distance from the top of the fill becomes greater, this interval is reduced until every third, and finally every second layer consists of a reinforced mat.

SOIL EROSION

359

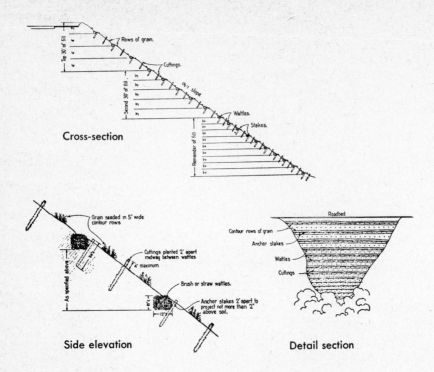

Fig. 7.25 Straw or brush wattle method for fill slope stabilization after construction.

1. After fill is constructed, beginning at toe of fill, dig a trench approximately 12 in. wide and 10 in. deep following the contour.
2. Pack leafy brush, straw, or a combination of both into a cable about 12 in. wide and 10 in. thick and lay it in the trench.
3. Drive 1 in. x 2 in. x 24 in. ± stakes at 2 ft centers below wattle and at right angles to the slope.
4. Partly cover wattle just placed with material excavated from next trench above.
5. After wattles are all placed, plant living cuttings not less than 1 in. in diameter and 24 in. to 30 in. long at 2-ft centers, in rows midway between wattles. Set cuttings in ground so that they protrude only 3 or 4 in.
6. Seed barley, rye grain, or alfalfa in rows 5 in. wide just above and just below each wattle, and broadcast additional seed evenly over surface of slope.

When wire mesh or fencing is used, the outer edge should be laid far enough inside the ultimate slope line not to be damaged during the rolling operation. Lengths of fencing should be overlapped and fastened together in order to take advantage of any structural strength and resistance to slumping which the wire may offer. The wire mat may then extend continuously for the full length of the fill, plus a short distance beyond the intersection of the embankment slope and original ground, where it should be secured.

The average cost per lin ft of these various methods, based on 1957 costs, is as follows:

Brush layers: $0.30 to $0.35
Wire reinforced brush mats: $0.85 to $1.10
Wire mesh mats (poultry netting) : $1.25 to $1.35

Straw, furnished and spread in two applications at rate of 6 tons per acre, averages about $65.00 per ton, or $390.00 per acre.

Cost of rolling or compacting slopes averages about $0.10 per sq yd, or $484.00 per acre.

Repair of failure on newly-stabilized slopes

The first winter after installation of the slope stabilization program is the critical one. Most failures occur at that time, before the vegetation had had a chance to consolidate the slope. The seriousness of the failure usually depends upon the intensity of the first severe storm. Prompt and effective repair of sections which have failed will forestall more serious trouble later.

The most frequent failure is surface slippage. If the slip starts at the top of the slope or near the top, then it is possible that seepage or percolation of water from above through a porous layer of subsoil is causing the damage. It may be intensified by standing water in a poorly graded intercepting ditch. Saturation of this sort is caused by water originating elsewhere than on the slope face, and corrective measures must be taken to repair defective drainage systems.

If the slip starts on the lower two-thirds of the slope or below, it is usually caused by saturation of the soil due to lack of sufficient compaction before the rains start. Where cut slopes have had the subsoil insufficiently roughened before the topsoil is applied, the tendency towards slippage is often increased. If such slippage occurs only in minor sections of the slope and remainder of the slope remains firm, only simple repair operations are necessary.

Failures appearing on slopes which have been given Type C stabilization treatment need not be backfilled as part of the repair process. Such procedure would only tend to increase the saturation point. Such areas need only to be fertilized and reseeded or planted. The most economical and satisfactory method for repairing surface slips is to fertilize the exposed subsoil heavily, reseed or plant, and apply a straw mulch held in place with brush or a few shovelfuls of loose soil. The sooner this method is employed, the better the chance for success.

Extensive gullies are caused by berm failures, plugged-down drains, or inadequate diversion ditches. Repairs are made only after the cause has been corrected. Usually it becomes necessary to backfill the gully, fertilize, seed, and mulch.

Repair of old eroded slopes

Old slopes which have never received a stabilization treatment and have eroded badly will require a light cultivation of the compacted soil before any other repair work can be undertaken. Such cultivation will smooth out small gullies and rills, break up channels of concentration, and make a more favorable seedbed. Cultivation should be followed by fertilization, seeding, and an adequate straw mulch.

Repair work on deeply eroded slopes is more or less a long-term proposition. Large gullies or slipouts in fill slopes usually require replacement of the material which has been lost in order to safeguard the roadbed. There are three methods which can be used which will provide control in a relatively short period of time. The first of these methods will need subsequent treatment to take care of the slumping. All slumping should be stabilized within two or three years, however.

1. A crib of logs and coarse brush is constructed at the toe of the fill to provide a solid foundation against which backfill material can settle. Loose brush is placed in the slope gullies and covered with a thick layer of backfill material. Additional brush is spread over the surface and covered with soil, and the process is repeated until the original fill contour is restored. The surface should be protected with one of the various stabilizing methods described. Since the backfill material is not compacted, there will be a certain amount of settlement and slumping. Usually such settling is near the top and can be easily backfilled and re-treated.

2. Where immediate protection is needed in order to protect a roadbed, this method will give good results. A log and brush crib is constructed at the toe of the fill to give a solid foundation against which the backfill can be compacted. Backfill material is furnished from the top, and a bulldozer is used to spread, compact, and shape this material to the original fill contour. Brush layers are installed at suitable intervals as the fill is built up. (See brush layer method detail sheet.) The completed slope is then given surface protection as described previously.

3. Another method is to use metal cribbing into which the backfill can be dumped. This is probably the most efficient and lasting method.

Reference: "Erosion Control on California State Highways." Material from this report is used by permission of the Department of Public Works, Division of Highways, State of California.

CHAPTER EIGHT

MAINTENANCE

OF ROADS

AND PARKING AREAS

MAINTENANCE OF BITUMINOUS SURFACES

Practically all of the access roads, service roads, and parking areas on public grounds have bituminous surfaces on crushed stone bases. The proper maintenance of bituminous surfaces should consist mainly of preventive measures such as skin patching, spot sealing or surface treating, when the first signs of failure appear, and not the patching of holes after they have formed. The most prevalent early sign of failure is the map cracking, checking, or alligatoring of the surface. This usually begins in small areas, and unless repaired may extend over the entire road surface, producing potholes and finally destroying the road surface and damaging the base.

Careful watching and attention to checked or alligatored spots will nearly eliminate the formation of potholes, and will result in much more effective maintenance, not only from the standpoint of cost, but also from the standpoint of service to the public. Except in unusual circumstances, such as severe ice and snow conditions or after heavy storms, there should never be a pothole of any appreciable size in a bituminous surface.

In maintaining bituminous surfaces, the following points should be observed and considered: checking, alligatoring, or map cracking; surface deterioration and raveling; potholes; corrugations or sharp irregularities; settlements and deformations; completely failed sections; slippery surfaces; shoulders and ditches.

Checking, alligatoring, or map cracking

Checking, alligatoring, or map cracking is caused by (1) soft subgrade material, (2) wet subgrade due to improper drainage, (3) drying out of the surfaces, (4) lack of sufficient thickness of the surface course, or (5) inadequate thickness of or lack of structural strength in the base course.

Repair by sealing with 0.15 to 0.25 gal per sq yd medium viscosity bituminous material and cover with 6–10 lb per sq yd No. 12 (No. 8 to $\frac{3}{8}$ in.) or No. 12-A (No. 100 to No. 4) aggregate. Rolling with a light roller is advisable, but should be omitted if the base is inclined to be yielding.

Bituminous material may be applied on small areas with hand spray. If areas are large, apply with pressure distributor, using bar widths as required. Care should be exercised not to apply an excess of bituminous material; it is always better to have too little than too much.

The principal rule about spot sealing of map-cracked areas is that it should be done whenever the telltale cracks appear, regardless of the season of the year, and regardless of whether the cracks are wet or dry. As long as the small sections of pavement surrounded by the cracks are reasonably dry, the treatment will hold and is effective in sealing out surface water.

Surface deterioration and raveling

Essentially the same defects as those described above for checking and alligatoring are responsible for surface deterioration and raveling. There is one additional cause of raveling: a deficiency of bitumen. Correction is also essentially the same, except that more bituminous material and a larger size aggregate should be used, to replace lost material.

Potholes

Either lack of proper surface maintenance or an uneven distribution of bituminous material may cause potholes. Also, movement of the base due to inadequate thickness of a yielding subgrade will cause the surface to break, thereby starting a pothole.

There are three important considerations in patching potholes: (1) Use essentially the same types of materials in the patch that are present in the base and the surface to be patched. (2) Tie or blend the patch into the area surrounding the patch; otherwise, two new potholes will develop—one on either side of the new patch. (3) Compact the material tightly into the cavity in approximately 3-in. layers, being careful to keep the surface of the layers parallel to the surface of the payment. The surface of the completed patch must conform with the surrounding pavement surface.

The three methods of patching potholes are illustrated in Fig. 8.1, 8.2, 8.3.

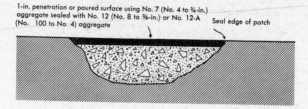

1-in. penetration or poured surface using No. 7 (No. 4 to ¾-in.) aggregate sealed with No. 12 (No. 8 to ⅜-in.) or No. 12-A (No. 100 to No. 4) aggregate   Seal edge of patch

Fig. 8.1   Repairing deep pot holes by restoring base to its original condition and then surfacing

Replacement to be comparable to original condition of base, containing the proper size of aggregate and filling material, and to be thoroughly compacted in not over 3–in. thick layers

Top of all layers to be parallel to finished grade.

The top of the restored base should be cleaned, and should be free of an excess of fine material before the bituminous surface course is placed. The application of a prime coat of bituminous material on the new base is advisable. Check the finished patch with a straight edge to insure a smooth riding surface.

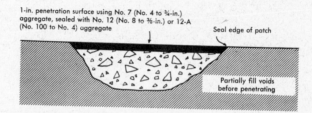

1-in. penetration surface using No. 7 (No. 4 to ¾-in.) aggregate, sealed with No. 12 (No. 8 to ⅜-in.) or 12-A (No. 100 to No. 4) aggregate   Seal edge of patch

Partially fill voids before penetrating

Fig. 8.2   Repair of deep pot holes by penetration method

Place No. 1 (1–in. to 3–½ in.) or No. 2 (1-in. to 3 in.) aggregate in layers approximately 3 in. thick when thoroughly compacted. Top of all layers to be parallel to finished grade.

To save bituminous material and to obtain better mechanical bond, the voids in the No. 1 or No. 2 aggregate should be partially filled with No. 12 (No. 8 to ⅜-in.) aggregate before penetrating with bituminous material. Check the patch with a straight edge to insure a smooth riding surface.

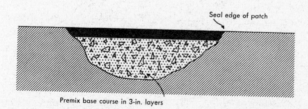

Seal edge of patch

Premix base course in 3-in. layers

Fig. 8.3   Repair of deep pot holes by use of premix base and top course material 1-in. to 1½ in. premix surface course

Place premix base course material in layers approximately 3 in. thick when thoroughly compacted. Top of all layers to be parallel to finished grade.

Check the patch with a straight edge to insure a smooth riding surface.

Corrugations or sharp irregularities

There are four common causes for corrugations or sharp irregularities: (1) the building up of a mat of small aggregate, together with an excess of bituminous material, (2) a base or surface inadequate for the type of traffic, (3) structural obsolescence, and (4) poor subgrade soil conditions.

A bituminous leveling course consisting of the following steps will be necessary to correct this situation:

Clean the surface thoroughly.

Patch potholes of surface breaks and spot-seal any cracked or alligatored sections. Care should be used in this operation, as an excess of bituminous material in patches or spot sealing will result in pot fat spots on the final surface.

Apply the appropriate grade of bituminous material in the correct amount (0.3–0.8 gal per sq yd) uniformly over the aggregate. (Avoid an excess of bitumen).

Immediately after the application of bituminous material, grade with blade at right angles in such a manner that material will be dragged from the high spots and spilled into the depressions.

Roll thoroughly with a 10-ton, 3-wheel roller.

Correct any remaining depressions or irregularities by placing an additional course where necessary.

Place required surface treatment.

The weight of surface treatment required to cover and protect this type of leveling depends on the type of original surface leveled. A standard 25-lb treatment is sufficient for leveling a reasonably tight bituminous surface.

The gradation of the aggregate used in leveling course also affects the weight of surface treatment required. Where a leveling course in which No. 37 (No. 4 to 1½ in.) aggregate has been used and covered with a 25-lb surface treatment and the amount of the tack coat should be increased 0.15–0.20 gal per sq yd. This material for the leveling course should be crushed stone, slag, or 100 per cent crushed gravel which meets the standard specifications for concrete aggregate. The depth of irregularities filled with one course should not be more than two to two and one-half times the maximum size of the aggregate. Courses of 30–60 lb per sq yd placed over the entire surface require No. 7 (No. 4 to ⅜ in.) gradation, and courses of 60–100 lb require No. 37 (No. 4 to 1½ in.) gradation.

Bituminous materials should either be RT-7 to RT-9 tar, the grade depending on the temperature and weather conditions at the time of application, or asphalt cutback or emulsion having comparable viscosity and penetrating qualities.

Settlements and deformation

The causes of settlements and deformation are (1) lack of adequate sub-grade support, (2) slipping or movement of the fill, (3) inadequate thickness of base, and (4) structural obsolescence. The placing of a patch affords only temporary relief unless the underlying cause of the subsidence is corrected. Lack of subgrade support is usually caused by a poor drainage condition which should be corrected before the finished patch is placed.

The slipping or movement of a fill is generally caused by lack of stability in the soil upon which the fill was placed, lack of stability of the fill material itself, or settlement from lack of compaction. Corrective measures should be applied before patching.

If the base is too thin or is structurally obsolete, then additional thickness should be provided prior to the patching.

If the settlement or deformation is not too pronounced, it may be corrected by placing a poured or premix patch; otherwise it may be necessary to bring the depression up approximately to grade with a base course material, and then resurface.

Completely failed sections

Poor drainage conditions, resulting in inadequate subgrade support, are responsible for completely failed sections. Remove the entire section of surface and base, and correct the drainage condition by installing underdrains or French drains. Place a blanket of granular material from ditchline to ditchline, as shown on Fig. 8.4, and then place a new base and surface.

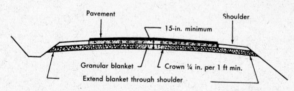

Fig. 8.4 Under-drainage for wet sections

Treatment as shown above is usually satisfactory for fill sections, and for sections having wide ditches and flat well stabilized slopes.

The granular blanket should be composed of a closely graded mixture of sand and gravel. Crushed stone, or slag is not advisable, because of the danger of clogging with subgrade soil, rendering the blanket ineffective for providing drainage and disrupting capillary action.

Slippery surfaces

The causes of slippery surfaces are an excess of bituminous material or improper gradation of the aggregate. Fat spots can be prevented by exercising care in the application of bituminous materials. It is better to have too little than too much, because if the surface lacks bituminous material more can be added, but if it is overbituminized, the removal of the excess is difficult and costly.

There are two practical and effective methods for the correction of slippery surfaces: (1) the application of a tack coat of tar or asphalt emulsion followed by an application of coarse, sharp sand, and (2) the application of a new heavy open-graded road or plant mix surface course.

Shoulders and ditches

It is important to keep the shoulders dressed or smoothed in such manner that there will be no holes, ruts, or high or low places to interfere with proper drainage of the edge of the pavement surface and the shoulders. High shoulders at the edge of the pavement hold surface water to soak down at the edge of the pavement. Ruts at the edge of the pavement also hold water which soaks into and softens the subgrade, resulting in pavement edge settlement.

Whenever practicable, the bottoms of the ditches should be below the subgrade elevation and should have sufficient fall to carry the water away quickly.

General

In placing patches of all types, extreme care should be exercised not to use an excess of bituminous material. An overbituminized patch will shove out of shape in hot weather and result in a fat, slippery spot and waste bituminous material.

Patching just ahead of resurfacing is important. The control of the bituminous material is particularly important; if an excess is used in the patches it is likely to come up through the new surface to form unsightly blotches and slippery spots. The patches should therefore be on the lean side and not tightly sealed, because their only function is to fill a subsidence; the new surface will insure the material's remaining in proper position.

Do not allow holes and broken places to accumulate in order to patch them all at once. This does not save costs; rather, it increases them. If repairs are neglected, the small holes and cavities develop into larger holes. and cavities and require many time the material and labor to repair. Such lack of constant maintenance results in numerous holes at all times, and particularly during wet and cold seasons. A patch placed during wet or cold weather remains in place almost as well as one placed in dry weather. See Fig. 8.5 for proper method and Fig. 8.6 (Sketches 1 and 2) for improper method. Fig. 8.7 indicates the method of repair of a series of holes of different areas and depths.

Fig. 8.5   Proper method of patching bituminous surfaces

Before the patch is placed the cracked and broken area of the bituminous surface should be thoroughly primed and treated with a bituminous material of a viscosity low enough to thoroughly penetrate the cracks and to liven up the old surface. This will rebond the entire structure, giving it strength while cutting off both the surface and sub-grade water.

Care should be taken, however, to avoid an excessive amount of bitumen in sealing the failed surface prior to placing the patch. Too much bitumen will work up through the patch and result in a "fat" (slick) area on the surface. Furthermore, an excess of bitumen may cause the patch to shove.

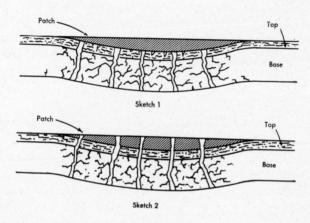

Sketch 1

Sketch 2

Fig. 8.6   Improper method of patching bituminous surfaces

A patch like that shown in Sketch 1, laid with premix material or paved with quick setting or high viscosity liquid bituminous material, will bridge over the cracks, with the result that the cracks, still open beneath the patch, will soon, under traffic, extend up through the patch (as shown in Sketch 2), allowing surface water to seep into the surface and base. This process results in disintegration, particularly during freezing and thawing.

MAINTENANCE OF GRAVEL OR TRAFFIC-BOUND SURFACES

A gravel surface road, if properly constructed, requires only ordinary drainage and grade maintenance common to all types of roads, together with the occasional blading of the surface. If chemicals are used, one or more light treatments will probably be required each spring. The blading of a

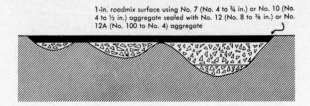

1-in. roadmix surface using No. 7 (No. 4 to ¾ in.) or No. 10 (No. 4 to ½ in.) aggregate sealed with No. 12 (No. 8 to ⅜ in.) or No. 12A (No. 100 to No. 4) aggregate

Fig. 8.7   Repair of a series of subsidences of different areas and depths

The subsidences are brought up to a point 1-in. below the finished grade with road mix leveling course using No. 38 (No. 4 to ½ in.) aggregate. The courses are to be 2 in. to 3 in. thick, and the top of each course is to be parallel to the finished grade.

Hot or cold-laid bituminous concrete base course and surface course may be substituted for road mix leveling and surface course.

gravel surface, whether chemically treated or not, should always be done soon after a rain, while more than the average moisture content is present in the top of the surface. If bladed while dry, some aggregate will be torn loose, leaving pits for the accumulation of water when rain comes. Loosened material will not recompact while dry, and general raveling of the surface will be encouraged.

TABLE 8.1/USE OF ASPHALT EMULSION

Type of work	Type and grade of bituminous material	Maximum application temperature (°F)	Minimum application temperature (°F)
Patching (late fall, winter, and early spring)	AE–1	130	70
Patching (summer)	AE–2	130	70
Light seals and light surface treatments	AE–3	130	70
	AE–5	130	100
Heavy surface treatments	AE–5	130	100
Road mixes	AE–4	130	70
Cold-laid plant mix	AE–3	130	70
Hot-laid plant mix	AE–3	130	70
Penetration macadam	AE–3	130	70
Crack filling (Impregnated with mineral flour)	AE–3	130	70
Primes:			
A. Knapped or macadam stone base	AE–6	150	100
B. Gravel base	AE–6	150	100
C. Traffic bound stone base	AE–6	150	100

TABLE 8.2/USE OF TAR

Type of work	Type and grade of bituminous material	Maximum application temperature (°F)	Minimum application temperature (°F)
Patching (late fall, winter, and early spring)	RT–6	150	80
	RT–7	225	150
Patching (summer)	RT–8	225	150
	RT–9	225	150
	RT–10	250	175
Light seals and light surface treatments	RT–6	150	80
	RT–7	225	150
	RT–8	225	150
	RT–9	225	150
	RT–10	250	175
Heavy surface treatments	RT–6	150	80
	RT–7	225	150
	RT–8	225	150
	RT–9	225	150
	RT–10	250	175
Road mixes	RT–6	150	80
	RT–7	225	150
	RT–8	225	150
	RT–9	225	150
	RT–10	225	175
Cold–laid plant mix	RT–8, 9 or 10		
	(8 and 9)	225	150
	(10)	250	175
Hot–laid plant mix	RT–12	250	175
Penetration macadam	RT–12	250	175
Crack filling (Impregnated with mineral flour)	RT–12	250	175
Primes:			
A. Knapped or macadam Stone base	RT–3, 4, or 5	RT–2:125	60
B. Gravel base	RT–2, 3, or 4	RT–3:150	80
		RT–4:150	80
C. Traffic bound Stone base	RT–2 or 3	RT–5:150	80

TABLE 8.3/USE OF ASPHALT

Type of work	Type and grade of bituminous material	Maximum application temperature (°F)	Minimum application temperature (°F)
Patching (late fall, winter, and early spring)	MC–2	200	150
	RC–2	175	100
	RC–3	200	150
Patching (summer)	RC–3	200	150
	RC–4	225	175
	MC–5	275	200
Light seals and light surface treatments	MC–3	250	175
	RC–2	175	100
	RC–3	200	150
Heavy surface treatments	MC–5	275	200
	RC–3	200	150
	RC–4	225	175
	AC–150–200 Penet.	300	200
Road mixes	MC–3	250	175
	MC–5	275	200
	RC–3	200	150
	RC–4	225	175
Cold–laid plant mix	AC–85–100 Penet.	340	275
Hot–laid plant mix	AC–85–100 Penet.	340	275
Penetration macadam (Impregnated with mineral flour)	AC–85–100 Penet.	340	275
	AC–150–200 Penet.	300	200
	RE–5	275	200
	AC–85–100 Penet.	350	275
Primes:			
A. Knapped or macadam Stone base	MC–1	125	80
B. Gravel base	MC–1	125	80
C. Traffic bound Stone base	MC–1	125	80
	MC–9	120	50

The regular use of a drag tends to cut away the crown and to dislodge aggregate, resulting in a flat, loose surface. The regular use of such equipment is not recommended. The modern tandem-drive power grader, however, is a flexible unit capable of handling ditching and shoulder grading, as well as surface grading, and is highly recommended.

If the surface becomes badly pitted or potholed, it will be necessary to blade deep enough to remove the material at the bottom of the pits or holes. The material is placed in a windrow at the center of the road, then bladed to either side and recompacted to proper shape. This should always be done after a rain.

Treatment of serious failures

Serious failures or break-ups which have been caused by frost action or inadequate subgrade can be repaired by light blading to reshape the surface, as early and as often as moisture conditions will permit, and by adding aggregate to the sections that have completely failed. A crushed material is more effective than round gravel for the stabilization of very soft sections, because the angular crushed particles will interlock much better, forming a mechanical bond which provides stability without the aid of cohesion.

Treatment to prevent dust

Calcium chloride is one of the chemicals most commonly used for retaining moisture on road surfaces. When used as a surface treatment it has the property of absorbing moisture from the air as well as retaining moisture. Calcium chloride should be applied when the surface is damp, thoroughly compacted, and free of loose material. It should be placed in increments of from 0.5 to 1.0 lb, and the entire treatment should total about 2.5 lb per sq yd. If it is necessary to apply calcium chloride during very dry weather, best results can be obtained by making the application at night or in the very early morning. Mechanical spreading gets better results than hand spreading. Lime spreader or chip or cinder spreaders can be used.

Sodium chloride (common salt) can also be used. Its main function is to retain moisture, and since it will absorb moisture from the air only under certain conditions of humidity, the surface should contain the proper amount of moisture when treatment is made.

If the surface does not contain enough moisture, it should be sprinkled just prior to treatment. Use the same method of application for salt as for calcium chloride. Another method of treating dry surfaces is to apply the salt in solution. This can be done with a pressure distributor or an ordinary sprinkling wagon. A total of about 3 lb per sq yd is required for the salt treatment.

Light asphaltic oil is frequently used as a dust palliative on gravel roads. It partially waterproofs the surface, reducing evaporation, and aids in maintaining stability. The usual application is from ¼–½ gal per sq yd.

General

The improvement of unsatisfactory gravel surfaces is accomplished by the addition of materials necessary to provide proper gradation and adequate thickness of surface; also, by proper shaping, by providing new or improvement of existing side ditches, and by installing under-drains where needed. Closer attention to requirements for stability and to proper drainage, and with a minimum of blading, will do much to improve the quality of the maintenance of gravel roads.

SHOULDERS AND DITCHES

The maintenance of shoulders and ditches is a type of maintenance work which must be carried on to some extent throughout the entire year. However, the majority of such work is confined to the fall and spring cleanup. The fall cleanup is to insure that the shoulders and ditches will go into the winter season in condition to effect proper drainage, and the spring cleanup is to dispose of the ravages of winter weather and its accompanying erosion and slides.

Shoulders

Shoulders are that portion of the roadway on each side of the pavement between the pavement edge and (1) the top of the inner ditch slope in cuts, or (2) the top of the fill slope on fills.

The dressing of shoulders is important because (1) if the surface of the shoulder is smooth and properly sloped it will drain properly, (2) a smooth shoulder adds to the safety of driving, and (3) a well-dressed shoulder adds to the appearance of a highway or access road.

Shoulders are to be maintained for their full width—except where the shoulders are unnecessarily wide—in a smooth condition, flush with the edge of the pavement at all times, and at a slope necessary to facilitate proper drainage of the roadway. As a general rule, slopes should be approximately ¾ in. per ft for earth shoulders, approximately ½ in. per ft for stabilized shoulders, and approximately 1 in. per ft for grass shoulders.

The regular blading of shoulders to keep them flush with the edge of the pavement is important because (1) if the shoulder is too high, water retained on the edge of the pavement causes surface deterioration or will soak down at the edge of the pavement and soften the subgrade, and (2) if the shoulder is too low, or if ruts and holes are permitted to remain in the shoulder at or near the edge of the pavement, a traffic hazard is created, or, as in bituminous surfaces, raveling of the edges is induced.

Grass covered shoulders invariably become "built up" to the point where they must be cut down to provide proper drainage. This cutting down of grass shoulders should be done in the early spring, as soon as weather conditions permit, in order that they will become grassed over again as quickly as possible. This cutting down must never be done in late summer and fall, because new ground cover will not have a chance to grow, and the shoulder will be severely damaged by erosion during the late fall and early winter months.

Regular mowing of grass shoulders during the growing season not only improves appearances, but causes grass to spread out from the base of the plants and give better cover. Regular mowing leaves relatively light cuttings that form a good mulch on the soil and hold moisture. Height of cut is determined by the area and specified on the plan of the individual area. Regular applications of fertilizer will improve both appearance and cover.

In blading and grading other than grass shoulders on fills which are protected with a guard rail, care should be exercised to leave no ridge of earth higher than the surface of the shoulder between, behind, or just in front of the guard rail posts, because a false ditch is formed, and erosion of the shoulder will result. The slope of the surface of the shoulder should extend entirely out to the fill slope line, in order that the surface drainage may run off uniformly for the entire length of the fill.

In numerous instances, pockets of water are impounded in low places on the shoulders at the edge of the pavement. Such places should be drained whenever observed. This applies also to earth or rock falls which block the ditch and interfere with proper drainage.

Ditches

The proper maintenance of ditches is of utmost importance. If the ditches are allowed to become filled with grass, weeds, leaves, earth, rock and other debris, they cannot function properly, and their effectiveness is definitely impaired.

During the winter, extensive ditch maintenance is very difficult. It is important, however, that rocks and slides which may block free drainage be removed as soon as they occur.

The leaves which fill ditches in woodland areas in the fall must be removed promptly; otherwise they will clog small pipe culverts. Furthermore, the presence of these leaves constitutes a definite fire hazard.

In blading ditches with a power grader, extreme care should be taken not to undercut the toe of the slope with the end of the blade, because wherever the toe of the slope is undercut, and the slope is left vertical, first the bottom of the slope and then material higher up will begin to slough into the ditch. Several points of maintenance require constant checking:

1. Late in fall, all weeds and tall grass should be cleaned from ditches in order that drainage of excessive water will be expedited.

2. Keep ditches low enough to maintain the water table below the subgrade.

3. Ditches should be watched in particular during and immediately after hard, washing rains; a little grading work at the time water is moving in the ditches will make the force of the water do a great deal of ditch and pipe culvert cleaning.

4. During the rainy seasons, inspections should be made at regular intervals to remove slides and debris.

Roadside cleaning

The average visitor often does not observe good maintenance details, and is only conscious of the over-all effect. The general appearance of access roads and service drives therefore plays an important part in the first impression a visitor receives of an area.

The general appearance of these roads and drives within an area is improved by giving special attention to the following details:

1. Pavement surfaces should be free of holes and bad deformations.

2. Center line strips should have good alignment and be kept well painted.

3. Signs should be kept properly placed and well painted.

4. Earth and traffic-bound shoulders should be free of ruts and well graded.

5. Grass shoulders should be kept well trimmed at all times.

6. Slopes should be kept trimmed reasonably close, with careful attention being given to selective pruning of shrubs and trees.

7. Guard rails should be kept lined up and properly painted. Temporary guard rails should be replaced with permanent guard rails.

8. Trash and other refuse should be kept off the right of way.

9. Slides and falls of rock or earth onto pavements should be promptly removed.

10. Wooded areas close to the pavement should be cleared of dead, down, and diseased material, and of vines and underbrush for a distance of approximately 50 ft on either side of the paved surface. This cleanup should gradually fade into the natural growth beyond.

11. No advertising signs should be permitted.

12. Eroded slopes and slopes with little or no cover should be regraded, fertilized, and planted. Steep slopes should either be mulched or have wattles built on them. The tops of such slopes should be rounded.

13. All important views should be preserved and cleared.

SPECIFICATIONS FOR CONSTRUCTION AND MAINTENANCE OF ROADS AND PARKING AREAS

The following specifications have been adapted from the specifications which have been used for many years by the Tennessee Valley Authority.

Excavation and backfill for concrete and masonry structures

Excavation should be made to the widths and depths necessary to provide satisfactory construction for the contemplated structure. Except where rock or unsuitable materials are encountered, the last of the excavation should be done by hand, and should not be carried to its final depth until immediately preceding the construction of the footing or base course. The excavation should then be completed to a smooth surface and to exact grade, so as to provide a foundation of undisturbed earth. Wherever possible, any excavation below the elevation of the top of footing or base course should be made to the neat dimension (exact size) of the footing.

Where rock is encountered, it should not be allowed to project within the lines of the structure shown on the drawings or established in accordance with the provisions of the drawings. Where rock exists under a portion of a footing which is otherwise to rest on an earth foundation, the rock should, when so indicated on the drawings or so directed, be removed to a depth of 6 in. below the under side of the footing and replaced with gravel or other approved fine materials.

All soft or unstable materials existing below the foundation elevation should be removed to the limits directed.

Preparation of foundation

The foundation of the footing or structure will depend upon the condition and character of the material encountered. Test holes should be driven or drilled in the foundation material, whether rock or other material, to a depth sufficient to establish its suitability for use as a foundation. They should be sunk by jackhammer drills or other suitable equipment.

Where concrete or masonry is to be placed on the existing surface of rock, all dirt and loose or disintegrated material should be removed to provide complete contact with the solid rock. Where the rock is to serve as a foundation for bridge abutments or other structures requiring additional stability, its surface should be roughened, or suitable anchors should be provided. Inclined surfaces of rock should be leveled in steps, as indicated on drawings or as directed, to prevent sliding. All dirt, mud, or loose material accumulating upon the foundation should be removed immediately before placing concrete. Any cracks or crevices in the foundation which are large enough to permit separation of the concrete materials should be filled with concrete or with suitable aggregate materials before concrete placing is begun.

Before concrete is poured in any footing of a foundation unit, all blasting necessary in excavating or shaping of all footings in the entire unit should be completed.

Any cavities resulting from excavation of either earth or rock below the foundation elevation should be backfilled with gravel, crushed stone, or other approved materials placed and thoroughly tamped in layers not more than 6 in. thick, or should be backfilled with concrete, as directed. Whenever the excavation in rock below the elevation of the top of the footing is carried beyond the neat lines (exact dimensions) of the footing course, the space so formed should be filled with concrete.

Backfilling

That part of the excavation which is not occupied by the structure should be refilled with acceptable material to the normal surface of the ground, unless otherwise directed, in layers not more than 6 in. deep. Both sides of the opening should be carried up at equal elevations, and each layer should be tamped thoroughly before the succeeding layer is placed. When the material does not contain enough moisture for thorough compaction, sufficient water for this purpose should be added. No backfilling should be done until the concrete around which backfilling is to be placed is at least 14 days old.

Excavation and backfill for pipe culverts

Excavation of trench for pipes shall be to the width necessary to provide space for thoroughly tamping the backfill material under the haunches and around the pipe, but where field conditions permit, the width should not be greater than required for this purpose. Except where rock or unsuitable foundation material is encountered, excavation of the trench should not extend below grade of the bottom of the pipe, and the bottom of the trench should be so excavated as to fit the lower part of the pipe exterior.

Where double lines of pipe are installed they should be spaced at least one and one-half diameters center to center.

Preparation of bed for pipe

Whether in trenches or under embankments, the pipe should be bedded in an earth foundation of uniform density, carefully shaped to fit the lower part of the pipe exterior for at least 10 per cent of its over-all height. This bed should be formed in undisturbed material wherever the nature of the site will permit. Where rock is encountered, in either ledge or boulder formation, it should be removed below grade and replaced with suitable materials in such manner as to provide a compact earth cushion having a thickness under the pipe of not less than 8 in. Where a firm foundation is not encountered at the grade established, because of the presence of soft, spongy, or other unsuitable soil, unless other special construction methods are called for, all of such unstable soil, under the pipe and for a width of at least one diameter on each side of the pipe, should be removed and replaced with gravel or other suitable material properly compacted to provide adequate support for the pipeline. Where drawings require that a portion of a pipe be on fill, the necessary fill should be built of approved earth materials and should have a top width of at least three diameters. The materials should be placed in 6-in. layers, which should each be moistened just enough for maximum compaction, and then thoroughly compacted by tamping.

Recesses of proper size to admit hubs or bells of pipe should be excavated across the trench so that the body of the pipe will rest upon the prepared bed.

Backfilling around pipe

Backfilling should be done with approved fine materials which should contain sufficient moisture to provide for compaction. Backfill material should be carefully tamped, in 6-in. layers or less, beneath and around the sides of the pipe, but not directly over it. Care should be taken that thorough compaction of the material under the haunches of the pipe is obtained, that the backfill material should provide a uniform support around all pipe, and that the joints and alignment should not be disturbed.

Pipe laid in trenches should be protected against displacement or injury by backfilling to a minimum depth of 12 in. above the top of the pipe as laying progresses, or as the entire line is laid. The remainder of the trench should be backfilled with material containing no stone exceeding 4 in. in diameter, and compacted by tamping in 12-in. layers. All sheeting used in trenches should be removed, and cavities left by its removal should be carefully filled with tamped materials.

Backfilling around pipe culverts projecting into the embankment should be completed before the adjacent embankment is constructed. The work should be done in such manner that there will be on each side of the top of the pipe, a berm of thoroughly compacted earth equal in width to the external diameter of the pipe and extending to a height of 18 in. above the top of the pipe.

Disposal of surplus materials

All material excavated should be deposited or disposed of in such a way that it will not obstruct water courses nor impair the function or appearance of the structure or other parts of the work. When the material is suitable, it should be used in the roadway embankment.

Measurement

The number of cubic yards of excavation for structures will be determined by measuring the volume of materials which lie within the limits defined hereunder, except that material required to be excavated in grading the roadway to its required limits in cut sections and that to be excavated within the finished limits of the channels beneath bridges will not be included.

The measurement of excavation for structures such as piers, abutments, box culverts, and headwalls will include the volume of all materials which lie between the surface of the under side of the structure and the normal surface of the ground, and which is bounded by vertical planes situated parallel to and 12 in. from the neat lines of the footing or base course. In rock excavations the measurement will extend to a depth of 6 in. beneath the footing or base course. The measurement of excavation for pipe culverts, or similar structures, will include the volume of all materials which lie between the grade of the under side of the pipe and the normal surface of the ground, and which are bounded at the sides of the pipe by vertical planes parallel to and equidistant from the axis of the pipe and at a distance apart which is 18 in. greater than the inside diameter of the pipe. Measurement along the pipe trench will extend to vertical planes 9 in. beyond the ends of the pipe, or to the limits of headwall or inlet excavations. In rock excavation, the measurement will extend to a depth of 8 in. below the grade of the under side of the pipe.

Where excavation of unsuitable material, other than rock is to be made below the structure or pipe, and where such material has not been rendered unsuitable through failure to protect the work properly, the measurement will include all material necessarily removed in the performance of such excavation to the limits directed.

Earth borrow excavation

Borrow pits should be excavated to regular lines as staked. The excavation should be carried only to the depth directed, and should be as uniform as practicable throughout the pit. Side slopes should not be steeper that $2\frac{1}{2}$:1, unless otherwise indicated on drawings.

The pits should be completed so that they will drain properly and should be left in presentable and satisfactory condition. Solid rock or boulders may be found in the borrow pit. Such rock should be excavated and moved in order to obtain the required amount of material and leave the borrow pit of uniform or regular shape, with proper drainage.

Measurement

The volume of material excavated and disposed of, as specified or directed, should be measured in its original position and computed by the method of average end areas. Rock excavated, as provided above, should be included in this measurement.

Unclassified excavation

Unclassified excavation refers to excavating cut sections of the roadway (including intersections and approaches); cutting or the improvement of ditches and channels; constructing embankments, roadbed, and so on, from suitable materials thus excavated; removal and disposition of all unsuitable and surplus materials; and performing all other work necessary to shape, complete, and maintain the graded roadway thus constructed.

Excavation and disposition of materials

Excavation should conform closely to the lines and grades given, and final slopes should be reasonably uniform and true to design requirements. Where changes in the character of materials or other unforeseen conditions make it necessary, the engineer may direct or permit the excavation to be made with slopes steeper than those originally indicated, but earth slopes should never be steeper than 2:1.

Changes in alignment or grade may be made by the engineer as the work progresses, or if additional excavations such as ditches or turnouts, are ordered. The engineer will then indicate lines, grades, and cross-sections for the additional work. The engineer should likewise designate the limits of excavations indicated on the drawings but not fully designed.

Excessive blasting or oversheeting should be avoided. Necessary precautions should be taken to prevent damage from blasting to structures within 200 ft. All blasting necessary to excavation of channels or ditches within 100 ft of designated structure locations should be done before construction of structure, and, when practicable, before completion of roadway cuts.

Unsuitable materials

All vegetation should be cut and removed from the site of excavations and embankments, including the slopes of existing embankments to be widened, before excavation or placement of materials is begun. Objectionable quantities of sod or leaves should not be placed in or left upon the site or an embankment 2 ft or less in depth between shoulder lines, but should be removed as directed. Such materials should be disposed of in a presentable and satisfactory manner beyond the roadway limits.

Where soft, spongy, or otherwise unsuitable materials are encountered in the excavation or upon the embankment site, they should be excavated to the limits directed and disposed of in a presentable manner beyond the limits of the work.

Rock below subgrade

The excavation of rock below roadbed elevation will not be required on any project unless called for on drawings. When called for, it should be excavated at the locations and to the limits and depths stipulated.

When excavation of rock below grade is called for on drawings, all stones of more than 4-in. size should be removed to the full width of roadbed, and to the depths indicated on drawings, so that no solid projections remain above these limits. The depth of excavation should be approved before backfilling is begun.

The cavities from which rock has been removed should be backfilled to the roadbed elevation with suitable earth or other acceptable material, all of which should pass a 3-in. sieve. The volume of rock excavated below roadbed elevation to the depths and limits designated should be measured.

Ditches and channels

Care should be taken in excavating to provide for proper drainage during construction, with a view to conformity with permanent drainage requirements. New ditches and channels should be cut, and existing ones improved wherever indicated on drawings or directed; all should conform to the designated cross-section and grade. Materials from ditch or channel excavation should be used in the embankment, if required. If they are not so used, they should be deposited a satisfactory distance from the ditch and shaped as directed to a neat and presentable appearance.

Terraces, existing roadbeds, and structures

Where embankments are to be constructed on existing ground slopes steeper than 1:3, contiguous deep steps or terraces at least 4 ft wide should be cut therein before placement of any material. Existing embankment slopes should be similarly terraced, except that the widths should be as directed by the engineer.

All portions of existing roadbed which are within 3 ft of the required surface of subgrade should be thoroughly broken up to a depth of not less than 6 in. Existing pavements within such depths, except those designated for removal under other items, should be broken up. If necessary they should be removed and scattered through the embankment in such manner as not to interfere with its construction, or should be disposed of outside the limits of the work as directed.

All portions of structures within embankment limits should be completed and any concrete thoroughly cured before grading operations are begun. If grading must be authorized before such construction is finished, a large enough section of the embankment should be omitted to allow for completion of the structure.

Embankment materials

All embankments—including channels, approaches, and other appurtenances—should be formed with suitable materials excavated within the roadway, and with necessary additional materials from borrow pits. Stumps, rubbish, sod, and other unsuitable materials should not be placed in embankments. The wasting of material should be carefully avoided, but where suitable material in excess of filling requirements as designed or directed is excavated, such excess material should be used to widen or flatten embankment slopes uniformly, or distributed otherwise, as directed.

Frozen materials should not be placed in embankments, and objectionable quantities of snow and ice should be removed from the ground surface before work is begun.

Formation of embankments

Embankments should be built to such height and width that after full shrinkage they will conform to the cross-sections shown on the drawings. The materials should be deposited in uniform, successive level layers for the full width of the embankment. No side casting of material into embankments without spreading and compacting in layers, in the specified manner, should be permitted. The top 12 in. of the embankment should always be built of earth, and no stone larger than 4 in. should be placed in this top layer.

In portions of embankments formed of materials which are principally rock, the thickness of the layers should not be greater than required by maximum size of stone, and should never exceed 4 ft. All earth and fine materials should be well distributed into the interstices of the larger stones. All interstices within 3 ft of the upper surface of such fills should be well filled with small stones and earth. Mixtures of earth should not be used below reservoir surcharge elevation, unless laid and tamped in 6-in. layers.

In the construction of earth embankments, the thickness of layers should not exceed 12 in. Earth embankments which will lie wholly or in part below reservoir surcharge elevation should be constructed in their entirety by depositing the material in uniform successive level layers not more than 6 in. thick, and the water content should be maintained within limits which permit the highest possible degree of compaction. The engineer will determine these limits from time to time, and when the material being placed contains insufficient moisture, sufficient water to bring the moisture content within the desired limits should be applied. Material containing excess moisture should not be placed in the fill until it has dried out so that the moisture content is within the proper limits. Water may be applied from a hose or similar equipment at the point where the material is being placed.

When new earth materials are placed against the slopes of an existing embankment, the hauling, spreading, and compacting operations over each layer should be so conducted as to provide a thorough bond between the new and old materials.

Each layer of an earth embankment should be thoroughly compacted. For earth embankments having any portion below pool level, compaction by the use of a sheepsfoot roller will always be required for a distance of 5 ft from each edge of each layer. The roller should be operated along the edges so as to overhang the edge of the embankment as far as practicable, and as many passages should be made in this position as are necessary to produce the maximum practicable degree of compaction. If the portions of the layers of reservoir fills are more than 5 ft from either edge of the embankment, or if the entire layers of embankments which are entirely out of the pool are compacted by hauling all materials in vehicles weighing at least 8 tons when loaded, and the vehicles are operated so as to distribute their tracks uniformly over the entire layer, no further compaction of these portions will be required, except where special requirements for compaction are made on drawings. Wherever the above requirements as to weight of hauling equipment and distribution of tracks are not met, compaction by the use of the sheepsfoot roller will be required.

When called for on drawings, compaction by use of sheepsfoot roller, or by such other means as may be called for, will be required on the embankments or portions of embankments in addition to those described above.

Wherever compaction by the use of sheepsfoot roller is required, the roller shall be operated uniformly over each layer as many times as necessary to obtain thorough compaction. The roller should pass over each portion of each layer at least five times, and the roller should weigh not less than 1,000 lb per lin ft of tread.

If any portions of earth embankments adjacent to structures are not thoroughly and uniformly compacted in the manner specified, these should be constructed by depositing and tamping suitable materials in 6-in. layers. The backfilling should progress at equal elevations on each side of the structure, and should be thus completed to sufficient height above the structure to protect the structure from injury by the equipment. These requirements should apply to the entire area of omitted sections of embankment which are of sufficient length to permit full compaction by the placement and compaction equipment.

Care should be taken to avoid damage to structures from impact of stones as well as from equipment. Any damage which does occur should be properly repaired to the satisfaction of the engineer.

Completion of grading

The completed roadbed should conform to the final grades given and to the cross-sections shown on drawings. It should be carefully finished by blading its entire surface until it is smooth and of uniform appearance, and should be maintained in such condition.

Measurement

The volume of excavation to be measured should be that of the material in its original position, computed in cubic yards by the method of average end areas. Each end area, whether of roadway cuts or of channel or ditches, etc., should be the cross-sectional area included between the original ground line and the theoretical lines of excavation, both as indicated on drawings. If any modifications or additional work are directed by the engineer, he should designate the lines, grades, and cross-sections for such additional work, and these should be used in computing end areas, replacing the cross-sections shown on drawings. The volume of any materials directed or permitted by the engineer to be left in place within these limits should be deducted from the quantities thus measured.

Metal plate guard rails

All posts, blockings, and anchors should be set in compact soil. The holes for posts should be dug to the required grade, and their bottoms should be thoroughly compacted by ramming until a stable foundation is provided. The posts should then be set plumb to exact intervals, and to the grade and alignment specified by the engineer. They should be set with front faces along a straight line on tangents, and at a uniform distance from the edge of the pavement on curves, except where varied to conform to a bridge or roadway section or to the manufacturer's approved plan for construction of the guard rail. Suitable material should be placed in layers not exceeding 4 in. and each layer rammed thoroughly with hand tamps in such manner as not to displace the posts from true alignment.

Anchors, bracing, and blocking should be installed in accordance with the provisions of the plans of the rail plate manufacturer so that the entire length of the rail plate will be maintained in uniform and taut condition. Anchors and blocking should be installed to the lines and grades given, and backfilled around with material applied and tamped in 4-in. layers.

Erecting steel rail plate

The rail plate should be erected to exact alignment and grade. It should be erected taut and firm and in full conformity with the provisions made in its design for maintaining its length and tautness under all temperature variations. After erection, the rail plates should be straight, and should not vary more than ½ in. from a straight line along either edge in a 16-ft span.

All lap joints should be made so that the end of the plate next to traffic will point in the direction of travel.

When finally accepted, the entire length of steel rail should be uniformly taut and in true alignment, with all posts plumb and firmly tamped and all connections and fastenings neat and secure.

Painting

Pressure treated and concrete posts will not be painted. All surfaces of posts and braces that will be in contact with the rail fittings should be brushed with two coats of white lead paint before the fittings are erected. After erection of the guard rail is completed, all posts and braces should be painted to a uniform line below the rail plate, as indicated on plans or designated by the engineer, with two coats of white lead paint. The remainder of the posts and braces to the surface of the ground should be painted with two coats of black carbon paint.

All metal parts of the guard rail, including rail plate and all supports and fastenings, should, after erection, be painted with two coats of white lead paint.

The entire head of the package should be removed and the paint kept thoroughly stirred and mixed at all times while being applied. If congealing makes it necessary to thin the paint in cool weather, this should be done only by warming the paint. Paint should not be applied when the air temperature is below 40°F, or when the air is misty, or when, in the opinion of the engineer, conditions are otherwise unsatisfactory for the work. It should not be applied upon damp or frosted surfaces.

Before any coat of paint is applied, surfaces to be painted should be thoroughly cleaned of dirt, oil, grease, and all other foreign substances. Bristle or wood fiber brushes should be used for removing dust.

Before paint is applied to galvanized metal surfaces they should be slightly etched with a dilute solution of vinegar, composed of 1 pt vinegar and 1 gal water.

Painting should be done in a thorough, neat, and workmanlike manner. Brushes should preferably be round or oval, but if flat brushes are used they should not exceed 4 in. in width. The paint, when applied, should be so manipulated under the brush as to produce a uniform, even coating in close contact with the surface or with previously applied paint, and should be worked into all corners and crevices. On surfaces which are inaccessible to paint brushes, the paint should be applied with sheepskin daubers especially constructed for the purpose. Each coat of paint should be thoroughly dry before the next coat is applied: at least 24 hours should be allowed between coats. Metal guard rails are measured by the linear foot, from end post.

Wire rope guard rails

The posts for wire rope guard rails should be brush-treated, butt-dipped, or pressure-treated timber posts or concrete posts, according to specifications on the drawings. Round posts should be grouped so as to minimize noticeable variations in size between successive posts, with larger size posts being placed at the ends of sections.

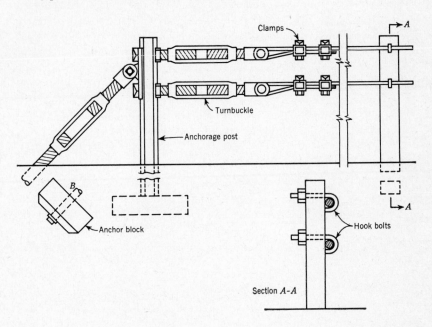

Fig. 8.8 Detail of wire rope and guard rail

The posts should be set at a uniform distance from the edge of pavement, except where it is necessary to vary this distance at approaches to bridges or culverts. They should be set in a compacted soil, and the bottoms of the holes should be compacted by ramming to provide a stable foundation. They should be set plumb to the lines and grades given by the engineers, and should be accurately aligned. Suitable backfill material should be placed in layers not exceeding 4 in. deep, and each layer should be rammed thoroughly with hand tamps in such a manner as not to displace the posts.

The anchors should be accurately located and aligned, and should be set with as little disturbance as possible of the material against which the anchor will bear. Holes should not be excavated larger than is necessary to permit installation of the anchors in the prescribed manner. The anchors should be backfilled around with materials placed and thoroughly tamped in 4-in. layers. If excavation of a trench is necessary to placing the anchor rods, such trench should be kept to the minimum width practicable.

Placing rope and fittings

After the posts have been set true and rigidly to the line and grade given by the engineer, the wooden reel should be mounted so that it will revolve, and the wire rope run off by pulling straight ahead. Rope should be wired to prevent unravelling before being cut. The wire rope should be supported by the hook of the bolt, which should be loosely in place, and then drawn taut by means of rods attached to an anchor buried securely in the ground as shown on the drawings. Intermediate turnbuckles should be installed in accordance with the provisions of the drawings. After the rope has been drawn taut and anchored, the hook bolts should be tightened and the nuts set with a set punch or small chisel so that they cannot readily be removed. When taut, the cable-tightening nuts should be approximately at the center of the threaded portion of the tightening rods.

Completion and measurement

When the guard rail is completed, all posts should be plumb, rigid, and accurately aligned. Each rope should be taut, held securely in position with all fittings snugly and securely fastened. The site should be left free of debris, and all excavated material should be neatly spread.

Wire rope guard rail is measured by the linear foot from end post to end post.

Timber guard posts

Round posts should be grouped so as to minimize any noticeable variations in size between successive posts, with larger posts at the ends of sections.

Unless otherwise indicated on the drawings or directed, the posts should be spaced 6 ft center to center. They should be set at a uniform distance from the edge of the pavement except where it is necessary to vary this distance at approaches to bridges or culverts. They should be set in a compacted soil, and the bottoms of the holes should be compacted by ramming to provide a stable foundation. They should be set plumb, to the lines and grades given by the engineer, and accurately aligned. Suitable backfilling material should be placed in layers not exceeding 4 in. in depth, and each layer should be rammed thoroughly with approved hand tamps in such a manner as will not displace the posts. Posts that are out of alignment should be realigned. Different types and shapes of posts should not be used on the same project unless otherwise indicated on the drawings.

Posts should be painted in accordance with instructions on page 386.

Guard posts are measured by a report of the number of posts of each type within the limits designated.

GUTTERS AND CURBS

Standards for construction of several types of gutters and curbs are given in detail in the following pages.

Grouted rubble gutters

The lines, grades, and cross-sections furnished by the engineer should be followed in the formation of subgrade. All soft and yielding or otherwise unsuitable material should be removed and replaced with fine material thoroughly tamped in thin layers. The excavation should be done by methods that will cause the least practicable disturbance of the material outside required section. Special care should be exercised to avoid disturbing the material that will form the earth shoulders along and above each edge of the gutter.

Grout

The grout should be composed of one part cement to two and one-half parts sand. It should be mixed to proper consistency and uniform color, using clean water. The mixing should be done in a suitable mechanical mixer or in a clean, tight mixing box. The mixture should be stirred at appropriate intervals to maintain proper consistency.

Laying gutter

Construction of gutter should begin at its lower edge, or should be integral with the toe wall when one is required. Just before the stores are set, a thick, plastic grout should be applied to the subgrade of the gutter to an approximate depth of 2 in. The stones should form a completed course not less than 6 or 10 in. thick, as called for on the drawings or directed. Each stone should extend entirely through the course, and the face exposed in the finished surface should be approximately flat. They should be set perpendicular to the slope, and generally have the longer axis of the exposed face perpendicular to the center line of the gutter. The stones should be set in contact, with all joints staggered, and should be worked or rammed to a firm bedding. The setting should be completed before initial set of the mortar begins. Chinking with spalls should be done as necessary. The finished surface should be reasonably smooth and regular, but local variations of not more than 2 in. from the surrounding surface may be permitted for 10-in. gutters.

As the setting of the stones is completed, grout of proper consistency should be poured and broomed or worked into the joints, so as to fill completely the spaces between the stones. Pouring should be done at stages and intervals to avoid overflow through the joints below. As the grouting proceeds, stone chips or gravel should be worked into the joints, but should not be allowed to prevent the grout from penetrating and filling all of the voids.

Joints need not be filled flush with the surface, but they should be filled to within 2 in. of the surface for 10-in. gutters, and within 1 in. for 6-in. gutters.

Where toe walls are required they should be constructed of stones specified for the gutter proper. The stones should be laid in courses with fully interlocked, spalled, and grouted joints.

Weather conditions

These gutters should not be constructed while the weather conditions are unfavorable or while the subgrade or materials are frozen. They should not be constructed when the air temperature in the shade is below 35°F and rising, or below 40°F and falling. If freezing temperatures are expected after the grout has been placed and before it has fully set, the gutters should be protected against freezing.

Shoulders

As construction of the gutter progresses, the earth shoulder along and above the edges of the gutter should be formed by placing suitable material, containing sufficient moisture to permit thorough compaction, and carefully shaping and tamping until the shoulders conform to the typical cross-section shown on the drawings, and are thoroughly compacted throughout.

Gutters are measured by the square yard along the surface of the gutter to the limits designated for construction.

Stone gutters

For construction of subgrade for stone gutters, see instructions for subgrade of grouted rubble gutters. All material unnecessarily excavated below the required subgrade should be replaced with gravel.

Laying gutters

The gravel course should be spread to the thickness shown on drawings and brought to a uniform surface. The stones should then be placed by hand

and worked or rammed to a firm bedding in the layer of gravel. They should be set in close contact, with the joints approximately perpendicular to the finished surface. Joints should be broken satisfactorily, and the stone should present an approximately flat surface uppermost, with the long dimension of the exposed face at right angles to the center line of the gutter. Use of too many stones may cause an excessive volume of joints, and should be avoided. The finished gutter should be full specified thickness and should present a reasonably smooth, uniform surface.

As the setting of the larger stones progresses, the spaces between them should be filled with smaller stones or spalls. Wherever practicable each void should be filled with a single spall, and each spall should be in contact with at least two of the adjacent larger stones. The spalls should be rammed firmly into place, with the upper surface of the spall below the top surface of the lowest adjacent larger stone. When complete, the gutter should be composed of a tightly keyed mass of stones.

Shoulders should be constructed as described for grouted rubble gutters, page 390.

Gutters are measured by the square yard along the surface of the gutter to the limits designated for the construction.

Concrete curbs and gutters

Subgrade should be constructed or excavated to required depth below the finished surface, in accordance with the cross-sections shown on the plans. All soft, unyielding, or other unsuitable material should be removed and replaced with suitable material; the subgrade should be compacted thoroughly in layers not exceeding 4 in. in thickness, and finished to a firm, smooth surface.

Base course

If it is specified on the plans, or if soil conditions during construction make it necessary or desirable, a base course of approved sand, common pit gravel, broken slag, or common crusher stone or other material should be applied and consolidated beneath the curb, gutter, or combination curb and gutter.

Drainage openings

Curbs or gutters should be provided with drainage openings as indicated or directed, and all castings, pipe, or other fittings should be set accurately as indicated. The curb or gutter should be depressed at openings, if so indicated or directed. Where weep holes are installed, the engineer may require that an appropriate quantity of coarse aggregate be placed behind each opening.

Forms

Either metal or wood may be used for forms. They should be straight and free from warp, and of sufficient strength when staked to hold the concrete true to line and grade without springing or distorting. Wood forms should be of selected and dressed material at least 2 in. thick, except that on curves of short radii the thickness requirement can be waived to permit use of flexible material. Form boards for exposed curb surfaces should be at least as wide as the exposed surface. The facing board used for the front face of the curb in combined curb and gutter construction should be so constructed and shaped that its lower edge conforms to the radius specified on the drawings or by the engineer. Metal forms should be of approved sections and should have a flat surface on top. The depth of the forms should be equal to the depth of the curbing. Adequate means should be provided for securely fastening forms together at the tops. Forms should be securely staked, braced, and held together to the exact lines and grades established by the engineer, and should be sufficiently tight to prevent the leakage of mortar.

Metal divider plates or templates should be not less than $\frac{1}{8}$ in. thick, and of such design as to remain securely in place and produce a straight, smooth joint after they are removed. They should be of the full dimensions of the curb or gutter cross-section. All forms should be thoroughly cleaned and oiled before each use.

Reinforcement

If the use of reinforcing steel is required by the drawings, the steel should conform to requirements as to design and spacing indicated thereon. Approved methods of support and placement which will insure maintaining the steel in correct position should be employed.

Joints

All curbs, gutters, or curb and gutter combinations should be constructed with $\frac{3}{4}$-in. expansion joints at intervals of 50 ft, except when other spacing or thickness of joints is indicated on the drawings. The expansion joints should be formed with premolded joint filler of the thickness of the joint. The filler should be cut to the full depth, length, width, and cross-section of the joint, and any portion that protrudes from the finished concrete should be trimmed as directed.

Unless curbs, gutters, or curb and gutter combinations are reinforced, they should further be divided into sections not more than 10 ft in length, or as otherwise indicated on the drawings. The length of the sections may be reduced to not less than 6 ft when necessary for closures. This division should be made by means of metal templates or divider plates, which would extend across the full width of the curb, gutter, or combination curb and gutter, and at least 1 in. below its bottom surface.

Either an expansion joint or a metal template joint should be formed at all intersections at the point where the straight and curved sections meet.

All joints should be constructed truly perpendicular to the face and top of the curb or gutter, and all templates should be held securely and rigidly in place.

Placing concrete

Concrete should not be placed when air temperature in the shade is below 40°F and falling, or until it is at or above 35° and rising. The subgrade should be clean, smooth, firm, and moist, but not wet or muddy, when the concrete is placed.

The concrete should be deposited in layers thin enough to permit thorough spading and consolidating. It should be spaded and tamped or vibrated sufficiently to produce a dense, homogeneous mass, and to bring the mortar to the surface. Particular attention should be given to spading along the surfaces of the forms to eliminate voids. When the forms are filled, the surfaces should be struck off and then finished smooth and even with a wooden float. In striking off gutter surfaces, a template of the form and shape of the gutter should be used. Before the concrete is given the final finishing, the surface of the gutter and the top and face of the curb should be checked with a 10-ft straightedge, and all irregularities of ¼ in. or more should be eliminated.

While the concrete is still soft, the exposed edges of all curbs and gutters should be rounded with appropriate edging tools to the radii shown on the drawings or directed by the engineer. Unless otherwise indicated on drawings or directed, the back edge of curbs and the front edge of gutters should be rounded to a radius of ¼ in. The metal templates for the joints should be removed as soon as the concrete has set sufficiently to hold its shape, and the edges of these joints and of the expansion joints should be rounded to a radius of ¼ in.

Finishing

The forms should be removed as soon as concrete is hard enough not to be easily injured and within 24 hours, unless otherwise directed. All minor defects should be eliminated by filling with a mortar composed of one part Portland cement to two parts fine aggregate. Plastering should not be done, and all unsatisfactorily constructed sections should be removed and replaced with properly constructed substitutes. As soon as the defects are corrected, and while the concrete is still green, all exposed surfaces of the curbs and gutters should be finished smooth and even, and all tool marks should be removed by means of a wooden float, which should be kept moist by wetting.

Any exposed surfaces against which some rigid construction is to be made should be left smooth and uniform so as to permit free movement of the curb, gutter, or combination curb and gutter.

Protection and curing

Immediately after the finishing operation is completed, the concrete should be covered with either moist burlap or moist cotton mats, and kept continuously moist for at least five days, or longer if directed. Moist earth, sand, or other approved material may be substituted for the burlap or cotton mats after the concrete has set sufficiently. Whenever, in the opinion of the engineer, the air temperature is apt to fall below 35°F, adequate and approved means of protection should be provided to maintain temperatures around the concrete at not less than 45°F for a period of five days after placement of the concrete.

Backfilling and cleaning up

After the concrete has set sufficiently, the spaces along the front and back of the curb or gutter should be backfilled to the required elevation with suitable material, which should be thoroughly consolidated in 4-in. layers by appropriate hand or mechanical tampers.

All waste or foreign materials should be disposed of as directed, and the entire work left in a neat and presentable condition.

Curb, gutter, or combination curb and gutter are measured by linear foot along the curb or gutter to the limits designated for construction.

ROAD SURFACE TREATMENT

Specifications for construction and maintenance of aggregate, bituminous gravel, and crushed stone road surfaces are given below.

Aggregate—stabilized subgrade

This specification covers the stabilization of subgrades for pavements or bases by applying and mixing a suitable aggregate into the soil.

The length, width, and depth of stabilization and the quantity of stabilizer aggregate to be added should be as called for on the drawing or directed by the engineer.

Material

The stabilizer aggregate should consist of crushed stone, gravel, or sand, unless otherwise indicated on the drawings or directed. It should be composed of sound, tough, and durable particles, which should meet suitable tests to demonstrate these properties, when required by the engineer. The material should be free from schist, shale, and slate, and from vegetable or other foreign matter. All stabilized aggregate should be well graded from coarse to fine, and should meet the following requirements:

Retained on ¾-in. sieve: none
Retained on No. 8 sieve: 10–50 per cent by weight
Retained on No. 200 sieve: 90–100 per cent by weight

Construction methods

The stabilized mixture should be prepared in layers 4 in. thick. This is the maximum thickness, but the layers may be thinner if so required on the drawings.

The cut sections should be excavated and the embankment sections constructed to the elevation required to provide for stabilizing the subgrade or roadbed to the specified thickness, width, and finished elevation. Except where rock is encountered in cut sections, the surfaces thus graded should be a sufficient height above the required underside of the stabilization to provide sufficient soil for the first layer. In rock cuts, the excavation should extend to the full depth of stabilization.

The stabilizer aggregate should be spread uniformly over the entire area to be stabilized, to the thickness or at the rate specified for one layer. See Fig. 8.9 and 8.10. After the stabilizer aggregate is spread, it should be thor-

Fig. 8.9 Aggregate spreader

Fig. 8.10 Aggregate and asphalt spreader

oughly and uniformly incorporated into the soil immediately thereunder, to the depth necessary to construct a compacted layer of the specified thickness, by scarifying, plowing, and harrowing with a satisfactory disc harrow having discs not less than 22 in. in diameter. The soil and stabilizer aggregate should be turned from five to ten times, and more if required by the engineer. The existing soil should be loosened and harrowed before stabilizer aggregate is applied on any areas where satisfactory results are not obtained by performing this work after the aggregate has been spread.

After the materials have been mixed as specified above, the entire layer should be thoroughly compacted by means of a sheepsfoot or tamping roller. Additional sprinkling should be done if necessary to secure thorough compaction.

Sprinkling with water should be performed with an approved type of mechanical distributor, and the amount specified by the engineer. The distributor should be in first class working condition, and should be so constructed and adjusted as to control, by units, the amount of water being sprinkled.

Each successive layer should be constructed by uniformly spreading the required amount of soil, followed by the stabilizer aggregate, on the preceding layer. The materials should then be mixed, sprinkled, and compacted in the manner specified for the first layer. The final layer should be shaped to correct cross-section and grade.

Shoulders

Where stabilization of the entire width of roadbed is required, the overlying shoulder material should also be stabilized unless otherwise shown on the drawings. Sufficient stabilized material for completion of the shoulders should be mixed at the same time as the remainder of the stabilized material. If construction of the pavement or base is not immediately to follow the stabilization construction, the material for the shoulders should be spread and compacted as a part of the final layer and later bladed to the shoulder before the construction of the base or pavement is started.

Maintenance

The entire stabilized area should be maintained in a satisfactory manner and condition until preparation of the subgrade for the base or pavement is begun in accordance with specifications. Ditches should be kept open during the period of construction and maintenance so that the roadbed will be adequately drained.

The aggregate stabilized subgrade is measured by the square yard.

Bituminous road mix

Adequate and suitable equipment of such capacity and character as to insure the completion of the work in proper manner should be provided. The equipment should be of approved design, and should be maintained in first-class working condition at all times.

The following requirements should apply to equipment used:

The roller should be of such design, weight, and power as to insure satisfactory compression. It should weigh not less than 8 nor more than 10 tons, and should exert a pressure of not less than 175 lb per in. width of rear tread. The roller should be equipped with an approved device for wetting or oiling the wheels to prevent them from picking up the surface material.

The pressure distributor should be equipped with pneumatic tires having sufficient width of rubber in contact with the road surface to prevent breaking the bond of or forming a rut in the surfacing. If the distributor is mounted on a truck having only four wheels, it should not be loaded in excess of 800 gal of bituminous material. The distance between the centers of openings of outside nozzles of the spray bar should be the same width as the surface to be treated in one application. The outside nozzles at each end of the spray bar should have an area of opening not less than 25 per cent nor more than 75 per cent in excess of the other nozzles, which should have uniform openings.

The distributor should be so constructed and equipped that it will spread the bituminous material evenly, uniformly, and under the constant pressure specified, over the entire surface being treated. It should be capable of being operated at the full required capacity both at the beginning and at the end of each spread.

The distributor should be equipped with a thermometer and suitable instruments for determining the rate of application, and with hand sprays consisting of a hose attached to the distributor and fitted with a proper nozzle.

The mixing equipment should consist of a blade grader either self-propelled or drawn by a tractor, a multi-blade planer, or other approved equipment.

If a self-propelled blade grader is used, it should weigh not less than 8,000 lb, and the tractor should be of adequate power and weight.

If a multi-blade planer is used, it should be of an approved design which should weigh not less than 4,800 lb, and should be adequate and suitable for the work to be performed.

Seasonal and weather limitations

Road mix construction should not be done between Oct. 15 and May 15. Mineral aggregate should be applied only when the base is dry, and bituminous material should be applied only when the aggregate is dry. Bituminous material should not be applied when the temperature of the air in the shade is below 50°F or has been below 45°F during the preceding four hours.

Protection of structures

The surfaces of all structures should be protected by satisfactory methods or devices against disfigurement by bituminous materials. Any surfaces becoming disfigured should be restored to a satisfactory appearance.

Application of mineral aggregate

This construction should not be begun until the prime coat has completely dried, and not until at least 48 hours after completion of the prime coat. The base course should be firm and smooth, and the prime coat uniform and unbroken and free from caked or loose dirt or foreign matter when the mineral aggregate is applied.

Wooden forms constructed of straight, sound timber 1 in. thick and not less than 4 in. wide should be set accurately to line and grade along the required edges of the surface course and securely fastened and braced.

Mineral aggregate should be spread directly from trucks by means of approved mechanical spreaders, and should be distributed uniformly between the forms at the rate of 100 lb per sq yd, on the basis of an aggregate weighing approximately 2,650 lb per cu yd in the surface dry condition. To obtain approximately the same thickness with aggregates weighing appreciably more or less than 2,650 lb per cu yd surface dry, the weight of material to be applied per sq yd must be correspondingly increased or decreased. The aggregate should be shaped to a uniform depth and surface.

Mineral aggregate should be spread uniformly between the forms directly from trucks by means of approved mechanical spreaders, at the rate of 100 lb per sq yd, and should be shaped to a uniform depth and surface.

Application of the bituminous material

The mineral aggregate should be uniformly distributed when the bituminous material is applied. The bituminous material should be applied by means of a pressure distributor at a uniform rate of not less than 0.65 gal per sq yd, and not more than 0.80 gal per sq yd. The exact amount that will provide a sufficient and proper coating for the aggregate is to be determined by the engineer. The material should be applied at a uniform pressure of not less than 35 nor more than 75 lb per sq in. and at a temperature high enough to insure proper distribution. However, cut-back asphalt and emulsified asphalt should not be heated to a temperature above 150°F. Grade RT-6 tar should not be heated above 200°F, and grade RT-7 tar should not be heated above 250°F.

The material should be applied to the full width of the surface coarse in a single application. In beginning a succeeding application, care should be exercised to secure a proper junction with the preceding work. If necessary, building paper should be spread over the treated surface for a sufficient distance back to insure that the nozzles will be operating at a full force when the untreated surface is reached. The building paper should then be removed immediately and destroyed.

Any excess of bituminous material where applications overlap should be removed and satisfactory correction made. Parts of the surface not reached or properly covered with bituminous materials directly from the distributor should be treated by means of a hand spray attached to the distributor, or with approved hand-pouring pots. If at any time distribution within the specified limits is not uniform, the process should be stopped until satisfactory adjustment can be made or the operator replaced.

Mixing, shaping and rolling

Immediately after application of the bituminous material, it should be mixed with the aggregate until the latter is thoroughly coated and a homogeneous mixture is obtained.

If a blade grade is used, the materials should be bladed to a windrow in the center of the road. This windrow should then be evenly divided and the halves bladed successively to the quarter points, edge of surface course, and back again to the quarter points and center of the road. When no further mixing is required for proper coating of the mineral aggregate, the mixture should be allowed to stand in a windrow until the mixture begins to set up.

If the mixing is done by means of a multi-blade planer, it should be continued until, in the opinion of the engineer, the materials are uniformly coated. During mixing, the equipment should be manipulated to mix the materials to their full depth without disturbing the underlying construction.

When, in the opinion of the engineer, the material has cured sufficiently, it should be spread to a uniform depth between the forms and shaped to the required crown and to a uniform surface. As the shaping is completed, the material should be compacted by rolling. Rolling should start at the edges of the pavement and progress toward the center, in passages parallel to the center line of the pavement. Each passage of the roller should overlap the preceding passage by at least one-half the width of the rear wheel. Rolling should be continued until the entire surface has been covered at least three times daily for three consecutive days, and until there is no appreciable movement in front of the roller wheels. The forms along the edges of the surface course should be removed before the final rolling.

As the rolling progresses, all depressions and areas containing voids should be filled with premixed material, until a uniform surface of the specified regularity and crown is produced. The surface should be such that when a 10-ft straightedge is placed parallel to the center of the road, in any position, the surface will not deviate more than $\frac{1}{4}$ in. from the straightedge.

After completion of this course, and before the surface becomes dirty, stone chips should be spread uniformly over the road mix construction at the rate of not less than 5 nor more than 8 lb per sq yd.

The road mix course should be maintained under traffic until the seal coat is applied. Side ditches should be kept open during the period of construction and maintenance, and all shoulders should be bladed and repaired as necessary to leave them in good condition with proper shape.

Bituminous surface treatment

Hot bituminous material is covered with coarse aggregate and a seal coat consisting of a layer of fine aggregate spread between two applications of lighter bituminous materials. The treatment should be constructed on a primed base in accordance with these specifications, and in conformity with the lines, grades, and cross-sections indicated or directed.

Equipment

Adequate equipment should be provided of capacity and character to insure the completion of the work in proper manner. The equipment should be of approved design, and should be maintained in first-class working condition at all times. The following requirements should apply to the equipment used:

The roller should be of a design, weight, and power to insure satisfactory compression. It should weigh not less than 5 nor more than 8 tons, and should exert a pressure of not less than 125 lb per in. width of rear tread. At least one roller should be supplied for each mile, or fraction thereof, of bituminous material applied in one day. The roller used in the seal coat construction should be equipped with an approved device for wetting or oiling the wheels to prevent picking up of the surface material.

The pressure distributor should be equipped with pneumantic tires having sufficient width of rubber in contact with the road surface to avoid breaking the bond of or forming a rut in the surfacing. If the distributor is mounted on a truck having only four wheels, it should not be loaded in excess of 800 gal of bituminous material. The distance between the centers of openings of outside nozzles of the spray bar should be the same width as the surface to be treated in one application. The outside nozzles at each end of the spray bar should have an area of opening not less than 25 per cent nor more than 75 per cent in excess of the other nozzles, which should have uniform openings.

The distributor should be so constructed and equipped that it will spread the bituminous material evenly, uniformly, and under the constant pressure specified, over the entire surface being treated. It should be capable of being operated at the full required capacity at both the beginning and the end of each spread.

The distributor should be equipped with a thermometer and suitable instruments for determining the rate of application, and with hand sprays, each consisting of a hose attached to the distributor and fitted with a proper nozzle.

The broom drag should be of a long base design suitable for distributing the aggregate as specified, and should have means for its adjustment to the crown of the roadway at widths not greater than one-fourth the width of the surface course. It should be rigid enough and of such weight or adjustability as to afford proper planing action.

Condition of base

The primed base should be properly cured and repaired and in a firm and uniform condition when construction of the surface treatment is begun. Before the bituminous material is applied, the entire primed surface should be swept with revolving brooms supplemented by hand brooms until cleaned of all loose or caked clay or other foreign matter.

Application of bituminous materials

Weather conditions should be considered when applying bituminous materials. They should not be applied to a wet surface, nor when the temperature of the air in the shade is below 50°F or has been below 45°F during the preceding four hours.

The bituminous material should be applied uniformly at a pressure of not less than 35 nor more than 75 lb per sq in. It should be applied to the full width of the treatment in a single application unless the engineer directs that the application be made to only one-half width at one time, in order to permit movement of traffic. Where one-half width applications are made, care should be taken to secure a complete coating of the area along the adjoining edges, without an excess or deficiency of material.

The distributor should be operated at the full required capacity at both the beginning and the end of each spread. It should be stopped before the application begins to run light, or whenever one or more nozzles becomes clogged. Before beginning a succeeding application, building paper should be spread over the treated surface for a distance sufficiently far back to insure that the nozzles will be operating at full force when the untreated surface is reached. The building paper should be removed immediately and destroyed.

Any excess of bituminous material at transverse or longitudinal junctions of applications should be removed and correction made. Parts of the surface not reached or properly covered with bituminous materials directly from the distributor should be treated by means of a hand spray attached to the distributor, or with approved hand-pouring pots. If at any time uniform distribution within the specified limits is not consistently obtained, the process should be stopped until the distribution is satisfactorily adjusted or the operator is replaced.

Spreading mineral aggregates

All mineral aggregates should have been satisfactorily air-dried before being applied. Seal coat aggregate should contain no more moisture than will dry out satisfactorily before the second application of bituminous material is made. Each application of aggregate should be spread directly from trucks by approved mechanical spreaders. Trucks or spreaders should not pass over the uncovered bituminous material. If bituminous material is being applied to less than the full width of the treatment at one time, the aggregate should be spread to within 8 in. of the inner edge of the first application, until the adjacent application has been made. The spreading of the aggregates should follow the application of bituminous material as closely as practicable. The application of bituminous material should never advance more than one distributor load ahead of the spreading of the aggregate. Hot bituminous material for mat course should be applied at a rate of not less than 0.40 nor more than 0.45 gal per sq yd.

Application of coarse aggregate

The aggregate should be spread uniformly over the hot bituminous material at a rate of not less than 45 nor more than 50 lb per sq yd. It should follow the application of bituminous material closely enough to be embedded in the bituminous material while it is still hot.

Immediately after the aggregate has been applied, it should be dragged with a drag broom and manipulated with hand brooms until an even spread of uniform texture is obtained. Additional aggregate should be placed by hand on any areas not properly covered.

As soon as the aggregate has been uniformly distributed, it should be rolled with a power roller. The roller should work in a longitudinal direction beginning at the outer edges of the treatment and progressing towards the center, with each trip overlapping the previous one by one-half the width of the roller. The first rolling should be completed within one hour after the application of the bituminous material. The rolling should be repeated as often as may be necessary to key the aggregate thoroughly to the bituminous material. When the aggregate has become sufficiently and satisfactorily embedded in the bituminous material, any loose aggregate remaining should be removed from the surface.

Slow-moving, light traffic may be permitted to use the road as soon as the coarse aggregate has been spread. The treatment should be maintained under traffic not less than 10 nor more than 60 days, as directed by the engineer. All defects occurring in the treatment from any cause should be corrected. The defective portions should be taken out and replaced or repaired in an adequate and workmanlike manner, as directed by the engineer, before construction of the seal coat is begun.

First application of bituminous seal coat material

Just before the first application of bituminous seal coat material, the entire width of the surface should be thoroughly swept and cleaned until free of caked or loose dirt, dust or other foreign matter. The surface should be firm, in satisfactory repair, and thoroughly dry.

The bituminous material should be applied in two approximately equal applications, which should produce a total deposit of not less than 0.30 gal per sq yd. The first application should be made before and the second after the seal coat aggregate is spread. The first application should not advance more than two distributor loads ahead of the second unless otherwise directed by the engineer. Bituminous materials should be applied at the temperatures within the limits indicated in Table 8.4.

TABLE 8.4/TEMPERATURES FOR APPLICATION OF BITUMINOUS MATERIAL

Material	Grade	Temperature (°F)
tar	RT–6	80–150
tar	RT–7, RT–8	150–225
cut-back asphalt	RC–1	80–125
cut–back asphalt	RC–2	100–175

The first application of bituminous seal coat material should receive at once a uniform covering of the seal coat aggregate, at the rate of not less than 20 nor more than 25 lb per sq yd. The aggregate should be free from moisture when the final application of bituminous seal coat is made.

After the fine aggregate has been evenly spread, the final application of bituminous material should be made, according to the procedure described above for the first seal coat application. Immediately after the final application of bituminous material, the seal coat should be dragged with a broom drag. The dragging should continue until all aggregate is thoroughly coated and is distributed to a smooth, even spread of uniform texture. The operations should be so conducted as to complete the mixing and spreading before the mixture becomes stiff and difficult to place.

As soon as the mixing and spreading have been completed, the seal coat should be rolled with a power roller. The rolling should proceed in the manner specified for rolling coarse aggregate. Rolling should be repeated from time to time while the seal coat is setting up, as may be necessary to embed the aggregate firmly in bituminous material and produce a uniformly closed surface.

When finally completed, the surface should be such that when tested with a 10-ft straightedge, parallel to the center of the road in any position, the surface does not deviate more than ¼ in. from the straightedge.

Traffic should not be allowed on the seal coat during the period that dragging and rolling are in progress, nor until the engineer is of the opinion that the mat will not be deformed or injured thereby.

Maintenance

The completed surface treatment should be maintained by the contractor for a period of not less than 30 days, and thereafter, if necessary. All failures or defects that may develop should be fully and satisfactorily repaired and corrected, so as to leave an even-textured, uniform surface of correct shape.

Side ditches should be kept open during the period of construction and maintenance, and all shoulders should be bladed and repaired as necessary to keep them in good condition with proper shape.

GENERAL SPECIFICATIONS FOR PROTECTIVE TREATMENT OF ASPHALTIC CONCRETE PAVEMENT (JENNITE J-16)

I. Objective

(A) To extend the service life of asphaltic concrete pavement by halting damage by the solvent action of petroleum derivatives, the drying and oxidizing effect of the sun, and the complex of troubles caused by water seepage, including frost action.

(B) To provide the pavement with an attractive and easily cleaned surface.

II. Material

J-16 shall be thoroughly stirred in its container, preferably by power or with mortar hoe, so that a creamy homogeneous consistency of all J-16 in the container is assured for ready application. No adulterants of any nature should be necessary.

III. Preparation of pavement

Areas to be sealed shall be cured, firm and clean.

To be cured, the asphaltic concrete shall be oxidized on the surface so that there is no concentration of light oils at that level. This can often be determined by pouring a bucket of water on an area of the surface in question; if the water picks up a film of oil, the surface is not yet sufficiently cured for sealing.

To be firm, the pavement base must be sound, and there must not be any soft spots in the pavement proper. All soft or oil-soaked pavement material shall be removed and repaired with new paving material having aggregate of similar size and well compacted in place.

To be clean, the surface shall be free from sand, clay, dust, grease, and other foreign matter. Areas shall be swept thoroughly by hand or power broom, then flushed with clear fresh water, and any additional small particles of imbedded foreign matter removed. Any accumulations of oil or grease should be scraped off the pavement, then this section should be cleaned with caustic solution, the residue of which shall be thoroughly flushed with clear fresh water before application of J-16.

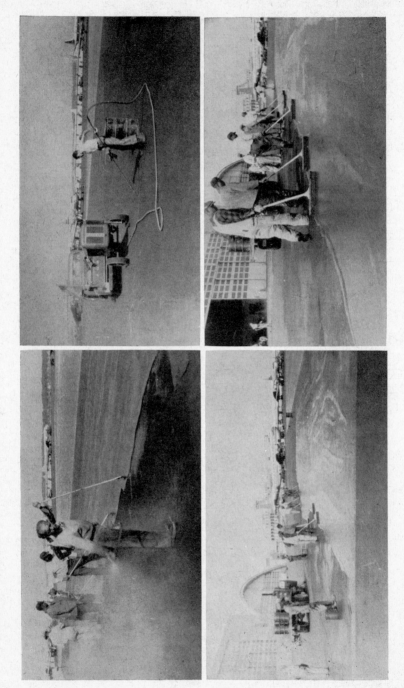

Fig. 8.11 Typical production jenniting by squeegee

GROUNDS MAINTENANCE HANDBOOK

IV. Application of material

Over damp pavement (free from standing water) prepared as described above, two uniform coatings of J-16 shall be applied. After the first coat has set, the second uniform application of J-16 shall be applied crosswise to the first application. The total application shall be equivalent to that provided by approximately 2 gal of J-16 per 100 sq ft, or 0.18 gal per sq yd.

Generally, application may be made by long handled 24 in. medium-soft rubber squeegee or long handled 18-in. nylon brush. Where pavement surface is unusually rough or very smooth, brush application is most suitable.

Application by distributor truck is most practical for sealing areas of over 40,000 sq yd.

Heavy duty compressed air spray equipment application is not recommended for application of J-16 over areas where fuel or oil spillage is prevalent.

Allow J-16 sealcoat to cure at least 24 hours before opening the roadway to traffic.

V. Notes

Weather: J-16 shall not be applied outside when weather is foggy or rainy, or when ambient temperature is below 45°F, nor shall J-16 be applied if such conditions are anticipated during the next eight hours.

Curing conditions: J-16 sets in approximately one hour at 77°F and 50 per cent relative humidity where circulation of air is present. If application is inside a building, ventilation should be provided for proper curing.

Precaution: Around fuel pumps, etc., where there may be intermittent gasoline or oil immersion, it is recommended that a third coat of J-16 be applied to cover any pinholes, voids, or holidays that may have been left inadvertently in the application of the first two coats.

Abrasive finish: If the surface texture of the pavement is such that a more abrasive treatment is desirable, the first coat application may be made with a homogeneous mix comprised of 2–4 lb of clean, sharp, well-graded sand for each gallon of J-16 distributed at the rate of approximately 0.1 gal per sq yd. The second coat of J-16 is then applied as described above, but without sand.

Cleaning tools: Application tools may be cleaned with water and/or coal tar benzene, xylene or toluene. This treatment (Jennite J-16) is excellent for many uses, such as playgrounds, tennis courts, driveways, airfields, paths, walks and parking areas.

Compacted gravel or chert surface course

All equipment used should be of adequate capacity and suitable character to perform the several operations as specified. The shaping and blading operations shall be done with a motor grader weighing not less than 7 tons, or with a blade grader weighing not less than 3 tons, which shall be drawn by a tractor of adequate power and weight. The blade of either grader shall not be less than 8 ft in length. Power rollers shall weigh not less than 8 tons,

Subgrade

The subgrade should be bladed and shaped true to line, grade, and cross section, and to a smooth, true surface. It should be of firm bearing throughout. Any unsatisfactory materials in the subgrade should be removed and replaced with suitable materials. When so indicated on the drawings or directed, the subgrade should be channeled to provide material for the completion of the shoulders. Side ditches should be kept open and the shaping should be so conducted as to insure against ponding of water on the subgrade during construction.

The subgrade should be kept prepared at an appropriate distance in advance of the surface course construction. Each section should be firm and free from irregularities at the time of placing surfacing materials.

Forms

Temporary wooden forms should be used where so indicated or directed, in order to confine and compact the material properly.

Spreading, shaping, and rolling

The gravel or chert should be applied to such loose thickness that the total compacted thickness of the completed surface course will not be less than that called for on the drawings. For example, a loose thickness of 6 in. would be compacted to 4 in. The material should be applied in two or more equal layers, whenever necessary to provide for satisfactory manipulation and compaction. The loose thickness of a layer should not be greater than 4 in., unless otherwise specifically directed by the engineer. The layer should be spread to a uniform depth and to the full width called for on the drawings, by means of an approved spreading device or from the tail gate of trucks so operated as to produce uniform distribution.

If unsatisfactory areas should be revealed due to a lack of reasonable uniformity in the material, mixing will be required to relieve this condition.

Where satisfactory results cannot be secured from mixing alone, coarse or fine material should be added, or the unsatisfactory material should be removed and replaced with appropriately graded material, as required or directed.

All hauling over the layer should be distributed over its entire surface in a manner to secure uniform compaction. The material should be kept bladed to a smooth surface during the hauling operations.

Where construction of surface in two or more layers is being done, the first layer should be placed and compacted before placement of the second layer is begun. The layer should be continuously maintained in a smooth condition, compacted either by traffic, or by rolling. Rolling should begin at the edges and progress towards the center of the roadway, with each trip of the roller overlapping the course of the preceding trip by at least 18 in. The first trip along the edge of the layer should lap on the shoulder by at least one foot. Rolling should continue until thorough compaction has been obtained.

If rutting or segregation of the material or other failures should occur at any time, such condition should be corrected by reshaping, remixing, or removal and replacement of the material as required to secure a uniform and well-compacted surface.

Whenever the material does not contain sufficient moisture to provide proper compaction, it should be sprinkled. When the sprinkling is being done before compaction of the layer is started, the material should be harrowed or otherwise manipulated, as required to distribute the moisture throughout the mass. Full advantage should be taken of weather conditions. The surface of the layer should be smooth and true to cross-section and grade when shaping and compacting are completed. The completed surface course should be well bonded and consolidated, with no tendency to ravel or form ruts under traffic.

Shoulders

Shoulders should be shaped and completed, as indicated on the drawing or as directed, with inner edges flush with the completed surface. If forms have been used, they should be removed and the spaces very carefully filled with compacted material.

The completed surface course should be maintained in a smooth and firm condition until taken over by agency or persons responsible for permanent maintenance.

Crushed stone surface course

If the stone does not contain sufficient fine materials having suitable binding properties to provide for a well-consolidated and bonded mass, additional binder should be added. This binder should consist of screenings, sand, clay, topsoil, other approved material. It should be clean material, of suitable gradation and binding value to correct deficiencies of these properties in the stone. The proportion of binder to be added to the stone will be determined by the engineer.

Equipment

The equipment used should be of adequate capacity and suitable character to perform the several operations as specified. The shaping and blading operations should be done with a motor grader weighing not less than 7 tons, or with a blade grader weighing not less than 3 tons, which should be drawn by a tractor of adequate power and weight. The blade of either grader should be at least 8 ft long. Power rollers should weigh not less than 8 tons.

Subgrade

Subgrade should be bladed and shaped to true line, grade and cross-section, and to a smooth, true surface. It should be of firm bearing throughout. Any unsatisfactory materials in the subgrade should be removed and replaced with suitable materials. When so indicated on the drawings or so directed, the subgrade should be channeled to provide material for the completion of the shoulders. Side ditches should be kept open, and shaped to prevent ponding of water on the subgrade during construction.

The subgrade should be kept prepared an appropriate distance in advance of the surface course construction. Each section should be firm and free from irregularities at the time of placing surfacing materials.

Temporary wooden forms should be used if required to confine and compact the material.

Application of stone

The stone should be applied at the rate called for on the drawings. This rate of application of stone should be maintained regardless of whether binder material is to be added. The stone should be spread uniformly upon the prepared subgrade, from vehicles with approved spreading devices, or from the tailgate of trucks if stone can be spread evenly and without segregation by this method. Material should never be unloaded on the subgrade in piles.

The material should be applied in two layers, whenever necessary, to provide for satisfactory manipulation and compaction. The loose thickness of any layer should not be greater than 4 in., unless otherwise specifically directed by the engineer.

Where the addition of binder material is necessary, it should be spread uniformly over the layer of stone at the rate directed. It should then be thoroughly mixed with the stone by blading, harrowing, or other appropriate methods. Or, instead of on the roadway, binder and stone may be mixed prior to application, if appropriate equipment is available.

As the spreading of the material proceeds, and after any mixing required to incorporate the binder has been completed, the layer should be shaped and smoothed to the required cross-section and to a uniform surface. All hauling over the layer should be distributed over the entire surface to secure uniform compaction. The material should be kept bladed to a smooth surface, both during the hauling operations and while the layer is open to traffic. If rutting or segregation of material should occur at any time, it should be corrected by reshaping, remixing, or removal and replacement of the material as required.

The surface course should be maintained and compacted until it becomes firm and well bonded, with no tendency to form ruts under traffic, and with no loose stone that will be displaced by traffic. Rolling should be done wherever hauling operations or traffic will not secure full bonding and compaction. Sprinkling should be done as required to aid compaction, and full advantage should be taken of weather conditions. Where construction in two layers is being done, full compaction of the first layer should be completed before placement of the second layer is begun.

Shoulders

Shoulders should be shaped and completed as indicated on the drawings or as directed, with inner edges flush with the completed surface. If forms have been used, they should be removed and the spaces very carefully filled with compacted material.

Maintenance

The completed surface course should be maintained in a smooth and firm condition, until taken over by the agency or persons responsible for permanent maintenance.

Hot bituminous seal coat

This seal coat of hot bituminous material and stone chips applied separately upon the bituminous road mix course or other designated surfaces, in accordance with the provisions of these specifications and in conformity with the lines, grades and cross-sections indicated or directed.

Equipment

Equipment of approved design and adequate to insure proper completion of the work should be provided, and should be maintained in first-class working condition at all times. The following requirements should apply to equipment used:

The roller shall be of such design, weight, and power as to insure satisfactory compression. It shall weigh not less than 5 nor more than 8 tons, and shall exert a pressure of not less than 125 lb per in. width of rear tread.

See specifications for pressure distributor as given under Bituminous Road Mix, page 398.

Seasonal and weather limitations

Seal coat construction shall not be done between October 15 and May 15.

The bituminous material should not be applied on a wet surface, nor when the temperature of the air in the shade is below 50°F or has been below 45°F during the preceding four hours.

The surface of all structures should be protected by satisfactory methods or devices against disfigurement by bituminous material. Any surfaces becoming disfigured should be restored to a satisfactory appearance.

Application of bituminous material

The entire surface to be covered should be swept and cleaned of all loose or caked foreign matter immediately before the application of bituminous material is started. The bituminous material should be applied uniformly at a pressure of not less than 35 nor more than 75 lb per sq in. It should be applied to the full width of the treatment in a single application, unless the engineer directs that the application be made to only half the width at one time in order to provide for movement of traffic. Where one-half width applications are made, care should be taken to secure a complete and even coating of the area along the adjoining edges of the applications.

The distributor should be operated at the full required capacity at both the beginning and the end of each spread. It should be stopped before the application begins to run light, or whenever one or more nozzles becomes clogged. Before each succeeding application, building paper should be spread over the treated surface, and so arranged that the nozzles will be operating at full force when the untreated surface is reached. The building paper should be removed immediately after the application and destroyed.

See specifications for treatment of excess bituminous material under Bituminous Road Mix, page 399.

The bituminous material should be applied at a uniform rate of 0.25 gal per sq yd. If asphalt cement is used, it should not be heated to a temperature greater than 350°F and should be applied at a temperature of not less than 300°F. If tar is used, it should not be heated to a temperature greater than 225°F, and should be applied at a minimum temperature of 175°F.

Application of stone chips

The stone chips should be satisfactorily air-dried before being applied.

The chips should be spread directly from trucks by means of approved mechanical spreaders. Trucks or spreaders should not pass over the uncovered bituminous material. If bituminous material is being applied to less than the full width of the treatment at one time, the chips should be stopped within 8 in. of the inner edge of the first application until the adjacent application has been made. The spreading of the chips should follow application of bituminous material as closely as practicable.

Stone chips should be spread uniformly over the hot bituminous material at a rate of not less than 20 lb per sq yd. They should follow application of the bituminous material as closely as necessary to insure their being embedded in the bituminous material while it is still hot. They should be uniformly distributed over the surface by dragging with a drag broom, supplemented by hand brooming as necessary.

As soon as the chips have been uniformly distributed, they should be rolled with a power roller. The roller should work in a longitudinal direction beginning at the outer edges of the seal coat and progressing toward the center, with each trip overlapping the previous one by one-half the width of the roller. The first rolling should be complete within one hour after the application of bituminous material. The rolling should be repeated as many times as may be necessary to key the chips thoroughly in the bituminous material. The surface should be covered by the rear wheels of the roller at least four times.

During rolling, the surface should be broomed to secure even distribution, and any areas containing an excess of bituminous material should have additional chips added and rolled in until the surface is uniform in appearance and texture.

At such intervals as may be necessary to avoid loss of chips from the surface, all chips should be swept from the edges of the pavement to the center and spread uniformly over the surface. This operation should be repeated until all chips are embedded in the surface. The surface may be rolled to expedite the embedment of the chips.

When finally completed, the surface should not deviate more than $\frac{1}{4}$ in. from a 10-ft straightedge placed parallel to the center of the road in any position.

Maintenance

The completed seal coat should be maintained for a period of not less than 30 days, and thereafter if necesary. All failures or defects that develop should be fully and satisfactorily repaired and corrected so as to leave an even-textured, uniform surface of correct shape.

Side ditches should be kept open during the period of construction and maintenance, and all shoulders should be bladed and repaired as necessary to leave them in good condition with proper shape.

Patching existing bituminous surfaces

Existing bituminous surfaces are patched by applying and compacting a mixture of mineral aggregate and bituminous material after suitable surface preparation. Areas which show indications of early failure should be repaired, as well as those which have already failed.

Areas to be patched should be prepared by digging out and removing all dirt and fine material and all surrounding surfacing material which has ravelled or disintegrated, or in which the bitumen has lost its bonding properties. These operations should be extended beyond the areas which have actually failed as far as necessary to obtain a firm, clean, well-bonded surface beneath and around the area to be patched. Apply patching material as soon as practicable after preparation of surface.

Patching material should not be applied when the surface to be patched is wet, or when the temperature in the shade is below 65°F, or has been below 55°F during the preceding four hours.

The surface to be patched and area of existing surfacing immediately adjacent thereto should be painted with a coat of tar of the grade specified above. When the tar has become tacky the previously mixed patching material should be applied.

Patching material should consist of a mixture of tar of the grade specified above, and of crushed stone. The proportions of the mix will be determined on the job by the engineer, and should be such that the surfaces of all particles of the aggregate will be thoroughly coated but there will be no excess of bituminous material, and the mixture will set up into a firm mass which will remain stable under the conditions of temperature and traffic to which it will be subjected.

Mixing should be done in an approved type of mechanical mixer, except that mixing by hand methods may be permitted by the engineer when the amount of patching to be done is small. In any case, the mineral aggregate should be dry before mixing and the materials should be thoroughly mixed to insure complete coating of the aggregate particles.

To keep the mixture from being displaced by traffic, the mixed materials should be kept in stock piles long enough to permit the volatile solvents to evaporate.

The mixture should be thoroughly tamped into place and shaped to be flush with the adjacent surfaces and to conform to the grade and section of the roadway. Enough stone chips to cover the bitumen should be spread over the patch and the immediately adjacent areas which were painted with tar.

Single bituminous surface treatment

Single surface treatment should consist of hot bituminous material and mineral aggregate in separate applications upon the primed base, in accordance with the provisions of the specifications and in conformity with the lines, grades and cross-sections indicated or directed.

See specifications for hot bituminous seal coat, above. The bituminous material should be applied at a rate of not less than 0.45 nor more than 0.50 gal per sq yd.

Application of mineral aggregate

The mineral aggregate should have been satisfactorily air-dried before being applied. The aggregate should be spread directly from trucks by means of approved mechanical spreaders. In no instance should the application of bituminous material advance more than one distributor load ahead of the spreading of the aggregate.

The mineral aggregate should be spread uniformly over hot bituminous material at a rate of not less than 45 nor more than 50 lb per sq yd. It should follow application of the bituminous material as closely as is necessary to insure its being embedded in the material while it is still hot.

Immediately after the aggregate has been applied, it should be dragged with a drag broom and manipulated with hand brooms until an even spread of uniform texture is obtained. Additional aggregate should be placed by hand on any areas not properly covered.

Stabilized base

Construction of a stabilized base should consist of base courses composed of natural or artificial mixtures of stone, slag, chert or gravel, with soil to which should be added calcium chloride and water. The base courses should be constructed in layers, to the lines, grades and typical cross-sections shown on the drawings or directed by the engineer, and in accordance with the requirements of these specifications.

Stone and slag

The stone or slag should be of such gradation that, when mixed with the soil to be used, it will meet the standards indicated in Table 8.5.

TABLE 8.5/GRADATIONS OF STONE AND SLAG IN BASE MIXTURES

Size of sieve passed	Minimum per cent of weight	Maximum per cent of weight
1–in.	100	
¾–in.	80	100
⅜–in.	50	90
No. 4	35	65
No. 10	22	50
No. 40	15	30
No. 200	5	15

If as much as 40 per cent of the mixture passes the No. 10 sieve, the fraction passing the No. 200 sieve should not exceed 50 per cent of the fraction passing the No. 40 sieve. If less than 40 per cent of the mixture passes the No. 10 sieve and the plasticity index of the mixture is low, the fraction

TABLE 8.6/GRADATIONS OF CHERT OR GRAVEL IN BASE MIXTURES

Size of sieve passed	Minimum per cent of weight	Maximum per cent of weight
2–in.		100
1½–in.	90	100
1–in.	75	100
¾–in.	60	95
½–in.	30	80
No. 4	25	60
No. 10	20	45
No. 40	15	35
No. 200	5	20

passing the No. 200 sieve may be not more than 65 per cent of the fraction passing the No. 40 sieve.

The fraction passing the No. 40 sieve should have a liquid limit of not more than 35 and a plasticity index of not more than 8.

Soil for binder

Soil for binder should be homogeneous material consisting primarily of fine soil particles and having such binding properities as to provide the physical structure and properties in the final mixture that are specified above. All soil should be obtained from sources approved by the engineer.

Chert or gravel

Local sources of chert or gravel and soil should be selected so as to produce a mixture of high density similar to the specifications given in Table 8.6, and having a maximum size of not more than 2 in.

If as much as 40 per cent of the mixture passes the No. 10 sieve, the fraction passing the No. 200 sieve should not exceed 50 per cent of the fraction passing the No. 40 sieve. If less than 40 per cent of the mixture passes the No. 10 sieve and the plasticity index of the mixture is low, the fraction passing the No. 200 sieve may be not more than 65 per cent of the fraction passing the No. 40 sieve.

The fraction passing the No. 40 sieve should have a liquid limit of not more than 35 and a plasticity index of not more than 8.

Calcium chloride should conform to the requirements of the Standard Specifications for Calcium Chloride, Designation D-98-34, of the American Society for Testing Materials.

Subgrade

The subgrade should be cut to the elevations established by the engineer, which in general will produce sufficient material for construction of the shoulders. It should be prepared true to the grade and to the lines and typical cross-sections shown on the drawings, or to authorized modifications thereof, and should be bladed and finished to a smooth and uniform surface. Adequate provisions should be maintained at all times to insure removal of water without ponding on or injury to the subgrade.

When properly shaled, the subgrade should be compacted to a firm and uniform bearing with a roller weighing not less than 8 tons. If necessary for good compaction, the subgrade should be moistened while it is being rolled.

The subgrade should be kept prepared an appropriate distance in advance of the placement of base materials. Any irregularities such as ruts, holes or the like which may develop should be corrected so that all material will be applied to a smooth, compact surface.

Guide planks

Unless otherwise indicated on drawings, guide planks having a nominal thickness of not less than 2 in. and a width equal to the loose thickness of the layer should be set for each layer of the base. They should be set to exact lines along the edges of the base, with top edges at a height above the subgrade, or the preceding layer, which is equal to required loose thickness of the layer under construction.

Mixed-in-place construction

The base should be constructed in approximately equal layers, the compacted thickness of which should not exceed 4 in. The base materials should be deposited along the subgrade or preceding layer in the quantities required for a complete layer and in the proportions fixed by the engineer. The calcium chloride should be spread uniformly over the soil in each layer at the rate of 1 lb per sq yd.

Water should be added to the materials in each layer of the base course prior to final mixing, so as to secure maximum compaction when rolled. The total quantity to be added should be determined by engineer. At the time of compaction, the total moisture content should equal approximately 8 per cent, by weight, of the base materials, or such other percentage as may be found appropriate from tests of the materials being used. The quantity added before mixing is begun should be sufficient to promote thorough and uniform moistening and proper workability without segregation of the materials.

The mixing should be done with a blade grader which should weigh not less than 8,000 lb. The grader should be drawn by a tractor of adequate power and weight. The materials should be turned from side to side until thoroughly mixed, the mixing equipment being manipulated so as to mix the materials to their full depth without appreciable disturbance of the underlying construction. When the mixing is completed, the mixture should be left in a windrow until it reaches the desired consistency, at which time it should be spread and shaped to a uniform depth and bladed to a smooth surface.

Before compaction of a layer is begun, shoulder material should have been placed adjacent to and flush with the guide planks to a width of not less than 2 ft, and tamped and shaped to a smooth surface. After the layer of base material is spread, the guide planks should be removed and the spaces left vacant filled and tamped.

Compaction of each layer should be done with a self-propelled roller weighing not less than 8 tons. The rolling should begin at the edges of the base, with the first course covering at least 1 ft of the shoulder, and should progress towards the center. Each track should overlap the preceding track by not less than 18 in. The rolling should continue until the entire surface of the layer is thoroughly and uniformly compacted. During the process of rolling, the moisture content should be maintained at approximately 8 per cent, and within such limits as the engineer may direct.

The surface of the final layer should not deviate more than $\frac{1}{4}$ in. from a 10-ft straight edge placed parallel to the center line of the road.

Pre-mix construction

Base materials may be combined in any suitable mixer before they are placed on the road. Enough water should be added to the materials during mixing operations to promote thorough mixing and to obtain the desired workability for handling and spreading without segregation.

Calcium chloride should be added in the proportions specified above before mixing is begun. The mixed materials should be spread on the road in approximately equal layers which will compact to a thickness not more than 4 in. As soon as any excess moisture has evaporated and the moisture in the mixture amounts to approximately 8 per cent, or such other percentage as may be determined from tests of the material being used to be appropriate, the layer should be shaped and compacted as specified for mixed-in-place construction.

Shoulders

The shaping and compacting of the final layer of the base should be followed as closely as conditions will permit by construction of such portions of the shoulders as have not already been completed. The necessary material should be placed, shaped, and compacted until the shoulders are firm and true to the cross-section shown on the drawings. The roller used for the base should be used to obtain thorough and uniform compaction of the entire shoulder.

Maintenance

Machining, rolling and sprinkling should be repeated frequently enough after completion of the base to maintain the surface smooth and compact. When maintenance is discontinued, both the base and the shoulders should be firm and smooth and true to the typical cross-section shown on the drawings.

Stabilizing subgrade with sheepsfoot roller

The subgrade and adjacent roadbed should be stabilized, where directed, by the use of a sheepsfoot roller in accordance with the methods herein specified. The engineer will determine the area to be treated after grading of the roadbed has been completed.

Construction methods

The section of roadbed to be stabilized should be shaped to conform to the subgrade on which the pavement is to be laid. The roadbed, to the width designed on the drawings or by the engineer, should then be loosened, by scarifying or other means, to a depth of not less than 6 in. below the final surface of the subgrade. The soil should be broken so that there will be no lumps more than 1 in. in diameter, and water should be added if necessary to bring the moisture content to that which is required by the engineer. The width of the roadbed being stabilized should then be compacted by rolling with an approved sheepsfoot roller until the roller will no longer sink into the soil. The soil should be so manipulated during the final stages of rolling that the subgrade under the proposed pavement will be at the proper lines, grades and cross-sections when the rolling is completed.

Tar prime coat

See specifications for equipment under Bituminous Surface Treatment, p. 401.

Preparation of base

The entire surface of the base should be firm, uniform, and of proper cross-section when the tar is applied. The prepared surface should be swept and cleaned of all loose material, dust, dirt, caked clay, and foreign material, to the full width to be treated immediately before being primed.

If the engineer so directs, the surface should be slightly damp when the priming is done, but should have no signs of free moisture on the surface, and should be firm enough not to show appreciable deformation under the rear tires of the distributor. If so directed, the base should be sprinkled for this purpose.

Rate of application

The prime coat should be constructed under "Tar Prime Coat—Single Application," or "Tar Prime Coat—Double Application."

When the prime coat is constructed under the single application, the tar shall be applied at a uniform rate of not less than 0.30 nor more than 0.35 gal per sq yd. It shall be applied in a single application except on portions of the surface where two applications are directed to prevent the tar from running.

When the prime coat is constructed under the double application, two applications of tar shall be made to the entire surface. The first application shall be made at a rate of approximately 0.25 gal per sq yd, and the second at approximately 0.15 gal per sq yd. The two applications shall not total less than 0.40 nor more than 0.45 gal per sq yd.

Method of application

The tar should not be applied when the temperature of the air in the shade is below 50°F or has been below 45°F during the preceding four hours. The temperature of the tar when applied should not be less than 80°F nor more than 150°F, and should be further limited if directed.

The bituminous material should be applied uniformly at a pressure of not less than 35 nor more than 75 pounds per square inch. It should be applied to the full width of the treatment in a single application, unless the engineer directs that the application be made to only one-half width at one time, in order to provide for movement of traffic. Where one-half width applications are made, care should be taken to secure a complete coating of the area along the adjoining edges of the applications without an excess or deficiency of material.

The distributor should be operated at the full required capacity at both the beginning and the end of each spread. It should be stopped before the application begins to run light, or whenever one or more nozzles become clogged. Before beginning a succeeding application, building paper should be spread over the treated surface for a distance sufficiently back to ensure that the nozzles will be operating at full force when the untreated surface is reached. The building paper should then be removed immediately and destroyed.

Any excess of bituminous material at transverse or longitudinal junctions of applications should be removed and correction made in a satisfactory manner. Parts of the surface not reached or properly covered with bituminous materials directly from the distributor should be treated by means of a hand spray attached to the distributor or with approved hand-pouring pots. If at any time uniform distribution within the specified limits is not consistently obtained, distribution shall be stopped until satisfactory adjustment of the distribution or replacement of the operator is made.

When the prime coat is being constructed in two applications, the second coat should not be applied until at least 48 hours after the first application, nor until all faulty distribution of the first coat has been corrected. The entire area should be free from dust, dirt, and other foreign matter and should be thoroughly dry when the second coat is applied.

Repairs

Any spots or areas that fail in any way after either prime coat application should be thoroughly cleaned out and the spaces filled either with material similar to that used in the base or with a mixture of seal coat aggregate and tar, as directed. The patching material should be thoroughly tamped as it is placed, and should be smoothed flush with the surrounding surface. When so directed, the exposed areas should be sprinkled before the patching is done. If material similar to that in the base is used, it should contain the proper amount of moisture for maximum compaction.

After this material has been placed, the surface should be primed by means of hand-pouring pots or other suitable equipment. If a mixture of tar and aggregate is being use, it should be prepared in the proportions of from 10 to 15 gal of tar to each cu yd of aggregate.

Traffic bound surface courses

Traffic bound surface courses should be prepared true to the lines, grades and cross-sections indicated or directed, and should be of firm and uniform bearing. They should be prepared by blading and shaping the roadbed constructed during grading of the roadway and by replacing any soft or unstable materials with suitable materials. Side ditches should be kept open, and the shaping should be so conducted as to insure against ponding of water on the subgrade during construction. The subgrade should be kept prepared an appropriate distance in advance of surface course construction. Each section should be firm and free from irregularities at the time of placing surfacing materials.

Application and shaping

All hauling operations should be conducted in such manner as to avoid rutting or displacement of the prepared subgrade or of surfacing material. Where such rutting or displacement occurs, it should be corrected by removal or reshaping of the materials so disturbed, so as to produce a finished surface course of uniform composition, stability, and thickness. The surfacing material should be applied at the rate specified on the drawings. It should be spread to proper width and thickness, and segregation and unequally compacted areas should be avoided.

All oversize material that may have been brought in should be exposed and either removed or broken down to meet the specification requirements. As the spreading of surfacing material progresses, the spread material should be leveled and planed to a smooth surface of the required cross section and crown.

Maintenance

Until the end of the maintenance period, surface course should be bladed as often as is necessary to prevent the development of holes, ruts, or waves. Full advantage should be taken of weather conditions in the blading operations.

At the end of the maintenance period, the surface course should be properly shaped and crowned and should present a smooth, firm, and uniform surface.

CHAPTER NINE

MATERIALS

SPECIFICATIONS

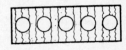

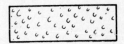

CHERT FOR TRAFFIC BOUND SURFACE COURSE

General requirements: The chert shall be composed of hard, durable, abrasion-resistant stone particles, together with clay or other satisfactory binding material, and shall be reasonably free from thin or elongated pieces.

Size requirements: The chert shall be composed of well-graded material, and shall meet the following requirements:

Passing 2¼-in. sieve: 100 per cent by weight
Passing 1½-in. square sieve: 80–100 per cent by weight
Passing No. 10 square sieve: 20–50 per cent by weight
Passing No. 200 square sieve: 0–25 per cent by weight

Sampling and testing: Samples shall be taken of the chert, and these shall be subjected to such laboratory determinations as may be needed for the particular deposit.

CHERT FOR COMPACTED SURFACE COURSE

General requirements: The chert shall be composed of hard, durable, abrasion-resistant stone particles together with clay or other satisfactory binding material, and shall be reasonably free from thin or elongated pieces. Chert that is not of uniform quality shall not be used.

Size requirements: The chert shall be composed of well-graded material, and shall meet the following requirements:

Passing 2-in. square sieve: 100 per cent by weight
Passing 1½-in. square sieve: 90–100 per cent by weight
Passing No. 10 square sieve: 20–50 per cent by weight
Passing No. 40 square sieve: 10–30 per cent by weight

The material passing the 40 sieve shall have a liquid limit not exceeding 45, and a plasticity index of 4 to 12, and shall contain clay in excess of silt.

Sampling and testing: Samples shall be taken of the chert, and these shall be subjected to such laboratory determinations as may be needed for the particular deposit.

COARSE AGGREGATES FOR PORTLAND CEMENT CONCRETE

General requirements: Coarse aggregate shall consist of crushed stone or gravel, having hard, strong, durable particles; free from disintegrated stone, salt, alkali, vegetable matter, or adherent coatings; and shall conform to the following requirements:

Physical properties:

Gravel

Wear (Modified Deval) Crushed particles,
   per cent by weight, not more than.........................20
Uncrushed particles, per cent by weight, not more than...........16
Soundness, sodium sulfate, 5 cycles..No marked disintegration

Crushed Stone

Wear (Deval), per cent, not more than.............6
Toughness, not less than........................6
Soundness, sodium sulfate,
   5 cycles...........No marked disintegration
Elongated pieces, per cent by weight, not more than...3

(An elongated piece is one which passes through a slot having a width equal to one-fifth the greatest dimension of the piece.)

Deleterious substances: The weight of deleterious substance in coarse aggregate shall not exceed the following percentage limits:

Material finer than No. 200 sieve: 1.00
Shale: 1.00
Coal and lignite: 1.00
Clay lumps: 0.25
Soft fragments: 5.00

Cinders and clinkers: 0.50
Shells: 1.00
Wet sticks: 0.025

The sum of all items noted in the above tabulation shall not exceed 5 per cent.

Gradation requirements: Coarse aggregate shall be well-graded between the limits specified and shall conform to the requirements given in Table 9.1.

TABLE 9.1/GRADATION OF COARSE AGGREGATES

Size no.	2.5 in.	2 in.	1.5 in.	1 in.	.075 in.	.375 in.	No. 4	No. 8
1	0	0–5	15–30	40–65	60–80	80–95	95–100	100
2		0	0–15	20–50	50–75	80–95	95–100	100
3		0	0–5	10–25	30–60	75–95	95–100	100
4			0	0–5	25–50	75–90	95–100	100
5				0	0–3	45–65	90–100	100

Sampling and testing: The sampling and testing of coarse aggregate shall be in accordance with the methods of the American Society for Testing Materials (ASTM), with subsequent revisions.

Sampling: ASTM D75–48
Wear of gravel: ASTM D289–46
Soundness: ASTM C88–46T
Wear of crushed stone: ASTM D2–33
Toughness of stone: ASTM D3–18
Material finer than No. 200 sieve: ASTM C117–48
Shale, coal and lignite, soft fragments, cinders and clinkers, shells, and wet sticks: Visual inspection
Clay lumps: ASTM C142–39
Sieve analysis: ASTM C136–46

In general, composite samples should weigh about 50 lb and should represent not more than 150 tons of material.

CRUSHED SLAG FOR BITUMINOUS SURFACE TREATMENT

Requirements: The crushed slag shall be made from air-cooled blast-furnace slag, and shall consist of angular fragments reasonably uniform in density and quality, and reasonably free from thin, elongated or glassy pieces, dirt, or other objectionable matter. The weight per cu ft of the crushed slag shall not be less than 75 lb. The crushed slag shall be uniformly graded from coarse to fine and shall meet the following grading requirements:

Retained on 1-in. square sieve: 0–5 per cent by weight
Retained on ¾-in. square sieve: 0–10 per cent by weight
Retained on ½-in. square sieve: 45–80 per cent by weight
Retained on ⅜-in. square sieve: 85–100 per cent by weight
Retained on No. 4 square sieve: 95–100 per cent by weight

Sampling and testing: The sampling and testing of the slag shall be done as specified by the American Society for Testing Materials, under the following designations:

Sampling: D75–42T
Weight per cu ft: C29–42

CRUSHED SLAG FOR MACADAM BASE AND SURFACE COURSES

General requirements: Crushed slag shall be air-cooled, blast-furnace slag, and shall consist of angular fragments reasonably uniform in density and quality, and free from thin, elongated, or glassy pieces, dirt, or other objectionable matter.

Properties: Crushed slag shall conform to the following requirements:

Weight per cu ft (dry rodded), not less than 70lb
Per cent of wear, not more than 15 lb

Gradation: The crushed slag shall conform to the following gradation requirements:

Retained on 1½-in. square laboratory sieve: 0 per cent
Retained on 1¼-in. square laboratory sieve: 0–75 per cent
Retained on ¾-in. square laboratory sieve: 20–75 per cent
Retained on No. 4 square laboratory sieve: 55–80 per cent

All aggregate shall be properly graded between the limits specified, and shall contain all material by crushing which will pass a No. 4 sieve.

Sampling and testing: The sampling and testing of crushed slag shall be done as specified by the American Society for Testing Materials, under the following designations:

Sampling: D75–48
Abrasion of rock: D2–33

CRUSHED STONE FOR BITUMINOUS ROAD MIX

General requirements: This material shall consist of clean, tough, durable pieces of stone, and shall be free from soft, thin, elongated, or laminated pieces and from disintegrated stone, vegetable matter, clay, silt, as well as all other deleterious substances. The crushed stone shall meet the following requirements:

Wear: not more than 6 per cent
Toughness: not less than 6

Size requirements: The crushed stone shall be uniformly graded from coarse to fine, and shall meet the following requirements:

Retained on 1-in. square sieve: 0–5 per cent by weight
Retained on ¾-in. square sieve: 20–50 per cent by weight
Retained on No. 4 square sieve: 95–100 per cent by weight

Sampling and testing: Crushed stone shall be sampled and tested as specified by the American Society for Testing Materials under the following designations:

Sampling: D75–42T
Wear: D2–33
Toughness: D3–18

CRUSHED STONE FOR BITUMINOUS SURFACE TREATMENT

General requirements: This material shall consist of clean, tough, durable pieces and shall be free from disintegrated stone, vegetable matter, clay, silt, or other deleterious substances. The crushed stone shall meet the following requirements:

Wear: not more than 6 per cent
Toughness: not less than 6

Size requirements: The crushed stone shall be uniformly graded from coarse to fine, and shall meet the following grading requirements:

Retained on 1-in. square sieve: 0 per cent by weight
Retained on ¾-in. square sieve: 0–10 per cent by weight
Retained on ½-in. square sieve: 45–80 per cent by weight
Retained on ⅜-in. square sieve: 85–100 per cent by weight
Retained on No. 4 square sieve: 95–100 per cent by weight

Sampling and testing: Crushed stone shall be sampled and tested as specified by the American Society for Testing Materials, under the following designations:

Sampling: D75–42T
Wear: D2–33
Toughness: D3–18

CRUSHED STONE FOR SINGLE BITUMINOUS SURFACE TREATMENT

General requirements: This material shall consist of clean, tough, durable pieces of stone, and shall be free from soft, thin, elongated or laminated pieces, from disintegrated stone, and from vegetable matter, clay, silt, or other deleterious substances. The crushed stone shall meet the following requirements:

Wear: not less than 6 per cent
Toughness: not less than 6

Size requirements: The crushed stone shall be uniformly graded from coarse to fine, and shall meet the following grading requirements:

Retained on ⅝-in. square sieve: 0–5 per cent by weight
Retained on ⅜-in. square sieve: 35–65 per cent by weight
Retained on No. 8 square sieve: 92–100 per cent by weight

Sampling and testing: The sampling and testing of crushed stone shall be done as specified by the American Society for Testing Materials, under the following designations:

Sampling: D75–42T
Wear: D2–33
Toughness: D3–18

CRUSHED STONE FOR MACADAM BASE AND SURFACE COURSES

Description: The crushed stone shall consist of crushed limestone, shall be free from disintegrated stone, salt, alkali, vegetable matter, and adherent coating, and shall be reasonably free from thin or elongated pieces.

The percentage of wear of the stone, as determined by Standard Method of Test for Abrasion of Rock, Designation D2–33, of the American Society for Testing Materials, shall not exceed 6 per cent.

Gradation: The crushed stone shall conform to the following gradation requirements:

Retained on 1½-in. square laboratory sieve: 0 per cent by weight
Retained on 1¼-in. square laboratory sieve: 0–5 per cent by weight
Retained on ¾-in. square laboratory sieve: 20–75 per cent by weight
Retained on No. 4 square laboratory sieve: 55–80 per cent by weight

All aggregate shall be well graded between the limits specified, and shall contain all material produced by crushing which will pass a No. 4 sieve.

CRUSHED STONE FOR SURFACE OR BASE

General requirements: The crushed stone shall consist of fragments of sound, durable stone, shall be free from disintegrated stone, salt, alkali, vegetable matter, or adherent coating, and shall be reasonably free from thin or elongated pieces. The percentage of wear of the stone shall not exceed 7.

Gradation: The crushed stone shall be well graded within the following limits:

Passing 1-in. sieve: 95–100 per cent by weight
Passing ¾-in. sieve: 70–100 per cent by weight
Passing No. 4 sieve: 30–65 per cent by weight
Passing No. 10 sieve: 15–45 per cent by weight
Passing No. 40 sieve: 8–25 per cent by weight
Passing No. 200 sieve: 0–10 per cent by weight

Sampling and testing: The crushed stone shall be sampled and tested as specified by the American Society for Testing Materials, under the following designations:

Sampling: D75–42T
Wear: D2–33

FINE AGGREGATE FOR PORTLAND CEMENT CONCRETE

General requirements: Fine aggregate for Portland cement concrete shall consist of natural sand or manufactured (stone) sand as specified below. Natural sand and manufactured sand shall not be used in the same structure.

Grading of the fine aggregate shall be held reasonably uniform. The vendor shall, when requested, submit samples proposed for use in the work.

Natural sand: Natural sand shall consist of clean, hard, strong, sound, durable, uncoated grains of silicious material, resulting from the natural disintegration of rock, or from the crushing of friable sandstone or conglomerate rocks. The weight of deleterious substances shall not exceed the following limits:

Material finer than No. 200 sieve: 3.0 per cent
Shale: 1.0 per cent
Coal and lignite: 1.0 per cent
Clay lumps: 1.0 per cent
Cinders and clinkers: 0.5 per cent

The sum of all material in the above tabulation shall not exceed 5 per cent.
The sand shall be free from injurious amounts of organic impurities.

Sand subjected to the colorimetric test and producing a color darker than the standard shall be rejected, unless the sand passes the mortar strength tests or it is established that such color is produced by lignite.

In the mortar strength test, a mortar made with natural sand is compared with a mortar of the same proportion and consistency made of the same cement and standard Ottawa sand. At the age of 7 or 28 days, the natural sand mortar should have a tensile or compressive strength of not less than 90 per cent of that developed by the Standard Ottawa Sand Mortar.

Manufactured sand shall be made from crushed stone manufactured by a commercial producer whose product has had a satisfactory record of durability for at least the past five years. The stone from which it is manufactured shall conform to the following requirements:

Wear: not more than 4 per cent
Toughness: not less than 6
Soundness, sodium sulfate, five cycles: no marked disintegration

Weights of deleterious substances shall not exceed the following limits:

Material finer than No. 200 sieve: 3.0 per cent
Shale: 0.5 per cent
Clay lumps: 0.5 per cent
Soft and flaky particles: 3.0 per cent

The sum of all material in the above tabulation shall not exceed 5 per cent.

Manufactured sand, when subjected to the mortar strength test, shall have a tensile or compressive strength at the age of 7 and 28 days of not less than that developed by mortar of the same proportions and consistency made of the same cement and Standard Ottawa sand.

Gradation requirements: The gradation of natural and manufactured sand, as determined by sieve analyses, shall conform to the following requirements:

Retained on ⅜-in. sieve: 0 per cent by weight
Retained on No. 4 sieve: 0–5 per cent by weight
Retained on No. 16 sieve: 15–45 per cent by weight
Retained on No. 50 sieve: 70–95 per cent by weight
Retained on No. 100 sieve: 95–100 per cent by weight
Fineness modulus: 2.25

Sampling and testing: Fine aggregate shall be sampled and tested in accordance with the methods of the American Society for Testing Materials (ASTM) and the American Association of State Highway Officials (AASHO) as follows:

Sampling: ASTM D75–48
Material finer than No. 20 sieve: ASTM C11-48
Shale: AASHO T10–35
Coal and lignite; cinders and clinkers: ASTM C123–44
Clay lumps: ASTM C142–39
Soft and flaky particles: visual inspection
Organic impurities: ASTM C40–48
Wear: ASTM D2–33
Toughness: ASTM D3–18
Soundness: ASTM C88–46T
Sieve analysis: ASTM C136–46
Tensile strength of mortar: AASHO T132–45
Compressive strength of mortar: AASHO T106–45

The fineness modulus is the sum of percentages in the sieve analysis divided by 100 when the sieve analysis is expressed as cumulative percentages coarser than each of sieves No. 100, 50, 30, 16, 8, 4, and so on.

In general, composite samples should weigh about 25 lb, and should represent not more than 150 tons of material.

GRAVEL FOR TRAFFIC-BOUND SURFACE COURSE

General requirements: The gravel shall be hard, tough, and durable, and reasonably free from thin, elongated, soft, or laminated pieces. It shall be homogeneous in character and free from injurious quantities of vegetable matter or other deleterious substances.

The loss by abrasion of the stone particles shall not be more than 25 per cent when tested in accordance with Tentative Method D289–42T of the American Society for Testing Materials.

Size requirements: The gravel shall be well graded between the following limits:

Passing 3-in. square sieve: 100 per cent by weight
Passing 2-in. square sieve: 90–100 per cent by weight
Passing 1½-in. square sieve: 70–100 per cent by weight
Passing No. 10 square sieve: 20–45 per cent by weight
Passing No. 200 square sieve: 0–25 per cent by weight

Sampling and testing: Samples of the gravel shall be taken and subjected to such laboratory determinations as may be needed for the particular deposit.

GRAVEL FOR COMPACTED SURFACE COURSE

General requirements: Material for compacted surface courses shall consist of a mixture of gravel, sand, and soil. The aggregate retained on the No. 10 sieve shall consist of hard, tough, durable particles which are sufficiently resistant to weathering and abrasion. All materials shall be uniformly graded, and shall be free from vegetable matter or other injurious or deleterious substances. All materials to be obtained from pits shall have been approved, after satisfactory laboratory tests, before being used. Pit-run gravel which is not of uniform quality shall not be used.

Size requirements: The material shall conform to the following gradation requirements:

> Passing 2-in. sieve: 100 per cent by weight
> Passing 1½-in. sieve: 90–100 per cent by weight
> Passing No. 4 sieve: 40–85 per cent by weight
> Passing No. 10 sieve: 35–75 per cent by weight

Material passing the No. 10 sieve, classed as soil binder, shall conform to the following gradation requirements:

> Passing No. 40 sieve: 35–95 per cent by weight
> Passing No. 200 sieve (combined with silt and clay): 10–40 per cent by weight

The fraction passing the No. 200 sieve shall be less than one-half of the fraction passing the No. 40 sieve.

SLAG CHIPS FOR BITUMINOUS SEAL COAT

Requirements: The slag chips shall be made from air-cooled, blast-furnace slag, and shall consist of angular fragments reasonably uniform in density and quality and reasonably free from thin, elongated or glassy pieces, dirt, or other objectionable matter. The weight per cubic foot of the slag chips shall not be less than 75 lb. The slag chips shall be uniformly graded from coarse to fine, and shall meet the following requirements:

> Retained on ⅜-in. square sieve: 0–5 per cent by weight
> Retained on No. 4 square sieve 50–90 per cent by weight
> Retained on No. 8 square sieve 92–100 per cent by weight

Sampling and testing: The slag shall be sampled and tested as specified by the American Society for Testing Materials, under the following designations:

Sampling: D75–42T
Weight per cu ft: C29–42

STONE CHIPS FOR BITUMINOUS SEAL COAT

General requirements: Stone chips for bituminous seal coat shall consist of clean, tough, durable pieces of stone, and shall be free from soft, thin, elongated or laminated pieces and from disintegrated stone, vegetable matter, clay, silt, or other deleterious substances. The chips shall meet the following requirements:

Wear: not more than 6 per cent
Toughness: not less than 6

Size requirements: The stone chips shall be uniformly graded from coarse to fine, and shall meet the following gradation requirements:

Retained on ⅜-in. square sieve: 0–5 per cent by weight
Retained on No. 4 square sieve: 50–90 per cent by weight
Retained on No. 8 square sieve: 92–100 per cent by weight

Sampling and testing: Stone chips shall be sampled and tested as specified by the American Society for Testing Materials, under the following designations:

Sampling: D75–42T
Abrasion of rock, per cent of wear: D2–33
Toughness of rock: D3–18

AGRICULTURAL LIMESTONE

Agricultural limestone may be of either of the two grades specified below.

Grade I: Grade I material shall contain calcium and magnesium carbonates equivalent to at least 80 per cent calcium carbonate, and must be fine enough for at least 80 per cent to pass through a 10-mesh sieve, provided that the relationship between these two percentages also meets the following requirement: When multiplied together, the two percentages expressed as decimals must be equal to at least 0.7200. (For example, 80 per cent $CaCO_3$ equivalent and 90 per cent passing a 10-mesh sieve would just qualify, because $0.80 \times 0.90 = 0.72$.) All the finer particles obtained in the production shall be included.

Grade II: Grade II material shall contain not less than 85 per cent of calcium carbonate or calcium carbonate equivalent. The material shall meet the following gradation requirements:

Passing No. 20 sieve, not less than 95 per cent by weight
Passing No. 60 sieve, not less than 55 per cent by weight
Passing No. 100 sieve, not less than 40 per cent by weight

Sampling and testing: Whenever the conditions so warrant, samples should be taken and tests and analyses made of the material.

Measurement: The weight of material to be paid for shall include the weight of moisture normally occurring in the material as delivered to the purchaser.

Note: The following weights of other compounds shall be considered equivalent to 100 lb of calcium carbonate:

Magnesium carbonate: 84 lb
Calcium hydroxide: 74 lb
Calcium oxide: 56 lb

ASPHALT CEMENT FOR MOP COAT

Properties: The asphalt cement shall be homogeneous and free from water, and shall conform to the following requirements:

Softening point (ring and ball method): 170–190°F
Penetration at 25°C (77°F), 100 g, 5 seconds: 25–90
Penetration at 0°C (32°F), 200 g, 60 seconds: not more than 15
Penetration at 46°C (115°F), 50 g, 5 seconds: not more than 70
Flash point (Cleveland open cup): not less than 205°C (400°F)
Evaporation loss at 163°C (325°F), 50 g, 5 hours: not more than 1 per cent
Penetration of residue at 25°C (77°F), 100 g, 5 seconds, as compared to penetration before heating: not more than 60 per cent
Ductility at 25°C (77°F): not less than 3.0
Amount insoluble in carbon disulfide: not more than 1.0 per cent

Sampling: Sampling and testing of the asphalt cement shall be in accordance with the Standard Method of Sampling Bituminous Materials, Method T40–42, of the American Association of State Highway Officials. Before samples will be taken the vendor shall furnish the sampler the data necessary to identify the shipment.

Method of testing: Testing of asphalt cement shall be in accordance with the following standard methods of the American Association of State Highway Officials:

Softening point: T53–42
Penetration: T49–42

Total bitumen: T44–42
Ductility: T51–42
Flash point: T48–42
Loss at 163°C (325°F) : T47–42

ASPHALT CEMENT

Properties: The asphalt cement shall be prepared from petroleum, shall be homogeneous, free from water, shall not foam when heated to 175°C (347°F) and shall conform to the following requirements:

Specific gravity, 25°/25°C (77°/77°F) : not less than 1.00
Penetration at 25°C (77°F), 100 g, 5 seconds: 150–200
Total bitumen (soluble in carbon disulfide) : not less than 99.5 per cent
Proportion of bitumen soluble in carbon tetrachloride: not less than 99.0 per cent
Ductility at 25°C (77°F) not less than 100 cm
Flash point: not less than 175°C (347°F)
Loss at 163°C (325°F), 5 hours: not more than 2.0 per cent
Penetration of residue at 25°C (77°F), 100 g, 5 seconds, as compared to penetration before heating: not less than 60.0 per cent

Measurement: Measurement of the volume of asphalt cement shall be based on the volume of the asphalt cement at 60°F. Volumes measured at temperature differing from 60°F shall be corrected by using an expansion coefficient of 0.0003 per °F. The gallonage from car weights shall be based on the specific gravity of the asphalt cement at 60°F, as shown by laboratory test reports.

Sampling: At least one sample of not less than one quart shall be taken from each lot or shipment of 10,000 gal or less. Samples shall be taken in accordance with the Standard Method of Sampling Bituminous Materials, Method T40–42, of the American Association of State Highway Officials.

Before samples will be taken, the vendor shall furnish the sampler the data necessary to identify the shipment.

Method of testing: Asphalt cement shall be tested in accordance with the following standard methods of the American Association of State Highway Officials:

Specific gravity: T43–35
Penetration: T49–42
Total bitumen: T44–42
Bitumen soluble in carbon tetrachloride: T45–42

Ductility: T51–42
Flash point: T48–42
Loss at 163°C (325°F): T47–42

CUT-BACK ASPHALT—RAPID-CURING TYPE

Properties: This material shall be the product of fluxing an asphaltic base with light volatile solvent. It shall be homogeneous and free from water, shall show no separation or curdling on standing, and shall meet the shown requirements in Table 9.2.

TABLE 9.2/SPECIFICATIONS FOR CUT-BACK ASPHALT

Grades	RC-1	RC-2
Minimum flash point (tag open cup)	80	80
Saybolt Furol viscosity at 50°C (122°F)	80–160	200–400
Distillation, per cent by volume:		
Minimum total to 190°C (374°F)	5	
Minimum total to 225°C (437°F)	12	10
Minimum total to 315°C (600°F)	20	15
Minimum total to 360°C (680°F)	40	35
Tests on residue from distillation		
Penetration at 25°C (77°F), 100 g, 5 seconds	70–120	70–120
Minimum ductility at 25°C (77°F) cm	60	60
Minimum solubility in CCl_4 (per cent)	99.5	99.5
Oliensis spot test	neg.	neg.

Measurement: Measurement of cut-back asphalt shall be based on its volume at 60°F. Volumes measured at temperatures differing from 60°F. Volumes at temperatures differing from 60°F shall be corrected by using an expansion coefficient of 0.0004 per degree Fahrenheit. The gallonage from car weights shall be based on the specific gravity of the cut-back asphalt at 60°F as shown by laboratory test reports.

Sampling: At least one sample of not less than 1 qt shall be taken from each lot or shipment of 10,000 gal or less. Samples shall be taken either at the source of supply or upon delivery, or both, in accordance with the Standard Method of Sampling Bituminous Materials, Method T40–42, of the American Association of State Highway Officials.

Water: T55–42
Flash point, tag open cup: T79–42
Viscosity, Saybolt Furol: T72–42
Distillation: T78–42

Penetration: T49–42
Ductility: T51–42
Solubility on carbon disulfide: T44–42
Oliensis spot test: T102–42

ASPHALT FILLER FOR JOINTS

Properties: The asphalt filler shall be prepared from petroleum, shall be homogeneous, free from water, shall not foam when heated to 175°C (347°F), and shall conform to the following requirements:

Penetration at 25°C (77°F), 100 g, 5 sec: 25–50
Total bitumen soluble in carbon disulfide: 99 per cent
Ductility at 25°C (77°F): not less than 4 cm
Flash point: not less than 205°C
Loss at 163°C (325°F), 5 hours: not more than 1 per cent
Penetration of residue at 25°C (77°F), 100 g, 5 seconds, as compared
to penetration before heating: not less than 60 per cent.

Measurement: Measurement of asphalt filler shall be based on its volume at 60°F. Volumes measured at temperatures differing from 60°F shall be corrected by using an expansion coefficient of 0.0003 per degree Fahrenheit. The gallonage from car weights shall be based on the specific gravity of the asphalt filler at 60°F as shown by laboratory test reports.

Sampling: At least one sample of asphalt filler of not less than one quart shall be taken from each lot or shipment. Samples shall be taken either at the source of supply or upon delivery or both, in accordance with the Standard Method of Sampling Bituminous Materials, Method T40–42, or the American Association of State Highway Officials.

Before samples will be taken, the vendor shall furnish the sampler the data necessary to identify the shipment.

Methods of testing: Asphalt filler shall be tested in accordance with the following standard methods of the American Association of State Highway Officials:

Penetration: T49–42
Total bitumen: T44–42
Bitumen soluble in carbon tetrachloride: T45–42
Ductility: T51–42
Flash point: T48–42
Loss at 163°C (325°F): T47–42

PREMOLDED EXPANSION JOINT FILLER

General requirements: The bituminous premolded joint filler shall be of the specified dimensions and of an asphaltic or tar composition of approved quality. The joint filler shall be of such character that it will not be deformed by ordinary handling during the hot summer months, nor become hard and brittle in cold weather. Thin strips of stiffener will be allowed. The bitumen shall be uniformly impregnated with suitable filler to reduce to a minimum its brittleness at low temperatures.

Physical properties: Premolded expansion joint filler shall conform to the following requirements:

Absorption: not more than 5 per cent
Distortion: not more than 1 in.
Brittleness: the joint shall not crack or shatter when subjected to the test for brittleness.

Method of sampling and testing: Where required, one section of premolded expansion joint filler at least 1 ft long and the full width of the joint shall be submitted from each consignment and shall be tested in accordance with the following method: Absorption: A specimen 2 in. by 6 in. is cut from the joint material in such manner that all edges are freshly cut. The specimen is weighed dry and then immersed in water for 24 hours, then removed and the surface water wiped off with a slightly dampened cloth. Specimen is then quickly weighed and per cent of absorption computed.

Distortion: A specimen 2 in. by 6 in., which is absolutely flat and straight, and has been cut parallel to the lay of the fiber, is clamped between two blocks so that the specimen cantilevers $3\frac{1}{2}$ in. horizontally. The clamp with the expansion joint is then placed for two hours in an oven maintained at 125°F. The deflection from the horizontal is then measured at the projecting end of specimen.

Brittleness: A specimen 2 in. by 6 in. is cut from the joint material parallel to the lay of the fiber and maintained at a temperature of from 4° to 6°C in water for at least two hours prior to testing. It is then clamped between two boards so that the specimen cantilevers $3\frac{1}{2}$ in. horizontally and is held in any suitable support. A cast-iron ball, weighing 0.95 lb and having a diameter of 1.875 in., is suspended by a cord which is tied to an eyelet soldered to the ball. For samples having a thickness of $\frac{9}{16}$ in. or less, the ball is suspended 1 ft above center of projecting portion of specimen. For samples over $\frac{9}{16}$ in. in thickness, the ball is suspended 2 ft above the specimen. Ball is released by burning string above eyelet.

DEFORMED STEEL BARS

General requirements: All bar reinforcement for concrete construction shall consist of deformed bars, and shall be either new billet steel of intermediate grade, or rail steel, conforming to the specifications of the American Society for Testing Materials, as follows:

Billet-steel bar for concrete reinforcement: A15–39
Rail-steel bars for concrete reinforcement: A16–35

Intermediate grade billet steel may be used for all bar reinforcement of concrete. Rail steel may be used only where specifically called for on the drawings. Rail steel shall in no case be used in concrete piling or where any bending of the bars in the field will be done. The form of the bars used shall be such as to provide a net section at all points equivalent to that of a plain square or round bar of equal nominal size.

All bars shall be free from mill scale, loose or thick rust, grease, paint, oil, dirt, or other defects affecting their durability or strength.

Bending: Bending shall be done in the fabricating plant before shipment. All bends shall be made when cold, and shall be carefully made to the dimensions specified, with a maximum tolerance of plus or minus $\frac{1}{2}$ in., except that the ends of hooks may have an unlimited overrun. The minimum radius of bends shall be four times the diameter of the bar, except as noted on drawings.

Testing: All reinforcing steel shall be tested and approved before being used.

Shipment: Bars shall be wired together in bundles for shipping, with all bars in any one bundle bearing same mark. To each bundle shall be securely attached a tag on which is plainly shown the mark of the bars in that bundle and an identification of the structure in which they are to be used.

CONCRETE GUARD RAIL ANCHORS

Casting: The anchors shall be cast in approved wooden or steel forms, which shall be tight and firm. During casting, the reinforcement shall be maintained securely in the correct positions. The concrete shall be thoroughly consolidated and spaded, and the exposed face struck off to a plane surface. All surfaces shall be free from honeycomb.

Curing: The anchors shall be cured by means of a wet covering for a period of at least seven days. Until removed from the forms, they shall be kept covered with wet burlap, which shall be placed as soon as the concrete has attained sufficient set to prevent its being marred. After the forms are removed, either the burlap or other approved coverings such as wet earth or sawdust may be used, or the anchors may be kept immersed in water.

STEEL PLATE GUARD RAIL FITTINGS

Rail plates: The rail plates shall be made from open hearth spring or semi-spring steel, properly tempered for toughness and high strength. The tensile strength of the steel plates from which the rail plates are made shall not be less than 75,000 lb per sq in. The rail plates shall have a thickness of not less than 12 gage, and a width after fabrication of not less than 12 in. If the average of five thickness measurements on a rail plate is more than 7 per cent lighter than the specified gage, or if the thickness at any one point is more than 10 per cent lighter than the specified gage, the plate shall be rejected. If 10 or more plates selected at random from a lot fail to meet the requirements, the entire lot shall be rejected. The plates shall be blanked to proper shape, punched, drilled, or fabricated, and ready for immediate assembly in the field, so as to conform readily to any alignment or grade existing at the locations where they may be required to be installed. Punching, drilling, cutting, or welding will not be permitted in the field. Warped or deformed pieces will not be accepted.

Provision shall be made in the design of the rail for automatic adjustment of its length sufficient to take up changes in plate length caused by the temperature variations to which it will be subjected.

If curved plates are used on any curve which is so sharp that the plates cannot be satisfactorily bent during construction, they shall be shaped to conform to the curvature during manufacture. The rail plates shall be galvanized or given a prime coat of red lead paint, uniformly applied to the entire surface.

The rail, when erected, shall have no sharp corners and no projections beyond the face of the rail of more than 3/8 in. Protruding heads of bolts shall be flattened and rounded.

Joints and fastenings: Brackets shall be designed to provide a spring action between the posts and the rail. They shall be made of spring or semi-spring steel, so constructed as to place the rail not less than 5 in. clear distance from the face of the posts. The brackets shall be bolted to the posts with not smaller than 5/8-in. bolts.

Joints between rail members after erection shall be such that they will withstand a tensional force applied to two adjacent rails of not less than 75 per cent of the specified strength of the full plate cross section, without permanent distortion. End joints shall have a minimum strength equal to that of the joints between rail members.

Splice bolts shall be buttonhead bolts provided with lock washers. End connections shall be of a type coinciding with the intent and design of the structure.

Galvanizing: Fastenings, spring brackets, and other fittings shall be galvanized by the hot-dip method and shall have a continuous coating of prime virgin spelter of uniform thickness, so applied that it will adhere firmly to the surface of the metal. This galvanizing shall withstand four immersions in a standard testing solution of copper sulfate as specified under the Preece test in the Standard Method of Determining Weight of Coating on Zinc-Coated Articles, Method T65-42 of the American Association of State Highway Officials. The first three immersions shall be for a period of one minute each, and the fourth immersion for a period of one-half minute.

When rail plates are galvanized, the coating shall be applied in the same manner and shall conform to the same test requirement specified for fastenings and fittings.

WIRE ROPE AND FITTINGS FOR GUARD RAIL

Scope: This specification covers ¾-in. and 1-in. wire rope and fittings for use in the construction of wire rope guard railings.

Wire rope: The wire composing the rope shall be galvanized annealed steel wire which shall be of such quality that the finished rope will meet the requirements specified below. The wire shall be cylindrical in form and free from scale, inequalities, flaws, and splits. All wires in the rope shall be of the same grade of steel and shall have approximately the same breaking strength.

Galvanizing: Each wire used in the rope shall be galvanized by the hot-dip process and shall have a continuous coating of zinc of uniform thickness so applied that it will adhere firmly to the surface of the wire. The weight of zinc coating for each wire shall be not less than 0.8 oz per sq ft of uncoated wire surface. The zinc-coated wires shall stand, without failure, four immersions of the Preece test. The first three immersions shall be for a period of one minute each, and the fourth immersion shall be for a period of one-half minute. The zinc shall be any grade that conforms to the requirements of ASTM specifications B6–37.

Rope construction: The ¾-in. rope shall be composed of three strands, each strand having seven wires. The diameter of the finished rope shall be not less than ¾ in. The lay of the finished rope shall be not more than 7½ in. The lay of the wires in the strand shall be not more than 4½ in. The diameter of the finished wires used in the rope shall be not less than 0.117 in., and not more than 0.124 in. The tensile strength of the rope shall be not less than 25,000 lb.

The 1-in. rope shall be composed of six strands with wire strand center, each strand having seven wires. The diameter of the finished rope shall be not less than 1 in. The lay of the finished rope shall be not more than 10 in. The lay of the wires in the strand shall be not more than $4\frac{1}{2}$ in. The diameter of the finished wires entering into the rope shall be not less than 0.105 in. and not more than 0.112 in. The minimum tensile strength of the rope shall be not less than 45,000 lb.

Fittings: Fittings shall include all metal parts required for anchorages, take-ups, and splices, and for attaching the wire rope to the posts or other supports. These parts shall include offset brackets, hook bolts, take-up bolts, cable ends, cable splicers, turnbuckles, anchor rods, plates, washers, nuts, and other fittings as called for.

All cable end, cable take-up and cable splice assemblies shall be equal in tensile strength to the minimum tensile strength specified for the wire rope. The tensile strength of anchor rods and fittings shall not be less than two-thirds of the total minimum tensile strength of all strands of rope in the railing.

All fittings shall conform to the specified requirements. Offset brackets shall be gray iron or malleable iron castings. Cable ends and cable splicers shall be steel forgings or malleable iron castings. They shall be of the locked variety. Hook bolts, take-up bolts, and anchor rods shall be made of suitable commercial quality steel. They shall be threaded to not less than the specified lengths. Washers and plates shall be of standard commercial quality steel.

Alternate fittings: Fittings that differ in design from the requirements will be considered for acceptance, provided they have the strength herein specified and are suitable for the purpose intended. Drawings or illustrative literature completely describing such fittings shall be submitted with the bids for approval.

Galvanizing fittings: Fittings shall be galvanized by the hot-dip process, using zinc that meets the requirements specified above for the wire rope. The galvanizing shall provide a uniform, continuous, coating which will adhere firmly to the surface of the metal. The weight of coating shall be not less than 2.0 oz per sq ft of surface. The coated metal shall stand, without failure, four one-minute immersions of the Preece test.

Marking and shipping: All wire rope shall be shipped upon substantial wooden or metal reels. The reel shall be mounted so that it will revolve and the rope can be run off by pulling straight ahead. All fittings shall be shipped securely wired together, or in suitable containers. All reels and packages of fittings shall be clearly and fully identified by a strong tag, firmly attached. Each reel shall be marked to show the length and weight of rope.

Methods of testing: Testing of wire rope and fittings shall be done in accordance with the following specifications of the American Society for Testing Materials or American Association of State Highway Officials:

Tests of wire rope (guard rail) AASHO: T39–42
Tests of weight of zinc coating, ASTM: A90–39
Tests of uniformity of zinc coating, Preece test, ASTM: A239–41

CREOSOTED YELLOW PINE PILES

Pressure treatment: All creosote oil used in preservative treatments shall be Grade 1 Creosote Oil, conforming to the requirements of Standard 4f of the American Wood-Preservers Association, or subsequent revisions thereof.

Fresh creosote oil shall meet every requirement of the specifications. The use of oil which has acquired water from previous treatments, but does not contain more than 5 per cent of water when reused, will be permitted if all other specification requirements are met. Whenever creosote oil containing more than 3 per cent of water is used, the entire percentage of water in the oil shall be deducted in computing the weight of oil retained. When the water in the oil does not exceed 3 per cent, no deductions for water will be made in computing the weight of oil retained.

Treatment process: The particular process to be used, and the amount of preservative to be retained, shall conform to the *Standard Specification for the Preservative Treatment of Yellow Pine Piles by Pressure Processes*, Standard No. 39b, of the American Wood-Preservers Association, as revised to date.

Handling: Treated piles shall be carefully handled to avoid breaking through the portions penetrated by treatment and exposing untreated wood. The use of chains, peavies, cant hooks, timber dogs, or other pointed tools on treated piles will not be permitted. Rope slings must be substituted.

Storage: The ground underneath and in the vicinity of all stored piles shall be free of vegetation, decaying wood material, and other rubbish.

TIMBER PILES

Note: These specifications are identical with the specifications of the American Society for Testing Materials, Designation D25–37, except with respect to the requirements for species of wood and knots.

Kinds of wood: Each class of piles shall be of the species of wood specified. Piles of different kinds of wood shall be delivered in separate lots.

Use classification: Timber piles are classified in these specifications under three general divisions according to the use intended, as follows:

Class A piles are suitable for use in heavy railway bridges and trestles. The minimum diameter of butt assumes the use of load-bearing timber caps 14 in. wide.

Class B piles are suitable for use in docks, wharves, highway work, and general construction. The minimum diameter of butt assumes the use of load-bearing timber caps 12 in. wide.

Class C piles are suitable for use in foundations which will always be completely submerged, for cofferdams, falsework, and sundry temporary work.

Class A and Class B piles, except as hereinafter provided, shall be free from any defects which could impair their strength or durability as piling. Such defects include decay, red heart, splits in piles to be treated or splits longer than the measured butt diameter of piles not to be treated, twist of grain exceeding one-half of the circumference in any 20 ft of length, unsound knots, numerous knots or holes, or shake more than one-third of the diameter of the pile. Piles which have been scored for turpentine shall be accepted, provided such scar does not exceed 36 in. and provided the scoring is of recent date, showing the scar to be entirely sound and free from insect damage.

Knots: The diameter of a sound knot shall not be greater than one-third of the minimum diameter of the pile at the section where it occurs, and shall not exceed 4 in. for piles 50 ft long or less. For piles over 50 ft long, knots between the section at mid-length and the butt shall conform to the limitation prescribed for piling under 50 ft. Between mid-length and the tip, single knots up to 5 in. in diameter will be permitted, provided they do not exceed one-half the minimum diameter of the pile at the section where they occur. The diameter of a knot shall be measured at right angles to the length of the pile. The sum of the diameter of all knots in any 6-in. length of the pile shall not exceed the maximum diameter specified for a single knot. The sum of the diameters of all knots in any 12-in. length of the pile shall not exceed one and one-half times the maximum diameter specified for a single knot.

General requirements: Class A and Class B piles shall be cut from sound, live trees, except that fire-killed, blight-killed, or wind-felled timber may be used if not attacked by decay or insects. Piles shall be cut above the ground swell. The tip shall be sound. The butt end shall be sound in cedar piles, which may have a pipe or stump rot hole not more than $1\frac{1}{2}$ in. in diameter. Piles shall have a gradual taper from the point of butt measurement to the tip.

All knots and limbs shall be trimmed or smoothly cut flush with the surface of the pile. Butt and tip shall be sawed square with the axis of the pile, or tip may be tapered to a point not less than 4 in. in diameter.

Sapwood: Piles for use without preservative treatment shall have as little sapwood as possible, and in exposed work the diameter of the heartwood shall not be less than $\frac{8}{10}$ of the actual diameter of the pile at the butt. Piles for use with preservative treatment shall have no sapwood restrictions, but preferably shall contain as much sapwood as is possible. In southern pine, the sapwood thickness shall not be less than $1\frac{1}{2}$ in., and in Douglas fir and larch, not less than 1 in. on the butt end.

Peeled piles: Peeled piles shall be peeled of bark, including the inner skin, soon after cutting, so that the piles are smooth and clean. Care shall be taken to remove as little sapwood as possible while peeling the bark. The piles shall be designated as piles for treatment. No pile shall be considered as thoroughly peeled unless all of the rough bark and at least 80 per cent of the inner bark which remains on the pile shall have been removed. There must be at least $\frac{3}{4}$ in. of clean wood surface between any two strips of inner bark.

The diameter of piles, measured under the bark, shall conform to the requirements shown in Table 9.3, subject to a permissible variation of $\frac{1}{2}$ in. in any diameter in not more than 25 per cent of the piles of that diameter.

The diameter of a pile, in cases where the tree is not exactly round, shall be determined either by measuring the circumference and dividing the number of inches by 3.14, or by taking the average of the maximum and minimum diameters at the location specified.

Length: All Class A and Class B piles shall be furnished on order cut to any of the following lengths: 16 to 40 ft in multiples of 2 ft, and over 40 ft in multiples of 5 ft. A variation of 6 in. in length shall be allowable, but the average length in any shipment shall be equal to or greater than the specified lengths. The length of each pile shall be legibly marked on the butt end with white or black paint.

Straightness: Piles shall be free from short or reversed bends, and free from crooks greater than one-half of the diameter of the pile at the middle of the bend. In short bends, the distance from the center of the pile to a line stretched from the center of the pile above the bend to the center of the pile below the bend shall not exceed 4 per cent of the bend, or $2\frac{1}{2}$ in. A line drawn from the center of the butt end to the center of the tip shall lie within the body of the pile.

Class C piles, in general quality, shall be of sound, live timber that will stand driving, and they need not be peeled if they are to be used without preservative treatment. They shall be free from decay and other imperfections, such as bad knots and shakes, which will materially affect their strength. Piles which have been scored for turpentine shall be accepted, provided such scars do not exceed 36 in., and provided the scoring is of recent date, showing the scars to be entirely sound and free from insect damage.

General requirements: The tip shall be sound. Piles shall have a gradual taper from the point of butt measurement to the tip. All knots and limbs shall

TABLE 9.3/DIAMETERS OF THREE CLASSES OF PILES

Length, ft	Class A Piles[1]			Class B Piles[1]			Class C Piles[2]		
	3 ft from butt		Tip	3 ft from butt		Tip	3 ft from butt		Tip
	Min.	Max.	Min.	Min.	Max.	Min.	Min.	Max.	Min.
					in.				
Douglas fir,[3] Southern pine									
under 40	14	18	10	12	20	8	12	20	8
40–50 incl	14	18	9	12	20	7	12	20	6
51–70 incl	14	18	8	13	20	7	12	20	6
71–90 incl	14	20	7	13	20	6	12	20	6
over 90	14	20	6	13	20	5	12	20	5
Chestnut, cypress, oak[4]									
under 30	14	18	10	12	18	8	12	20	8
30–40 incl	14	18	9	13	20	8	12	20	8
over 40	14	18	8	13	20	7	12	20	6
Cedar									
under 30	14	22	10	12	22	8	12	22	8
30–40	14	22	9	13	22	8	12	22	8
over 40	14	22	8	13	22	7	12	22	7

[1] Classes A and B differ in size only.

[2] Class C differs form Classes A and B in size and quality. In Class C piles a minimum diameter (at cut-off) of 10 in. may be specified for lengths of 20 ft and under.

[3] Where larch, lodgepole, or Norway pine, spruce, or tamarack poles are specified, their dimensions shall correspond to the requirements shown for Douglas fir and southern pine.

[4] Including black oak, pin oak, post or burr oak, red oak, white oak, or willow oak.

be trimmed or smoothly cut flush with the surface of the pile. Butt and tip shall be sawed square with the axis of the pile, or top may be tapered to a point not less than 4 in. in diameter.

Sapwood requirements shall be identical with those for Class A and Class B piles, as specified in "Sapwood," page 445.

The requirements for peeled piles shall be identical with those for Class A and Class B piles, as specified in last paragraph, page 445. The methods of measurement of diameter and the permissible variations in diameter shall be identical with those for Class A and Class B piles as specified above. The recommended sizes are given in Table 9.3.

The requirements for length shall be identical with those for Class A and Class B piles, as per paragraph above.

The requirements relating to straightness shall be identical with those for Class A and Class B piles, as specified above.

ALTERNATE SHORT FORM PROCUREMENT SPECIFICATION

Class A and Class B piles—General requirements: The piles shall meet the requirements of ASTM Specifications D25–37, except that the sum of the diameters of all knots in any 6-in. length of the pile shall not exceed the maximum diameter specified for a single knot, and the sum of the diameters of all knots in any 12-in. length of the pile shall not exceed one and one-half times the maximum diameter specified for a single knot.

Kinds of wood: The piles shall be of the species of wood indicated on the drawings or otherwise specified.

Class C piles—General requirements: The piles shall meet the requirements of ASTM specifications D25–37.

REINFORCED CONCRETE CULVERT PIPE FOR HIGHWAYS

General: This specification covers reinforced concrete pipe intended to be used for the construction of culverts. The several classes of pipe shall conform to the requirements of specification C76–41 of the ASTM, or the latest revision thereof, subject to the modifications and additional requirements specified herein.

Reinforced concrete culvert pipe furnished under these specifications shall be of the three classes as follows:

Standard-strength
Extra-strength
Double-strength

Requirements for all classes of pipe: All pipe shall be circular in cross-section, and all circumferential reinforcement shall be circular. The pipe joints shall be either bell-and-spigot or tongue-and-groove design. Either type will be acceptable, except when the contract or purchase order specifies that a particular one of these types is to be furnished.

All sizes of bell-and-spigot pipe shall have a line of circumferential reinforcement in the bell equal in area to that of a single line within the barrel of the pipe.

Tongue-and-groove pipe, 36 in. in diameter and larger, shall have a line of circumferential reinforcement in the tongue and in the groove equal in area to that of a single line within the barrel of the pipe. In sizes of pipe containing two lines of circumferential reinforcement, one line shall be near the inner surface and the other near the outer surface of the pipe shell, subject to the specification requirements that the minimum cover over the reinforcement shall be not less than 1 in.

Additional requirements for double-strength pipe: The shell thickness, the compressive strength of the concrete, and the number of lines of reinforcement for double-strength pipe shall meet the requirements specified for extra-strength pipe.

The double-strength pipe shall meet strength test requirements $33\frac{1}{3}$ per cent greater than those specified for extra-strength pipe.

Marking: There shall be clearly stenciled or indented on the inner surface of the barrel of the pipe: (1) a symbol identifying the class of pipe, (2) the date of manufacture, and (3) the name or trademark of the manufacturer.

Alternate types: Proposals for furnishing pipe that does not fully conform to the requirements of this specification will be considered, provided that such pipe shall be circular in cross-section and all circumferential reinforcement shall be circular, and provided further that it shall meet the requirements of this specification with respect to the strength of the pipe, absorption, and physical defects. The bidder shall furnish with his proposal a statement showing in detail the respects in which the pipe that he proposes to furnish does not meet the specification requirements, and, when so required, he shall also furnish drawings showing the complete design for the several sizes of pipe of each class, together with complete specifications.

OVAL REINFORCED CONCRETE CULVERT PIPE

This specification covers reinforced concrete culvert pipe having a shell composed of two semicircular segments joined by two straight parallel segments, each approximately equal in length to the thickness of the shell.

The several classes of pipe shall conform to the requirements of specification C–76–41 of the ASTM, or the latest revision thereof, subject to the modifications and additional requirements specified herein.

Classes: Reinforced concrete culvert pipe furnished under these specifications shall be of the three following classes:

> Standard-strength
> Extra-strength
> Double-strength

Requirements for all classes of pipe: The pipe shall have a single line of circumferential reinforcement which shall be circular. This line of reinforcement shall meet the requirements of ASTM C76, the specification that applies to elliptical pipe, except as otherwise specified herein. All sizes of pipe shall have a line of circumferential reinforcement in the bell equal in area to the circumferential reinforcement required in an equal length of the barrel of the pipe. The pipe joints shall be of the bell-and-spigot type only.

Additional requirements for double-strength pipe: The shell thickness and the compressive strength of the concrete for double-strength pipe shall meet the requirements specified for extra-strength pipe. The double-strength pipe shall meet strength test requirements 33⅓ per cent greater than those specified for extra-strength pipe. The quantity of circumferential reinforcement in double-strength pipe shall be 33⅓ per cent greater than that specified for extra-strength pipe.

Marking: A symbol identifying the class of pipe, date of manufacturer, and the name or trade mark of the manufacturer shall be clearly stenciled or indented on the inner surface of the barrel of the pipe.

Alternate types: Proposals for furnishing pipe that does not fully conform to requirements of this specification will be considered, provided such pipe shall be of the cross-section described above, and all circumferential reinforcement shall be circular, and provided further that such pipe shall meet the requirements of this specification with respect to strength of the pipe, absorption, and physical defects. The bidder shall furnish with his proposal a statement showing in detail the respects in which the pipe he proposes to furnish does not meet the specification requirements, and he shall also furnish drawings showing complete design for the several sizes of pipe of each class, together with complete specifications.

CAST-IRON CULVERT PIPE

This pipe may be smooth, corrugated, ribbed, or of other approved design. It shall be of good quality, free from scales, lumps and holes, blisters, and all other defects tending to impair its strength or durability. It should be solid and round, with inner and outer surfaces of true concentric cylinders. It shall be furnished in lengths of 3 ft or more, measured longitudinally along the inside of the pipe. All pipe shall be provided with bell and spigot, or other approved means of fastening the joints so as to prevent displacement. The pipe shall be thoroughly cleaned of rust, scale, grease, and dirt, and then coated inside and out by dipping in coal-tar pitch varnish. It shall not be tacky or brittle, nor have any tendency to scale off.

Classes of pipe: Pipes are classified as "standard strength" and "extra strength." All pipe of each class furnished shall have such strength that, when tested by the three-edge bearing method, they will support, without cracking, a load not less than that specified below for that class.

TABLE 9.4/STRENGTH REQUIREMENTS FOR PIPE

Class of pipe	Load (in lb per ft of laying length)
Standard strength pipe	$2,000 \times D$
Extra strength pipe	$3,000 \times D$

(D = nominal inside diameter of pipe specimen in feet.)

Test requirements: The thickness of the steel shall be measured, and if so directed the contractor shall be prepared to have sections of the pipe weighed. In any event, the contractor shall furnish duplicate copies of the bill of lading of each car of pipe, together with a statement of the number of feet of each size of pipe contained in the car.

Samples of pipe shall be selected and tested as prescribed in the Standard Method T33–42, of the American Association of State Highway Officials, submitting the pipe to the maximum load required only for the time necessary to obtain the stipulated data, unless initial cracking occurs, in which event the test will be carried to utter collapse. The load-supporting capacity of the pipe will be determined by the 3-edge bearing method.

CORRUGATED GALVANIZED METAL CULVERT PIPE

Corrugated metal pipe culverts shall be fabricated from corrugated galvanized sheets, the base metal of which shall be made by the open hearth process and shall conform to the chemical requirements of one of the types shown in Table 9.5.

TABLE 9.5/CHEMICAL REQUIREMENTS: BASE METAL FOR CORRUGATED CULVERT PIPE

Elements (per cent)	Pure iron	Copper-bearing pure iron	Copper iron	Copper-molybde-num iron	Copper steel	Tolerance by check of fin-ished sheet
Carbon, max.	—	—	—	—	—	—
Manganese, max.	—	—	—	—	—	—
Phosphorus, max.	0.015	0.015	0.015	0.015	—	—
Sulfur, max.	0.040	0.040	0.040	0.040	0.050	0.010
Silicon, max.	—	—	—	—	—	
Copper, min.	—	0.20	0.20	0.40	0.20	0.02
Molybdenum, min.	—	—	—	0.05	—	—
Sum of first five elements, max.	—	0.10	0.25	0.25	0.70	0.04
Sum of first six elements, max.	0.10	—	—	—	—	0.04

All rivets shall be of the same material as the base metal specified for the corrugated sheets. They shall be thoroughly galvanized or sheradized.

Spelter coating: The base metal sheets shall be galvanized on both sides by the hot-dip process, after which these sheets may be sheared to proper sizes. Sheets perforated for drainage shall be galvanized after drainage perforations have been punched. A coating of prime western spelter, or equal, shall be applied at the rate of not less than 2 oz per sq ft of double-exposed surface. If the average spelter coating, as determined from the required

450

samples, is less than 2 oz, or if any one specimen is less than 1.8 oz of spelter per sq ft of double-exposed surface, the lot sample shall be rejected. The finished sheets shall be of first-class commercial quality, free from injurious defects such as blisters, flux, and uncoated spots.

Sampling: Chemical analysis of the base metal of the finished sheet, when required, may be made of the samples taken for weight of spelter-coating test. For testing coating of sheets before fabricating, a sample strip about 3 in. wide shall be cut crosswise or on a diagonal across the sheet, the full width, from one sheet of each lot of the same identification symbol. From this strip and along the newly sheared edge, samples $2\frac{1}{4}$ in. square, or of equivalent area, shall be cut from the middle and near each end. For testing coating of fabricated culverts, when these tests are required, at least one sample $2\frac{1}{4}$ in. square, or a sample of equivalent area, shall be selected from 20 culverts of a shipment, provided that not less than three samples, each from a different section, shall represent any one shipment.

Analysis of finished sheets: When not otherwise provided, chemical analysis, when required, shall be in accordance with the methods of *Chemical Analysis of Steel, Cast Iron, Open-Hearth Iron and Wrought Iron, Designation E30–46T*, of the American Society for Testing Materials.

Tests for spelter coating: Where tests for weight of spelted coating are required, they shall be made in accordance with the *Standard Methods of Determining Weight of Coating on Zinc-Coated Articles, Method T65–42*, of the American Association of State Highway Officials.

Identification: No pipe shall be accepted unless the metal is stamped on each section to show: name of sheet manufacturer, name of brand and kind of base metal, gage number, weight of spelter coating, and identification symbols (heat number and pot number). The identifying brands shall be placed on the sheets by the manufacturer of the sheets, in such way that when rolled into culverts such brands shall appear on the outside of each section of each pipe. Pipe having any sections not so sampled shall be promptly rejected.

Corrugation: Corrugation shall not be less than $2\frac{1}{4}$ in. nor more than $2\frac{3}{4}$ in. center to center. Corrugations shall have a depth of not less than $\frac{1}{2}$ in.

Gage determination and tolerance: The gage of culvert sheets shall be determined by weight only. Pipe which is more than 5 per cent under the U.S. Standard Gage will be rejected.

FABRICATION

Shape: Culverts furnished under this specification shall be of the full-circle riveted type with lap joint construction.

Dimensions: The widths of laps, lengths of sheets, and gages shall be as specified in the following tabulation. The dimensions given for diameter of pipe are nominal.

TABLE 9.6/DIMENSIONS FOR CORRUGATED CULVERT PIPE

Nominal diameter, in.	Length of sheet before forming. in.	Minimum width of lap, in.	Galvanized sheet gage number	Connecting bands galvanized sheet gage number (minimum)
8	28.5	1.5	16	16
10	35	1.5	16	16
12	41	1.5	16	16
15	50.5	1.5	16	16
18	60	1.5	16	16
21	69.5	1.5	16	16
24	80	2	14	16
30	98	2	14	16
36	117	2	12	14
42*	137	3	12	14
48*	156	3	12	14
54	1–80 1–98	3	12	14
60	2–98	3	10	12
72	2–117	3	10	12
84	2–137	3	8	12

* Two sheets may be used by allowing sufficient total sheet lengths to provide for an additional standard lap.

Rivets and riveting: Rivets shall be of the following diameters for the gages specified:

TABLE 9.7/DIAMETERS OF RIVETS

Gage material	Diameter of rivet (in.)
No. 16	$5/16$
No. 14	$5/16$
No. 12	$3/8$
No. 8	$3/8$

All rivets shall be driven cold in such manner that the plates shall be drawn tightly together throughout the entire lap. The center of no rivet shall be closer than twice its diameter to the edge of the metal. All rivets shall have neat, workmanlike, and full hemispherical heads; they shall be driven without bending, and shall completely fill the holes. Longitudinal seams shall be riveted with one rivet in the valley of each corrugation. The longitudinal seams of all pipe 42 in. or more in diameter shall be double-riveted. Circumferential, shop-riveted seams shall have a maximum rivet spacing of 6 in., except that six rivets will be sufficient in 12-in. pipe.

The length of culvert specified shall be the net length of the finished culvert, which does not include any material used to procure an end finish on the pipe. If the average deficiency in length of any shipment of pipe is greater than 1 per cent, the shipment shall be rejected.

End finish: The inlet and outlet of all culverts fabricated of 16- or 14-gage sheets shall be reinforced.

Coupling bands: Field joints shall be made with bands of the same base metal as the culverts, and shall be not less than 7 in. wide for diameters of 8 to 30 in., inclusive; 12-in. bands are required for culverts with diameters 36 to 48 in., inclusive, and 24-in. bands for culverts with diameters 54 to 84 in. inclusive. Such bands shall be so constructed as to lap on an equal portion of each of the culvert sections to be connected, and preferably shall be connected at the ends by galvanized angles having minimum dimensions of $2 \times 2 \times \frac{3}{16}$ in. The 7-in. band shall have at least two galvanized bolts not less than $\frac{1}{2}$ in. in diameter. The 12-inch band shall have three and the 24-in. band shall have five $\frac{1}{2}$-in. bolts.

Workmanship: It is of the essence of these specifications that in addition to compliance with the details of construction, the completed pipe shall show careful, finished workmanship in all particulars. Culvert pipe on which the spelter coating has been bruised or broken, either in the shop or in shipping, or which shows defective workmanship, shall be rejected. This requirement applies not only to the individual pipe, but to the shipment on any contract as a whole. Among others, the following defects are specified as constituting poor workmanship, and the presence of any or all of them in any individual culvert pipe or, in general, in any shipment shall constitute sufficient cause for rejection:

Uneven laps
Elliptical shaping
Variation from a straight center line
Ragged or diagonal sheared edges
Loose, unevenly lined or spaced rivets
Poorly formed rivet heads
Unfinished ends
Illegible brand
Lack of rigidity
Bruised, scaled, or broken spelter coating
Dents or bends in the metal itself
Variations in diameter from nominal by more than $\frac{1}{2}$ in.

Field inspection and acceptance: The field inspection shall include an examination of the culvert pipe for deficiency in lengths of sheets used, nominal specified diameter, net length of finished culvert pipe, and any evidence of poor workmanship as outlined above. The inspection may include the taking of samples for chemical analysis and the determination of weight of spelter coating. The pipe making up the shipment shall fully meet the requirements of these specifications, and if 25 per cent of the pipe in any shipment fails to meet these requirements, the entire shipment may be rejected.

PAVED CORRUGATED METAL CULVERT PIPE

This pipe shall conform to all of the requirements as to materials, fabrication, inspection, test, and so on, except that the base metal shall conform to the requirements for either pure iron, copper-bearing pure iron, or copper molybdenum iron. The pipe shall be paved with bituminous material or some other satisfactory wear-resistant material.

If other types of invert paving materials are approved, requirements setting forth the value and methods of application of such pavements shall be drawn and become part of these specifications.

Bituminous coating: All pipe shall be coated inside and outside for at least the lower half of its circumference with an asphalt coating not less than 0.05 in. thick.

Invert pavement: In the bottom one-sixth of the circumference of the pipe there shall be applied one or more smooth pavements, which, except where the upper edges intersect the corrugations, shall have a minimum thickness of $\frac{1}{8}$ in. above the crests of the corrugations; or the bottom one-sixth shall be paved with an asphalt pad so disposed as to be of substantially equal thickness on the peaks and in the valleys of the corrugations as measured along a longitudinal section, and not less than $\frac{3}{8}$ in. in thickness.

Test requirements: The bituminous material shall be capable of meeting the requirements specified in the following tests.

Resistance to spalling test: A steel ball $2\frac{1}{4}$ in. in diameter and weighing 1.67 lb shall be dropped from a height of $7\frac{1}{2}$ ft through a vertical tube of 3-in. inside diameter, upon the outside crest of a representative sample. This test shall be conducted with the specimen at a temperature of 30°F. Failure of the material is indicated by its spalling from the metal on the inside of the pipe, or by the formation, on the inside of the pipe, of cracks longer than $\frac{1}{2}$ in. from the point of impact.

Stability test: Parallel lines shall be drawn along the valleys of the corrugations of a representative sample of coated pipe, and the specimen placed on end in a constant temperature oven, with the parallel lines in a horizontal position. The temperature of the specimen shall be maintained within 2° of 150°F for a period of four hours. At the end of this time, no part of any line shall have dropped more than $\frac{1}{4}$ in.

Permeability test: A 25 per cent solution of sulphuric acid, or a 25 per cent solution of sodium hydroxide, or a saturated salt solution (such as sodium chloride) shall be held in the valley of a corrugation for a period of

48 hours, during which time no loosening or separation of the bituminous material from the galvanizing shall have taken place.

Erosion test: A representative sample consisting of a 2-ft length of pipe, with ends closed by suitable bulkheads, shall be loaded with an erosive charge consisting of 3 gal of water, and 50 lb of brick. The brick must meet requirements for grade MW building brick to the Standard Specifications for Building Brick, Designation C62–44, of the Society for Testing Materials, and shall be broken into pieces 2 to 3 in. in diameter. The apparatus shall be arranged so that the sample of pipe may be revolved end-over-end about its tranverse axis in such manner that the erosive charge shall roll alternately along the inner surface of the top and bottom of the pipe (as when installed in service), and so that at least 75 per cent of the sample of pipe shall be immersed, as it revolves, in a bath of water maintained at a temperature of 50° to 55° F.

The sample shall be revolved at a speed of 3.7 rpm. The test shall continue for 50 hours, with a new erosive charge being used for each five-minute period. At the end of the test, the paving on the bottom portion of the pipe shall show no areas of bare metal more than 2 in. in length, nor on more than four of the seven corrugations.

Distortion requirements: Pipe 42 in. or more in diameter shall have its vertical diameter uniformly elongated by approximately 5 per cent. This shall be accomplished by shortening the horizontal diameter by means of threaded rods passing through holes not more than 6 ft apart, longitudinally, drilled through the sides of the pipe at the ends of the horizontal diameter. These rods shall be provided with nuts and washers, and the pressure necessary to shorten the diameter shall be applied to the pipe at both ends of the rods through wooden blocks of a size sufficient to prevent damage.

Care should be taken to avoid damage to structures from impact of stones as well as from equipment. Any damage which does occur should be properly repaired to the satisfaction of the engineer.

The metal of the pipe exposed by drilling or distorting operations shall be protected against rust by a coating of approved material. The pipe may be distorted either at the fabricating plant or on the job. If it is to be distorted on the job, holes of the required size and spacing to receive the distortion rods shall be drilled before shipment. Any injury to the pipe which may occur in drilling holes or distorting pipe shall be sufficient cause for rejection of the pipe.

VITRIFIED CLAY CULVERT PIPE

Material and manufacture: Clay pipe shall be manufactured from surface clay, fire clay, shale, or a combination of these materials. These materials, or any combination thereof, shall, when molded into pipe and subjected to suitable temperatures, produce a product that will be strong, durable, serviceable, free from objectionable defects, and that will conform to these specifications. Pipe shall be of the bell and spigot type, with inner and outer surfaces of true concentric cylinders, and shall be furnished in lengths of not less than 2 ft.

Classes of pipe: Pipe are classified as standard strength and extra strength. All pipe of each class furnished shall have such strength, that when tested by the three-edge bearing method, they will support an ultimate load in lb per lin ft equal to that specified in Table 9.8 for that class.

TABLE 9.8/STRENGTH FOR VITRIFIED CLAY CULVERT PIPE

Class of pipe	Ultimate load per ft of laying length (lb)
Standard-strength	$2000 \times D$
Extra-strength	$3000 \times D$

D = Nominal inside diameter of pipe specimen, in ft. The absorption of tested specimen of pipe shall not exceed 8 per cent.

Workmanship and finish: Each section of pipe shall be straight, with the planes of the ends of pipe perpendicular to its longitudinal axis. Pipes shall be substantially free from fractures, large or deep cracks, large blisters, laminations, and surface roughness.

The glaze shall consist of a continuous layer of salt glaze which shall be substantially free from large blisters or large pimples. No blisters shall exceed 3 in. in diameter, and no blisters or pimples shall project more than $\frac{1}{8}$ in. above the surrounding surface of the pipe for sizes up to and including 18 in. internal diameter. For sizes over 18 in. internal diameter, no blisters shall exceed in diameter more than 2 in. per ft of the internal diameter of the pipe, nor project above the surrounding surface of the pipe more than $\frac{1}{8}$ in. per ft of internal diameter of the pipe.

Not more than 10 per cent of the inner surface of any pipe barrel shall be bare of glaze except the socket, where glaze may be entirely absent. Glazing shall not be required on the outer surface of the barrel at the spigot end for a distance from the end of the pipe equal to the specified depth of socket. There shall be no well-defined network of crazing lines or hair cracks. Each section of pipe, when placed on end and dry-tapped with a light hammer, shall give a clear ringing sound.

Marking: Each length of pipe shall bear the name or trademark of the manufacturer, the location of the mill, and the class of pipe. The markings shall be on the exterior of the pipe, and shall be plainly legible for purposes of identification.

Inspection and rejection: Pipes shall be subject to rejection on account of the following:

1. Fractures or cracks passing through the shell or socket, except a single crack at the spigot end of the pipe not exceeding 75 per cent of the depth of the socket, or a single fracture in the socket not exceeding 3 in. in width nor 2 in. in length.

2. Chips or fractures on the interior of the pipe exceeding 2 in. in length, 1 in. in width, and a depth more than ¼ of the thickness of the shell.

3. Fire cracks or hair cracks sufficient to impair the strength, durability, or serviceability of the pipe.

4. Variation of more than ⅛ in. per lin ft in alignment of a pipe.

Testing: When the testing of pipe for strength and absorption is required, it shall be done as specified in *Standard Methods of Testing Concrete, Cast-Iron and Vitrified-Clay Culvert Pipe and Drain Tile, Designation T33–42,* of the American Association of State Highway Officials.

BITUMINOUS-COATED CORRUGATED METAL PIPE

Bituminous coating: All pipe shall be completely coated, inside and outside, with an asphalt cement which shall adhere to the metal tenaciously and shall not chip off in handling. The coating shall have a minimum thickness of 0.05 in., measured on the crest of the corrugations. The asphalt cement shall be 99.5 per cent soluble in carbon disulphide.

Test requirements: The bituminous material shall be capable of meeting the requirements specified in the following tests, which shall be made whenever required:

Test for resistance to spalling: A steel ball, 2¼ in. in diameter and weighing 1.67 lb, shall be dropped from a height of 7½ ft through a vertical tube of 3-in. inside diameter, upon the outside crest of a representative sample. This test shall be conducted with the specimen at a temperature of 30°F. Failure of the material is indicated by its spalling from the metal on the inside of the pipe, or by the formation, on the inside of the pipe, of cracks longer than ½ in. from the point of impact.

Stability test: Parallel lines shall be drawn along the valleys of the corrugations of a representative sample of coated pipe, and the specimen placed on end in a constant temperature oven, with the parallel lines in a horizontal position. The temperature of the specimen shall be maintained within 2° of 150°F for a period of four hours. At the end of this time, no part of any line shall have dropped more than ¼ in.

Permeability test: A 25 per cent solution of sulfuric acid, or a 25 per cent solution of sodium hydroxide, or a saturated salt solution (such as sodium chloride) shall be held in the valley of a corrugation for a period of 48 hours, without causing any loosening or separation of the bituminous material from the galvanizing.

Erosion test: A representative sample consisting of a 2-ft length of pipe, with ends closed by suitable bulkheads, shall be loaded with an erosive charge consisting of 3 gal of water and 50 lb of brick. The brick shall meet the requirements for grade MW building brick of *Standard Specifications for Building Brick, Designation C62–44,* of the American Society for Testing Materials, and shall be broken into pieces 2 to 3 in. in diameter. The apparatus shall be arranged so that the sample of pipe may be revolved end-over-end about its transverse axis in such manner that the erosive charge shall alternately roll along the inner surface of the opposite sides of the pipe, and so that at least 75 per cent of the sample of pipe shall be immersed, as it revolves, in a bath of water maintained at temperature of 50° to 55°F. The sample shall be revolved at a speed of 3.7 rpm, and the test shall continue for five hours. At the end of the test the pipe shall show no areas of bare metal more than 2 in. in length, nor on more than four of the seven corrugation.

Distortion requirements: Pipe 42 in. or more in diameter shall have its vertical diameter uniformly elongated approximately 5 per cent. This shall be accomplished by shortening the horizontal diameter by means of threaded rods passing through holes not more than 6 ft apart, longitudinally, drilled through the sides of the pipe at the ends of the horizontal diameter. These rods shall be provided with nuts and washers, and the pressure necessary to shorten the diameter shall be applied to the pipe at both ends of the rods through wooden blocks of a size sufficient to prevent damage.

The metal of the pipe exposed by drilling or distorting operations shall be protected against rust by a coating of approved material. The pipe may be distorted either at the fabricating plant or on the job. If it is to be distorted on the job, holes of the required size and spacing to receive the distortion rods shall be drilled before shipment. Any injury to the pipe which may occur in drilling holes or distorting the pipe shall be sufficient cause for rejection of the pipe.

WEEP HOLE AND UNDERDRAIN PIPE

Weep hole pipe shall be concrete pipe of specified diameter, and meeting the requirements for *Farm Drain Tile of the Standard Specifications for Drain Tile, Designation C4–24,* of the American Society for Testing Materials.

Vitrified clay pipe for underdrains shall be of the full circular, bell and spigot type, and shall meet the requirements of *Standard Specifications for Clay Sewer Pipe, Designation C13–44T,* of the American Society for Testing Materials.

Concrete pipe for underdrain shall be of the full circular, bell and spigot type, and shall meet the requirements of *Tentative Standard Specifications for Concrete Sewer Pipe, Designation C14–41*, of ASTM.

Perforated corrugated metal pipe shall be of the full circular type having either helical or annular corrugations. The gage for 6-in. pipe shall be the same as specified for 8-in. pipe. The perforations for both annular and helical pipe shall be approximately ¼ in. in diameter after galvanizing ,and shall be located on the inside crest of all corrugations. The perforations shall be in longitudinal rows, which shall be spaced on centers of not less than 1 in., measured circumferentially. The rows may be divided into equal groups so as to leave an unperforated segment in the bottom equal to approximately one-fourth of the periphery of the pipe. The number of rows of perforations in each pipe shall not be less than specified in the following tabulation:

6-in. pipe: 6 rows	15-in. pipe: 10 rows
8-in. pipe: 6 rows	18-in. pipe: 14 rows
10-in. pipe: 8 rows	24-in. pipe: 20 rows
12-in. pipe: 10 rows	30-in. pipe: 20 rows

Helical corrugated metal pipe shall be fabricated by welding or by forming a continuous lock seam running parallel with the helical corrugations. The seam must be continuous and so constructed as not to impair the shape and nominal diameter of the pipe. The corrugations shall not be greater than 2 in. center to center, nor less than ¼ in. in depth.

Connecting bands for helical pipe shall be not less than 7 in. in width, shall have corrugations that mesh with the corrugations in the pipe, and shall be fastened by not less than two ⅜-in. diameter galvanized bolts, if a one-piece band is used, or by not less than four ⅜ in. diameter galvanized bolts, if a two-piece band is used.

BRUSH TREATED TIMBER POSTS

Brush-treated timber posts may be produced from black locust, chestnut, post oak, white oak, cedar, black walnut, cypress, mulberry, or osage orange. All posts shall be sound and straight, and shall have the bark and inner skin removed for the entire length of the post, and all knots closely trimmed.

The posts shall be round and shall have a diameter at the small end of not less than 7 nor more than 11 in. The length of the posts and their shape at the small end shall be as directed. Unless a different method of shaping is required, a 1½-in. bevel shall be cut around the circumference of the small end. The beveling may be done either before or after the posts are set, unless otherwise directed.

Creosote oil: Creosote oil shall conform to the requirements of *Standard 4f* of the American Wood Preservers' Association for Grade 1 oil.

Brush treatment: All posts shall be brushed with two coats of hot creosote oil from the bottom of the post to a line which will be 1 ft above the ground after the posts are set. The brushing shall not be done until the posts have cured satisfactorily, nor while they are wet from rain. At the time they are treated, the entire surface shall be thoroughly clean and entirely without bark. Each coat shall be uniformly and thoroughly applied to the entire surface, and in all cracks and crevices. The first coat shall be allowed to dry thoroughly before the second coat is applied.

BUTT-DIPPED TIMBER POSTS

Posts, braces, and blocking: For use in guard rail construction, all posts, braces, and blocking shall be of black locust, chestnut, white oak, post oak, red cedar, black walnut, cypress, mulberry, osage orange, catalpa, cherry or long-leaf pine. They shall be cut from live timber and shall not contain unsound material or wormholes. The pieces shall have at least 80 per cent heartwood on any girth. The posts shall be sawed to specified dimensions. Braces and blocking shall be sawed to specified dimensions, or to such other dimensions as may be approved for metal plate guard rail construction, in order to conform to the guard rail design. All pieces shall be square edge, except that wane not exceeding one-eighth of the width of the face and one-fourth of the length of the post on one corner, or the equivalent on two or more corners, will be permitted on not more than 10 per cent of the posts constituting any one shipment.

The posts, braces, and blocking shall be free from loose, decayed, or clustered knots, or knots more than 2 in. in size, size being taken as one-half the sum of the maximum length and width of the exposed face of the knot. All pieces shall be free from splits, shakes, or checks which are longer, measured across the end of the piece, than one-third the width of the end.

All timbers shall be properly seasoned, before being treated. Timber which has been wet by rains shall be allowed to dry before being treated.

Preservation treatment: The preservative used for treatment of the posts, blocking, and braces shall be Grade 1 Creosote Oil conforming to the requirements of *Standard 4f* of the American Wood Preservers' Association, as revised.

The posts shall be butt-treated to a height of 4 ft 10 in., by the open tank method. Treatment shall consist of immersion first in a hot bath and then in a cooling bath of the preservative. All blocking, and all braces to a height of 10 in. above the ground, shall be treated by the same method.

460   GROUNDS MAINTENANCE HANDBOOK

The timbers shall be continuously immersed in the preservative and maintained at a temperature of 230°F, ± 5°, for a period of six hours. They shall then be transferred directly from the hot bath to the cooling bath, and continuously immersed therein for a period of not less than two hours, the temperature of the cooling bath being maintained between 150°F and the temperature at which solids forms in the preservative. The posts shall be immersed to the same depth and the preservative maintained at the same level in each bath. The exchange between hot and cooling solution shall be completed within 10 minutes.

Handling and storing: The treated portion of the posts, braces, or blocking shall not be handled with cant hooks, carrying tongs, or other tools which might puncture it.

Stored posts, braces, and blocking shall be piled at least 18 in. above the ground, on treated timbers or metal skids which will not sag nor allow distortion of the timber, and in a location which is well ventilated and free from vegetation.

CONCRETE GUARD RAIL POSTS

Casting: The posts shall be cast either in steel forms or in the approved wooden forms, dressed on all four sides. Forms shall be sufficiently braced so that no irregular lines or surfaces shall be produced. During casting, the reinforcement shall be maintained securely in the positions specified. When complete, posts shall conform to dimensions shown on the drawings, and each face shall be true and uniform in appearance, with no surface flaws or irregularities.

Curing and finishing: Within two hours after the posts are poured, they shall be covered with burlap, and this covering shall be kept continuously saturated until the forms are removed. Immediately after the forms are removed, the upper 3 ft of the posts shall be given a "rubbed" finish. Upon completion of this operation, the posts shall be immersed in water or covered with burlap, tarpaulin, or a heavy layer of earth or sawdust. The covering shall be kept thoroughly moist for not less than seven days. Care shall be exercised in handling and storing to avoid damage to the posts. Any posts which become cracked, broken, or objectionably chipped, or in which reinforcement is exposed, shall be rejected and immediately removed from the work.

PRESSURE TREATED TIMBER POSTS

These posts may be either round or sawed, unless otherwise indicated or directed, but different types shall not be used on the same job.

Round posts: Round posts shall be of sound southern yellow pine timber, and shall be straight and free from defects such as worm holes, unsound or loose or clustered knots, injurious shakes and checks, or other defects which might impair their strength or durability.

The posts shall have the bark and inner skin removed from their entire length, and all knots closely trimmed. They shall have a length of 7 ft and a diameter at the small end of not less than 7 in. nor more than 11 in. The posts shall be cut to exact length, and the small ends beveled 1½ in. around the circumference before being treated.

Sawed posts: Sawed posts shall be manufactured from southern yellow pine timber, and shall meet the requirements of the Southern Pine Association for *Dense Structural Square-Edge and Sound Timbers.* The posts shall be of the dimensions and shape specified. All cutting and shaping shall be done before treatment.

Pressure treatment: All operations in the pressure treatment of guard posts shall conform to the *Standard Specifications of the American Wood Preservers' Association,* as revised to date. The posts shall be treated to not less than 8 lb per cu ft final retention of creosote oil, by the empty-cell process.

Creosote oil: All creosote oil used in preservative treatments shall be Grade 1 creosote oil, conforming to the requirements of *Standard 4f of the American Wood Preservers' Association,* as revised to date.

All fresh creosote oil shall meet every requirement of the specifications. Use of oil which has acquired water from previous treatments, but does not contain more than 5 per cent of water when reused, will be permitted if all other specification requirements are met. Whenever creosote oil containing more than 3 per cent of water is used, the entire percentage of water in the oil shall be deducted in computing the weight of oil retained. When the water in oil does not exceed 3 per cent, no deductions for water will be made in computing the weight of oil retained.

Handling and storing: The treated portion of the posts shall not be handled with cant hooks, carrying tongs, or other tools which might puncture it.

Stored posts shall be piled at least 18 in. above ground, on treated timbers or metal skids which will not sag or allow distortion of the timber, and in a location which is well ventilated and free from vegetation.

TIMBER FENCE POSTS

General requirements: The posts and braces shall be produced from cedar, white oak, post oak, black locust, black walnut, mulberry, chestnut, cypress, or osage orange. They shall be thoroughly sound and free from defects such as wormholes, injurious splits and shakes, unsound knots, or clustered or large knots that materially impair the strength of the post.

The posts and braces may be round, split, or sawed, unless specific forms are required. Round or split posts and braces shall have all knots closely trimmed. Unless specifications state that unpeeled posts and braces are acceptable, the bark and inner skin shall be removed in a workmanlike manner, soon after cutting.

Size requirements: The length of the posts and braces shall be as specified. Except as otherwise noted, the cross-sectional dimensions of the posts and braces, or of the logs from which they are produced, shall conform to the following requirements, at the point where the cross-section is smallest:

Round posts and braces
Corner posts: 8 in.
Line posts: 4 in.
Braces: 4 in.

Split posts and braces
Quarter circle corner posts: diameter of log 16 in.
Half-circle line posts: diameter of log 8 in.
Quarter-circle line posts: diameter of log 10 in.
One-sixth circle line posts: diameter of log 12 in.
Braces: Requirements as for line posts

Sawed posts and braces
Corner posts: 7 in. x 7 in.
Line posts: 4 in. x 5 in.

Tapered line posts
Bottom cross-section: 4 in. x 6 in.
Top cross-section: 4 in. x 5 in.
Braces: 4 in. x 4 in.

BARBED WIRE FOR FENCES

All wire which is used in making of barbed wire shall be composed of basic open-hearth steel, and shall be galvanized. The wire shall have a tensile strength of not less than 70,000 lb per sq in. and shall stand tight winding around wire of the same size without sign of fracture. The wire shall be cylindrical and free from inequalities, flaws, splits, and scale.

Copper content: Copper content shall be not less than 0.20 per cent, unless it is specified that no copper content is required.

Galvanizing: The wire shall be galvanized by the hot dip process, with any grade of zinc that conforms to *ASTM Specification B6–37*. The weight of coating on each size of wire shall be not less than 0.6 oz per sq ft of wire surface, and the coating shall be capable of withstanding three one-minute immersions of the Preece test.

Manufacture: Barbed wire shall consist of two strands of wire twisted together, with wire barbs twisted around one or both of the strands of wire at uniform intervals. The barbs shall have sharp points approximately ½ in. long. The twist in strands of wire shall be uniform throughout, and shall be so made that the strain will come equally on both wires.

Styles and gages: This specification covers the following styles and gages of barbed wire. The particular style and gages to be furnished in each case shall be as called for on the drawings.

TABLE 9.9/STYLES AND GAGES FOR BARBED WIRE

Style no.	Use	Strand gage	Barb gage	Barb points	Barb spacing	Barb shape
A3	Hog	12½	14	2	3 in.	Round, wrapped twice around one strand
A4	Cattle	12½	14	2	5 in.	
B3	Hog	12½	14	4	4 in.	Round, interlocked and wrapped around one strand
B4	Cattle	12½	14	4	6 in.	
F3	Hog	12½	14	4	4 in.	Half-round, interlocked and wrapped around one strand
F4	Cattle	12½	14	4	6 in.	
G1	Hog	14	16	2	3 in.	Round, wrapped twice around one strand
G2	Cattle	14	16	2	3 in.	

Packaging and marking: The wire shall be compactly wound on strong metal or wooden spools. Each spool shall be legibly marked to show the style of barbed wire, length of wire in the roll, and the name or trademark of the manufacturer.

Methods of test: The wire shall be tested in accordance with the following specifications of the American Society for Testing Materials:

> Tensile strength of wire: E8–42
> Weight of galvanized coating: A90–39
> Uniformity of galvanized coating: A239–41

WOVEN-WIRE FENCING

The wire used in the fabrication of fencing shall be composed of basic open-hearth steel, and shall be annealed and galvanized. The wire shall have a tensile strength of not less than 70,000 lb per sq in., and shall stand tight winding around wire of the same size without sign of fracture. The wire shall be cylindrical and free from inequalities, flaws, splits, and scale.

Copper content of wire shall be not less than 0.20 per cent, unless it is specified that no copper content is required.

Galvanizing shall be by the hot-dip process, using any grade of zinc that conforms to ASTM specification B6–37. The weight of coating and uniformity of coating shall meet the requirements of Table 9.10.

TABLE 9.10/SPECIFICATIONS FOR GALVANIZED WOVEN WIRE FENCING

Size of Wire	Min. weight of coating, oz per sq ft of uncoated wire surface	Minimum number of dips of Preece Test
9 to 12½ gage, inclusive	0.8	4
14 gage and smaller	0.6	3

Manufacture: The woven fencing shall be of hinged-joint type, unless welded or wrapped stiff-stay joints are specified. All line wires shall have a tension crimp in each space between the stay wires. The fencing shall be so fabricated as not to remove any of the galvanizing or impair the tensile strength of the wire.

Styles and gages: The styles of fencing and corresponding gages of wire specified below conform to *Simplified Practice Recommendation R9* of the U.S. Department of Commerce. The particular style of fencing, gage of top and bottom line wires, gage of filler wires, and spacing of stay wires to be furnished in each case shall be as called for on the drawings. See Table 9.11.

TABLE 9.11/STYLES AND GAGES FOR WOVEN WIRE FENCES

Style of Fencing*	Top Line Wire Gage Number	Bottom Line Wire Gage Number	Filler Wire Gage Number	Spacing of Stay Wires (In.)
11–55, 10–47, 9–39,	(9	9	9)	Either 12
8–32, 7–26	(9	9	11)	or 6
	(10	10	12½)	
9–49, 8–45, 6–35	(9	9	9)	
	(9	9	11)	12 only
	(10	10	12½)	
9–39, 8–32, 7–26	11	11	14½	6 only

*The first two digits of the style number indicate number of line wires in the fencing; the last two digits indicate the width of the fencing. Example: number 11–55 represents a fence that has 11 line wires and is 55 in. wide.

Spacing of line wires: In the number 11–55, 10–47, 9–39, 8–32, and 7–26 styles of fencing the spacing of line wires shall not exceed 3½ in. at one edge and shall increase towards the opposite edge in a uniform manner such that the spacing in the 55-in. fencing will not exceed 9 in. In the number 9–49, 8–45 and 6–35 styles of fencing the spacing of line wires shall not exceed 9 in. at one edge, and shall decrease towards the opposite edge in a uniform manner, so that the minimum spacing in the 49-in. fencing will not exceed 4 in.

Packaging and marking: Each roll of wire fencing shall be tightly rolled and firmly tied. Each roll shall carry a tag showing the style of fence, gages of wire, length of wire in the roll, and name or trademark of the manufacturer.

Methods of test: The methods of testing for the wire shall be in accordance with the ASTM specifications as follows:

> Tensile strength of wire: E8–42
> Weight of galvanized coating: A90–39
> Uniformity of galvanized coating: A238–41

PAINT VEHICLE MATERIALS

Linseed oil shall conform to the requirements of the Standard Specification for Raw Linseed Oil, Designation D234–28, of the ASTM.

Turpentine shall conform to the requirements of the Standard Specifications for Spirits of Turpentine, Designation D–13–34, of the ASTM.

Drier shall be resin-free, and composed of lead, manganese, or cobalt, or a mixture of any of these elements combined with a suitable fatty oil and mineral spirits or turpentine; or a mixture of these solvents. It shall be reasonably free from sediment and suspended matter.

The drier when flowed on metal and baked for two hours at 100°C (212°F) shall leave an elastic film. It shall mix with raw linseed oil in the proportion of one volume of drier to 19 volumes of oil without curdling, and the resulting mixture when flowed on glass shall dry in not more than 18 hours. When mixed with pure raw linseed oil, in the proportion of one volume of drier to 8 volumes of oil, the resulting mixture shall be no darker than a solution of 6 g of potassium bichromate in 100 ml of pure sulfuric acid of specific gravity 1.84.

RED LEAD PAINT

Composition of red lead paint shall be as follows, by weight:
    Pigment: 75–79 per cent
    Vehicle: 21–25 per cent

Pigment: Red lead pigment shall conform to the requirements of *Standard Specifications for Red Lead, Designation D83–41,* of the ASTM, for 95 per cent grade dry pigment.

The method of test shall be in accordance with the *Standard Methods of Routine Analysis of Dry Red Lead, Designation D49–44,* of the ASTM

Vehicle: The vehicle shall have the following composition:

Raw linseed oil: 90 per cent
Turpentine: 5 per cent
Drier: 5 per cent

Consistency: Red lead paint bought in containers shall not show evidence of long standing by caking hard in shipping cans. Caked paint will be subject to rejection.

Shipment: Paint shall be delivered in containers of not more than 5-gal capacity.

WHITE LEAD PAINT

Composition: The composition of white lead paint shall be as follows, by weight:

Pigment: 66–69 per cent
Vehicle: 31–34 per cent

Pigment: The pigment shall have the following composition, by weight:

Basic carbonate white lead, basic sulfate white lead, or a mixture thereof: 75–80 per cent
Zinc oxide: 20–25 per cent
Magnesium silicate: 0–5 per cent

The several components of the pigment shall conform to the requirements for dry pigment specified by the ASTM under the following designations:

Basic carbonate white lead: D81–43
Basic sulfate white lead: D82–44
Zinc oxide (American process): D79–44

Magnesium silicate shall be white, finely ground, and free from admixtures of china clay or silica.

The method of test of pigment shall be in accordance with the Standard Methods of Routine Analysis of White Pigments, Designation D34–47, of the American Society for Testing Materials.

Vehicle: The vehicle shall have the following composition:

Linseed oil: 90 per cent
Turpentine: 5 per cent
Drier: 5 per cent

Shipment: Paint shall be delivered in containers of not more than 5-gal capacity.

BLUE LEAD PAINT

Composition: The composition of blue lead paint shall be as follows:

Pigment: 100 lb
Raw linseed oil: 2⅔ gal
Turpentine: 1½ pt
Drier: 1 qt

Pigment: Blue lead pigment shall be a sublimed blue lead in oil paste, the composition of which shall conform to the requirements for paste in oil of *Specifications for Blue Lead: Basic Sulfate, Designation D405–41*, of ASTM.

The method of analysis shall conform to the *Standard Methods of Routine Analysis of Yellow and Orange Pigments containing Chromium and compounds, Blue Pigments and Chrome Green, Designation D126–36*, of ASTM.

Shipment: Paint shall be delivered in containers of not more than 5-gal capacity.

ALUMINUM PAINT

Composition and properties: Paint shall be mixed in the proportion of 2 lb of pigment to 1 gal of vehicle. The resulting paint shall have good leafing quality and satisfactory brushing and leveling properties. When applied to a vertical, smooth, steel surface, it shall not break nor sag, shall set to the touch in not more than three and one-half hours, and dry hard and tough in not more than 18 hours, at a temperature of 20° to 30°C. The paint shall be mixed at the site of the work, and only sufficient quantity for one day's application shall be mixed at one time.

Pigment composition shall be an approved disintegrated-aluminum powder paste prepared by suitably grinding together in a ball mill a mixture consisting of not less than 63 per cent aluminum bronze powder (99 per cent pure) and not more than 35 per cent mineral spirits.

Aluminum paste shall conform to the following requirements:

Not less than 97 per cent of the aluminum particles shall pass a No. 325 sieve.

The liquid with which the aluminum powder is compounded to form the paste shall be completely volatile at 105°C.

There shall be no appreciable settling out of the metallic portion of the paste in the container; that is, no free liquid shall be present.

The aluminum paste shall show a minimum leafing percentage of 60 per cent before and after heating in a closed vessel for three hours at a temperature of 45°C.

The methods of test for the above requirements shall be in accordance with the methods prescribed in the pamphlet *Characteristics and Specifications for Alcoa Albron Paste* of the Aluminum Company of America.

The vehicle shall be Chinawood oil, 100 per cent phenolic resin varnish, which conforms to the following requirements:

The varnish shall be clear and transparent, and not less than 50 per cent by weight shall consist of nonvolatile oil and resin. The oil-resin ratio shall not exceed 33 gal of oil to 100 lb of resin.

The entire oil content shall be Chinawood (tung) oil.

The resin content shall be 100 per cent phenol-formaldehyde condensate, free from resin, ester gum, or other nonphenolic resins. The volatile thinner shall contain not less than 20 per cent high-flash solvent naptha, and shall be free from toxic hydro-carbons, such as benzol.

The viscosity shall be between 0.50 and 0.85 poises at 25°C corresponding to "Tubes Ato C" of the Bardiner-Holt Air Bubble Viscometer.

The flash point shall be not below 30°C in a closed cup tester. The varnish shall pass a Kauri Reduction Test of 140 per cent, using the method described in Paragraph F–2g, *Federal Specification TT–V–81a, Varnish; Mixing (for) Aluminum Paint.* The varnish shall show no skinning after 48 hours in a three-fourths filled tight container.

Flow-out films on tin plate panels dried 72 hours shall withstand immersion in cold water for 96 hours and in water at 77°C for six hours without whitening, dulling, checking, or showing other signs of deterioration.

Films on two 6- by 1-in. test tubes, secured by immersion in the varnish to a depth of 4 in., and drying in an inverted position for 72 hours, shall show no permanent whitening, dulling, or visible attack when immersed to a depth of 2 in. for 24 hours at 20°C, one in a 5 per cent solution of sodium hydroxide and the other in a 4 per cent solution of acetic acid.

When applied to a vertical, smooth, steel surface, the varnish shall not break or sag, shall set to the touch in not less than one and one-half hours nor more than three and one-half hours, and shall dry hard and tough in not more than 18 hours at a temperature of 20° to 30°C.

BLACK CARBON PAINT

Composition of black paint shall be as follows, by weight:

Pigment: 28–32 per cent
Vehicle: 68–72 per cent
Water: 0–0.5 per cent
Coarse particles and skins: 0–1.5 per cent

Coarse particles and skins shall be taken as the weight of pigment in the residue retained on a No. 325 sieve.

The pigment shall consist of carbon, lead oxide, and insoluble mineral material, and, at the option of the manufacturer, oxide or iron. It shall show on analysis not less than 20 per cent of carbon and not less than 5 per cent of lead oxide calculated as Pb_3O_4. The total of the lead oxide, iron oxide, insoluble mineral material, and loss on ignition shall not be less than 90 per cent.

The vehicle shall have at least 80 per cent linseed oil, the balance to be combined drier and thinner.

Black carbon paint shall be well-ground, shall not settle badly or cake in the container, shall be readily broken up with a paddle to a smooth, uniform paint of good brushing consistency, and shall dry within 18 hours to a full oil gloss, without streaking, running or sagging.

The weight per gal shall be not less than 9 lb. Shipment shall be in containers of not more than 5-gal capacity.

Analysis of black carbon paint shall be in accordance with Federal Specification TT–P61a.

THE USE OF PAINT

Selection: It requires as much labor and time to apply a poor paint as it does to use good paint. It is an accepted fact that the material cost constitutes 10 to 20 per cent of the expense of a painting job, and labor the other 80 or 90 per cent. With that breakdown in mind, it becomes apparent that the durability of the paint, all conditions considered, is of the greatest importance, and prices per gallon is secondary.

Assuming that we use a good quality of paint, we still have to choose among flat, semigloss, and enamel products, selecting paint suitable to the construction of the building, the type of occupancy, frequency of cleaning and washing, etc. Generally, ceilings are painted with flat paints; upper walls with semigloss; and dadoes, machinery, and equipment with enamel. In this the most durable finishes are put where the usage is the most severe.

Proper surface preparation is of the utmost importance, for even the best quality paint will give poor performance if applied over an improperly prepared surface. The surface to be painted must be clean, dry, and firm. Dust and dirt can be removed by brushing, blowing, scraping, or washing; grease must be removed with grease solvents, hot water, or steam cleaning devices. Rust, scale, and lose paint on metal should be removed by hand wire brushes, power-driven wire brushes, or sand blasting. Tests show that improper cleaning causes most adhesion failures.

Mildew, sappy woods, pitch pockets, glassy surfaces, rust, water-painted surfaces, cement, plaster, old paint, galvanizing, zinc, tin and copper surfaces, asbestos, masonry, composition board, etc., all require specific preparation before painting. The large paint manufacturers will be glad to furnish information on any surface preparation problems.

Applicators: Paint is usually applied in what is called the "good old-fashioned way," with a brush, but recently the roller paint applicator has been gaining favor in domestic and some industrial work. Spray guns, dipping, and even push brooms are also used to apply paint—wire fences, for example, can be painted faster and better with a hair push broom than with a brush. About 75 per cent of all industrial paints are sprayed, and many rough or hard-to-reach surfaces can be spray-painted more quickly and effectively than they can be brush-painted. The development of low-pressure guns that reduce the "over-spray" has made spray painting practical in many areas where it was questionable a few years ago.

Dipping is probably the most important of industrial painting methods for such small manufactured parts as tools. These are suspended from hooks or racks during the drying process.

The roller paint applicator is especially favored by the amateur house painter in decorating ceilings and interior walls. Any flat surface that can be hand brush-painted can be painted with a roller, with considerable saving of time and effort. Roller paint applicators can now be purchased with pressure paint feeds.

Drying: Probably no painting factor causes quite so much grief as faulty drying. Assuming that the right kind of paint has been used, there are five conditions which can affect the drying of any paint. They are:

1. Excessive film thickness
2. Slow thinners
3. Improper cleaning before painting
4. Inadequate ventilation during the drying period
5. Improper drying temperature

The first three factors require no special comment, but the necessity for proper ventilation and proper drying temperatures should be stressed. Many people do not realize that stagnant air, saturated with paint or lacquer solvents, will retard or prevent the drying of any finish. The condition is exactly the same as the one the housewife encounters when she attempts to dry laundry on a damp, windless day. Both laundry and paint dry best when the surrounding air is clean, pure, dry, and in constant circulation. An air-dried finish will not dry at a temperature below 50°F, and if applied in the hot sun it will dry so fast that it may wrinkle.

Paint failures: Good materials and proper methods of surface preparation and application have a great deal to do with the life of the paint job. This will insure the maximum satisfaction under the conditions to which the surfaces are subjected. There are, however, quite a few things which can happen to a well-meant paint coating. Some of these are desirable. Failures occur because of careless application, atmospheric conditions, or moisture.

Chalking: It is usual for paint to wear off by a process called "chalking." Surface oils are destroyed by light, heat, and moisture. Loose particles appear. This may be normal paint wear and is not, in itself, a sign of poor paint or poor workmanship. Before a heavily chalked surface is recoated, all chalk should be removed by scrubbing with water or by brushing with a stiff brush.

Checking, Cracking, Flaking, Scaling: Short narrow breaks in the surface are known as "checks." If the breaks are long and deep, they are called "cracks." Checks and cracks are caused by the shrinking and hardening of the film to such an extent that it can no longer expand and contract with changing atmospheric conditions. Later, the edges curl and the paint between the cracks loosens and falls off. These processes are referred to as "flaking" or "scaling." This type of failure may be delayed or controlled by using a reliable brand of paint and by steering clear of thick coatings. Thick coats may be avoided by sanding down all paint before recoating.

Washing: Sometimes the softening and washing away of the outer layer reveals a soapy condition of the painted surface. This sometimes indicates that the paint contains water-soluble materials formed because of poor drying during damp and cold weather. To avoid washing, all coats must contain sufficient quantities of thinners and dryers to give a hard-drying, firm foundation.

Wrinkling: Applying too thick a coat may cause wrinkling. The surface dries quickly, but there is an undried portion underneath. As the under part dries and contracts, the top surface wrinkles. This can be avoided by adding thinner to over-thick paint (about one-half pint to the gallon) or by vigorously brushing out the paint to avoid thick films.

Alligatoring: The pattern of breaks in alligatoring is rather large and has the appearance of an alligator hide. It is usually caused by the application of hard finishing coats over a soft primer—especially before the primer has thoroughly dried. A priming coat should be allowed to dry thoroughly. It should always be as hard as or harder than the outer coats.

Gas discolorations: Hydrogen sulfide fumes from sewage, industrial plants, and other sources tend to darken some paints to a metallic gray resembling graphite. Sponging the surface with hydrogen peroxide or other bleaches—or a dilute solution of muriatic acid—will quickly remove the discoloration.

Metal stains: Corrosion from screens, gutters, flashings, downspouts, nails, hinges, and other hardware often produces stains. Painting or varnishing these surfaces will reduce the amount of stain they cause.

Suction spotting: Greater paint absorption in some areas than others may cause suction spotting. If surfaces are properly prepared, if suitable primers are used (primers with a high pigment content and a properly treated vehicle) and if sufficient coats are applied, this kind of spotting can be prevented.

Mildew: Dampness and warmth encourage mildew, the spores and threads of which are somewhat hard to dispossess. Before mildewed surfaces are painted, they should be washed with alkaline cleaning solutions and flushed with clean water. A hard film will resist both dirt collection and mildew growth. Materials know as "mildewcides," which prevent the growth of mildew, may be added to paints.

Blistering: Condensation of moisture within or upon the surface to which the paint is applied may cause blistering. As a rule, such moisture comes from new plaster inside a building, from moisture arising within kitchens and bathrooms and laundries in old houses, or from overhumidified dwellings. The moisture passes through the siding and collects on the underside of a paint film, causing blisters. All paint in the blistered areas should be removed before recoating. The best way to prevent blistering is to remove as much moisture as possible from the building before painting the siding, and to take steps to block the further entrance of moisture.

Discoloration from wood: Dark brown spots on painted sidings of red wood and cedar are caused by water accumulation back of the siding. The moisture from newly plastered inside walls migrates through the siding and through the paint, carrying with it the natural staining matter in these types of wood. The spotting can also be caused by faulty flashings over windows, and by roof leaks. Often the spots may be removed by sponging the surface with a 50 per cent solution of alcohol and ammonia. If this does not work, recoating may be necessary.

The same measures prescribed for blistering will prevent wood spotting. Mend faulty flashings and leaks, ventilate walls, and keep the following points in mind:

1. Be sure that the surface is dry, and that no moisture will appear from beneath the film later on.

2. Be sure that the coats are not too thick as they are applied. Remove part or all of the old coatings that have become too thick.

3. Be sure that each coat has an opportunity to dry thoroughly before another is applied.

4. Be sure that adjoining metal is also painted.

5. Be sure that the proper type of paint is selected and that quality products are used.

FIFTEEN SIMPLE PAINTING RULES

The Canadian Paint, Varnish and Lacquer Association has issued 15 "rules" for painting. Some of these may be new, but most of them are long established and fundamental. All are simple and it is suggested that they be reviewed and observed when a paint job is to be done.

1. Use a good quality paint. If the job is worth spending time on, it deserves a paint that will give best results.

2. Stir the paint thoroughly before using. Everyone knows that this should be done, but many people still are inclined to skimp on the stirring.

3. Be sure that the surface to be painted is absolutely free from dirt, oil, and grease—and of course make sure it is dry.

4. Follow the directions on the can—the manufacturer has spent a lot of time and money to find out how his product should be used.

5. Thin paint sparingly—with turpentine. Do not thin with linseed oil; the paint may go farther if you do, but it will not stand up so well, because the oil upsets the careful balance between oils and pigments.

6. Use a good quality brush. It pays off in a better paint job.

7. Soak new brushes 24 hours before using them.

8. Use a brush of suitable size. Don't try to do a wall with a little brush, and don't try to do fine work, or to get into tight corners, with a big brush.

9. Allow enough time between coats for the paint to dry hard and firm; absence of tackiness is not sufficient.

10. Paint when the air is warm and dry, for best results. In interior painting, make sure that there is plenty of air circulating.

11. In choosing paint colors from color chips in paint dealers' stores, remember that the color of the finished job will be somewhat deeper than that of the color chip, because the color has been applied to a greater area.

12. If the surface hasn't been painted before, use a good primer sealer undercoating for the first coat.

13. Two thin coats are always better than one thick coat.

14. Remember the simple rules of color—that blues, greens, and allied tints are "cool" colors, and that yellow and orange shades are "warm"; also that light colors in a room give an impression of greater spaciousness; darker shades do the opposite.

15. Ask your paint dealer for advice on particular problems, or telephone or write any reputable paint manufacturer whose product you are using.

The section on the "Use of Paint" is adapted from information written by Edgar P. Romilly, Superintendent of Maintenance, Forest Preserve District of Cook County, Ill. Other references were the National Paint, Varnish and Lacquer Association, Inc., Pratt and Lambert, Inc., and Canadian Paint, Varnish and Lacquer Association.

TRANSIT MIXED CONCRETE

Aggregates: Coarse aggregate for each unit shall be one of the following sizes:

Class A concrete: Aggregate 3 or 4
Class B concrete: Aggregate 2 or 3
Class C concrete: Aggregate 1 or 2
Class S concrete: Aggregate 4 or 5

Storage of Materials: Stored materials shall be so located as to facilitate inspection. After aggregates are screened and graded, they shall be stored in bins, on wooden platforms, or on other hard, clean surfaces, and placed under cover when directed. Different types and sizes of fine and coarse aggregates shall be stored separately, in such a manner as to prevent the material from becoming intermixed. Materials having different specific gravities shall be considered different types.

If aggregates are stockpiled after being screened and graded, such piles shall be built up in layers not to exceed 3 ft in height, and each layer shall be completely in place before the next is begun. Coning or building up of stockpiles by depositing materials in one place should not be permitted.

Cement shall be properly protected from weather, dampness, or other destructive agencies. If it is necessary to store cement after its arrival at the loading plant, an approved weatherproof building adequate to protect cement from deterioration shall be provided. Adequate secondary protection such as straw or canvas, or both, shall be provided if necessary. Sacks shall be piled in layers on a suitable floor, with the sides of the pile at least 12 in. from the side walls. Cement from different mills shall be piled separately.

CLASSES AND PROPORTIONING OF CONCRETE

Classes: Concrete shall be divided into four classes: A, B, C, and S.

Proportions: The several classes of concrete shall be mixed in the proportions given in Table 9.12.

TABLE 9.12/PROPORTIONS FOR CLASSES OF CONCRETE

Class of concrete	Water-cement ratio: Max. gal of water per sack of cement	Mix* by volume: Parts cement	Max. parts aggregates	Cement factor: Min. sacks cement per cu yd concrete
A	6.0	1	5.5	6.0
B	6.5	1	6.5	5.2
C	7.5	1	8.0	4.4
S	5.6	1	4.5	7.0

*Approximate

In the above proportions the quantity of water is the total water in the mix, including the free water in the fine and coarse aggregates.

The proportion of aggregates to cement shall never permit the cement factor to fall below the minimum stated in the above table for the given class of concrete. If, with the maximum water-cement ratio permissible for the given class of concrete, the mixture is too dry for workability, the proportion of aggregate to cement paste (cement and water) shall be reduced until the proper workability and consistency as specified hereinafter are obtained.

If, with the maximum water-cement ratio permissible, the mixture is too wet for workability, the water-cement ratio shall be reduced until the proper workability and consistency are obtained.

Measuring Materials: One sack of cement (94 lb) shall be considered as 1 cu ft of cement. The fine and coarse aggregates shall be measured by weight. The weight of fine and coarse aggregates to be used shall be determined from the weight per cu ft of the materials, the estimated amount of moisture contained in the aggregates at the time of weighing, and the proportions by volume specified above. All aggregates shall be weighed on scales graduated to 2 lb and accurate to 0.4 per cent of the total load. Weighing equipment for aggregates shall further comply with the following conditions:

1. At least that part of the total load weighed which is a fraction of 100 lb shall be indicated on a graduated beam or scale.

2. The weighing equipment shall be so arranged that when operating the bin gates the operator will have the weighing beam or dial in full view, and can conveniently shovel material from the weighing hopper.

3. Ten 50-lb weights, each accurate within one-half lb, shall be available at all times for use in checking the scales.

The water shall be measured by a suitable device mounted on the truck mixer. The device shall be readily accessible and adjustable, and under all operating conditions shall be accurate to 0.5 per cent or less of its maximum capacity. The device shall be fitted with suitable means for locking. In addition to the measuring device, the tank shall be fitted with a glass gage. Provision shall be made to allow accurate checking of the measuring device by drawing the water off into an independently calibrated container. The unit of measure of the water shall be the United States gallon (231 cu in.).

Consistency: In general, the consistency of concrete mixtures when deposited in the structure shall be such that: (a) the mortar clings to the coarse aggregate, (b) the concrete is not sufficiently fluid to segregate when transported to the place of deposit, (c) the concrete, when dropped directly from the discharge chute of the mixer, shall flatten out at the center of the pile but stand up and not flow at the edges, (d) the mortar shall show no free water when removed from the mixer, (e) the concrete shall settle into place when deposited, and shall slide and not flow when directed to place through chutes or troughs at an angle of 30 degrees with the horizontal, and (f) the upper layer of the set concrete shall show a cement film upon the surface, but shall be free from laitance.

Mixer: The concrete drum shall be watertight when closed. It shall be equipped with a discharge mechanism which will insure the discharging of the mixed concrete without segregation. The mixer shall also be equipped either with a bath meter and locking device which will automatically prevent the discharging of the mixer drum prior to the completion of required number of drum revolutions, or with a counter mounted on the truck-mixer, allowing resetting for each trip at the loading plant and reading at the destination. The inside of the drum shall at all times be free from hardened mortar or concrete, and the blades shall be not less than 85 per cent of the original size.

Loading: The maximum size of batch shall not exceed the rated capacity of the mixer as stated by the manufacturer and stamped in metal at a prominent place on the mixer drum, except that a fractional part of a cubic yard in excess of the rated capacity may be permitted for one batch when ordered to complete any unit of a structure that is to be poured monolithically. In no instance, however, shall the load exceed by more than 10 per cent the rated capacity of the mixer. The quantity of aggregate for each batch shall be exactly sufficient for one or more full sacks of cement; batches requiring fractional sacks will not be permitted.

Not less than 90 per cent of the estimated quantity of water required in the batch shall be introduced into the mixer drum before the mixer leaves the loading plant. If more water is added after the mixer reaches the discharging point, the mixer drum shall not be discharged until at least 10 revolutions have been completed after introduction of the additional water.

Mixing: Mixing shall be started as soon as water has been introduced into the drum. For each batch the drum shall make not less than 50 nor more than 150 revolutions at the rate of rotation specified as mixing speed. Thereafter, until the batch has been entirely discharged from the drum, the drum shall revolve continuously at the rate of rotation specified by the manufacturer for agitation.

Delivery: Concrete shall be delivered to the site of the work, and discharge from the hauling container shall be completed within a period of one and one-half hours after the introduction of the mixing water to the cement and aggregates, or the cement to the aggregate. This maximum time shall be decreased as directed when it is justified by the time of initial set, or by loss of plasticity of the concrete.

Temperature: Concrete delivered in outdoor temperatures lower than 40°F (5°C) shall arrive at the work having a temperature not less than 60°F (15°C) nor greater than 100°F (38°C) unless otherwise specified or permitted.

Discharging: The equipment and methods used in discharging the mixer drum shall be such as will insure the placing of the fresh concrete without segregation.

Enough delivery units of adequate size shall be kept in operation for each structure to furnish a continuous supply of fresh concrete at the rate at which it is needed, and to guard against interruption or delay of the placement of any layer for a period of more than one-half hour after the preceding layer has been placed.

Measurement: The basis of measurement of the volume of concrete to be paid for shall be the cubic yard. The quantity of concrete produced by a given combination of materials shall be calculated from the absolute volumes of the separate ingredients as determined from the weight of each used in a batch and its specific gravity. The volume of cement and water shall be assumed as follows:

1 sack cement = 0.48 cu ft
1 gal water = 0.13 cu ft

CHAPTER TEN

MAINTENANCE

OF PICNIC AREAS

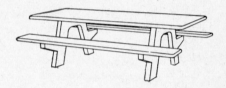

Picnicking is an important part of all recreational activity. It is an activity in which persons of all ages indulge; unfortunately the public is generally lax in cooperating to keep the picnic premises clean and sanitary. The carelessness and vandalism that result add considerably to maintenance costs. Few seem to realize that all picnic areas on public grounds are tax supported, and by misusing them the public is penalizing itself for its own carelessness.

The term "picnic area" includes many different types of facilities. It includes structures such as shelters, comfort stations, and even refectories and bandstands. It includes roads, parking spaces, walks, trails, steps, guard rails, drinking fountains, and signs. It includes the primary facilities such as water supply, tables, benches, fireplaces, and sanitary conveniences.

CARE OF GROUNDS

One of the most essential elements of proper care of picnic areas is the degree to which the grounds are maintained. The public is quick to recognize and respond to an efficient maintenance program, and equally quick to criticize and aggravate a situation where the grounds remain littered with trash. Each area's maintenance crew should regulate its schedule so that during the summer season the picnic area is thoroughly cleaned early in the day—before 10 o'clock if possible. The schedule should provide for daily policing, depending upon the use and season. In addition, the schedule should provide for extra maintenance whenever the occasion demands, such as periods immediately following holidays and weekends, or other periods of concentrated use. It is very important that trash and garbage should not be permitted to accumulate over the weekend, or it is conceivable that the grounds might become so littered as to be unsanitary as well as unattractive.

The preservation of existing ground cover, trees, and shrubs is highly important. It is much too expensive to provide extra picnic areas in order that one badly deteriorated can be retired from use until it is reclaimed and made serviceable once more. Also, it is impossible to replace full grown trees. Therefore, the only alternative and the most economical method is to preserve the existing cover. All of the gorund area of the intensive use sections of picnic areas should receive annual light cultivation and fertilization. If the forest cover is dense and grass will not grow, a heavy mulching of leaves (held in place by well-rotted sawdust) after the area has been fertilized and cultivated, will replace the normal ground cover worn thin by constant use. Another method, but more expensive, is to cover the area with tanbark or ground coconut hulls. This surface treatment is used in many city parks where there is a heavy concentrated use. This ground cover replacement should be done after the picnic areas are no longer in heavy demand, usually in late fall or early winter.

Care of public facilities

The old log or wood picnic table has proved to be a major maintenance and replacement problem. This problem has been met by the design of attractive concrete tables.

In order to reduce maintenance costs as much as possible, anchor all tables to the ground. It has been definitely proved that maintenance costs increase if the public is permitted to move the tables at will. In addition, each table should be placed on a paved level terrace in order to protect adjacent trees, prevent erosion, and make policing of the grounds easier.

Maintenance crews should make daily inspections of all picnic tables during the summer season. Such inspections should reveal immediately any need for repairs. A continuous repair and inspection program will greatly increase the life of the tables and reduce total maintenance costs.

Concrete tables

Maintenance costs can and have been reduced by the use of concrete tables in picnic areas. These tables will require periodic scrubbings with soap and water, frequency depending upon use. Concrete table tops can be treated with Amercoat solution No. 1254, clear or equal, to aid in cleaning. Such treatment reduces the amount of staining caused by grease, bottles, or food. Protect the wood seats with annual applications of a good wood preservative. Because it is toxic, do not use creosote or any preservative with a predominance of creosote. Treatment with Wood-Tox and two or three coats of marine varnish will give good protection.

Wood tables

There are many designs of wood tables, but only those which provide a combination of stability, durability, reasonable cost, and an attractive appearance should be used. Low annual cost of maintenance should be the guide. The following points are offered as a maintenance guide:

1. Avoid using resinous woods such as yellow and Norway pines for replacement of seats and tops.

2. Norway pine is the most economical in the long run for legs and braces.

3. Use a good grade of lumber, such as redwood, cypress, or oak for tops and seats.

4. Treat all wood with a good wood preservative such as Wood-Tox, Cuprinol etc. Do not use creosote.

5. Paint all tables with a good, durable grade of paint, preferably marine paint. Do not use stain, since stains are ineffective and shorter-lived than paint.

6. Use bolts for seats and at all important connections, with screws for the tops.

7. Separate top boards by 3/8-in. cracks for drainage.

8. Chamfer or round all outside edges of the seats and tops.

Fireplaces

In recent years the fireplace has gradually become an essential part of every picnic area. It does not need to be an elaborate arrangement of grates and fireboxes, but should be efficient for cooking, safe against spread of fire, and reasonably inexpensive to maintain.

It is very difficult to build an outdoor fireplace which is entirely efficient for cooking. Experience has shown that a fireplace built with an enclosed chimney provides too much draft, which draws most of the heat up the chimney and away from the cooking. In addition, fireplaces of this type are slow cookers and extravagant of fuel. A fireplace, to be most useful, should be built without a chimney and with the grate depressed between the sides of the fireplace. Such fireplaces confine the fire and decrease both the time and amount of fuel to prepare an outdoor meal.

Since most picnic areas are located in wooded areas, it is necessary that every precaution be taken to eliminate fire hazards. A correctly built fireplace, protected from prevailing winds, will give this protection. To provide the maximum safety the fireplace should be enclosed on both sides and one end, and located at right angles to prevailing winds.

Maintenance cost will vary with the type of fireplace and degree of use. There are three general types now popular: the concrete type, the masonry type, and the round steel type. From a maintenance standpoint, the concrete fireplace is easy to maintain. Under most conditions the concrete fireplace is used until it has become so cracked and broken that it is unserviceable and unsightly, at which time it is removed and a new one installed. This type deteriorates rapidly under intense heat, and probably needs replacement every four or five years.

The masonry type is, in general, built of stone, with the firebox lined with firebrick. If properly constructed, a masonry fireplace will last indefinitely, because loose brick and stones can be replaced. The grate will tend to warp and twist under constant use, but it is so constructed that it can be removed and replaced when no longer of service. The maintenance crew should check each fireplace daily so that minor repairs can be made immediately. Such checking will help to reduce the need for major repairs.

In order to protect the existing forest cover from ravage by picnickers, firewood should be provided in convenient locations and in proper size. Most areas will have an abundance of dead and down trees and wood salvaged from power line clearances to maintain a supply for many years.

Probably the most economical and easiest fireplaces to maintain are the upright steel charcoal burners. These are practically indestructible, except by rust. They have been used, regardless of treatment, for more than six years. As firewood grows scarce installation of good charcoal burners will become essential.

Utilities

Water for drinking is essential and should be furnished at convenient locations in the picnic area. There are three types of water outlets in general use: the concrete fountain type is used in areas where the predominant construction material is concrete. Very little maintenance is necessary except to check all working parts to be sure they are performing properly, to check for leaks, and to cut off water at proper time to insure against freezing.

The masonry type of water outlet is used in areas where the predominant construction material is stone and where the shelters and picnic area are entirely separate from major installations. The same type of maintenance is required as specified for concrete outlets.

The upright hydrant type of outlet, without fountain, is installed wherever a picnic area is close to a public building or to a parking area with drinking fountains installed. Maintenance on this type is essentially the same as specified above.

Some areas have been experiencing maintenance difficulties with upright water hydrants, which develop leaks that are difficult to repair. The difficulty seems to be in the type of cut-off, which is metal-to-metal and requires a good hard turn. Most people using the fountain do not bother to apply the pressure needed, and as a result the hydrant drips or runs constantly.

Another problem has been the waste water sumps at these fountains. These sumps may fill up with water rapidly, indicating that the ground drainage from the sump is poor. There are several methods by which this can be corrected. One is to redig the sump and enlarge it to twice its size and depth. If the sump is in impervious clay, use a crowbar to break up the bottom. If the sump is in rock, it will probably be necessary to add a small drain field to take the water away from the hydrant, or to pipe the waste water from the hydrant into a natural drain away from the hydrant or to a sump located in an area where good drainage can be obtained.

It may be advisable to install a cut-off valve at some convenient point in the water line servicing the picnic area. This cut-off should be provided with a drain and located at the lowest point of the line between the main line and the picnic line, thereby permitting the picnic area line to be thoroughly drained for the winter seasons. When it is cut on again in the spring, all water outlets in the picnic area should be opened wide in order to flush the line thoroughly. The line should be sterilized before it is put back into use. The local health and safety authorities should be consulted on this point.

Power

Wherever possible, sufficient power should be provided to light the area adequately for night use. Lighting arrangements do not need to be extensive, but fixtures should be numerous enough to permit use of the area without endangering the safety of the public. Generally, lighting standards should be located adjacent to paths and parking areas. All service lines within the area should be underground. Where underground lines are impractical to install, overhead lines may be used, but they should be located in such manner as to be inconspicuous.

Sanitary facilities

There are two types of sanitary toilet facilities in use: dry pit and flush type. The dry pit privy, usually considered temporary, should be replaced, as funds become available, by the flush type. Maintenance of the flush type sanitary facilities is as follows:

1. Keep lavatories, stools, and cell interiors clean and sanitary at all times. This means daily cleaning during normal summer use. During periods of intensive use—weekends and holidays—it may mean hourly checking and cleaning. The intensity of use will determine how often a facility must be cleaned in order to be neat and sanitary at all times.

2. Maintain an adequate supply of paper, soap, and towels.

3. Check all plumbing for leaks or faulty operation, and repair at once.

4. Keep interiors clean and neat.

5. Repaint all interiors and exteriors as needed. This will vary with locality, use, and weathering conditions. Repainting should never be deferred longer than four years under any conditions.

6. Maintain proper lighting.

The dry pit should be built in accordance with state's health department recommendations. It is essential that the privies be located in convenient places, sufficiently screened and marked. Do not hide them or place them in some out-of-the-way place where they may become useless. Maintenance of the dry pit privy is simpler, but it is more difficult to keep clean. Periodic liming is necessary to keep down odors, and daily washings with soap and disinfectant water are necessary during the summer season. As the privies fill up, the simplest process is to move to a new location and seal the old pit. Since all pit privies are of frame construction, they will require periodic painting and repair.

Play equipment

Some suitable equipment—swings, seesaws, sand boxes and jungle gyms for the children, and horseshoe and badminton for adults—should be provided. Maintenance of such facilities is simple and inexpensive.

Trash and garbage disposal

Choosing the proper location and number of trash and garbage cans insures: (1) convenience to the public (2) convenient truck access for efficient collection (3) good appearance, and (4) maintenance of grounds in a sanitary condition.

All trash and garbage cans must be located where picnickers will use them instead of throwing everything on the ground. This may mean that every two or three tables will require a trash or garbage container, depending upon the spacing or grouping of the tables. Do not place the containers where they may detract from a view.

The design for the picnic area should provide a service drive for small trucks, with easy access for efficient collection of garbage. This drive should be located so that it comes within a relatively short distance of the trash and garbage containers. A wide trail will suffice for both truck and pedestrian access. Workmen sometimes have a tendency to disregard the design of the area and locate all containers at some central point, easily reached by truck, but every effort should be made to discourage this practice. In mountainous areas, where many of the picnic tables are inaccessible except by foot trail, small hand dollies can be used to reduce the number of trips and to make handling easier. Trash and garbage containers should be well labeled and in conspicuous places, and should also be kept clean, well painted, and well maintained. Battered old cans make a poor appearance and are more difficult to handle.

The number of trash and garbage cans required for any particular picnic area depends upon use of the area and the number of picnic tables. One method of estimating the required number in a new area is to place one container for three picnic tables, and add more containers as demand or need increases.

Each garbage can should be placed in a permanent holder to prevent animals from tipping the can over and spreading the refuse over the ground. This holder may be either a concrete base with four steel uprights holding the can in place, or concrete container large enough to hold a can. Both lids and cans should be fastened to the base by means of a chain or cable which can be locked.

MISCELLANEOUS

Barricades: Unless the area is designed for such use, no cars should be permitted to drive into the picnic area in order to park adjacent to a table. In order to prevent this, it is necessary to confine all cars to designated parking areas, and to barricade entrances to service drives. All places where cars might be able to cross grass areas from access roads should be barricaded with posts or bounders, depending upon the locality.

There are several ways to confine cars to designated parking areas:

1. Curbs, either stone or concrete
2. A combination of guard rails and posts
3. Guard posts spaced close enough to prevent cars from driving between them
4. Stone boulders spaced as above

Guard posts should be constructed of concrete, and guard rails should be steel. Log construction should be avoided.

Barricades to service drives should be concrete or steel posts, or masonry piers at either side of the drive with a chain or cable connecting the posts and securely locked. All posts should be anchored in the ground. There have been instances where posts have been pulled from the ground by a car's pushing against them and loosening the post enough to let it be pulled out. This can be overcome by setting the posts in a concrete base, or by setting them 3–4 ft in the ground.

If concrete posts are used, very little maintenance is necessary. Broken posts should be removed as soon as possible and new ones installed. Loose posts should be replaced as rapidly as possible with concrete posts and steel rails. While awaiting replacement, they should be treated as often as needed with creosote or other wood preservatives. Steel guard rails should be painted as often as necessary to maintain a good appearance.

Tree maintenance

Since practically all picnic areas are located in heavily wooded areas, considerable attention should be given to the maintenance of existing trees. Under conditions where the natural litter of the woods is annually destroyed by continued use, trees will suffer, become diseased, and eventually die. It is therefore important that the soil improvement program mentioned in the first part of this chapter be followed. The picnic area should be checked at least once a year, and all dead and dangerous trees should be removed and all dead branches in good trees properly removed. This practice lessens one danger to the public—falling limbs and trees.

Some localities are subject to severe wind storms during the summer season. The picnic area should be checked immediately after each storm and all down trees removed and damaged trees either repaired or removed. All other debris left by such storms should be removed.

The maintenance of roads and parking areas is covered in Chapter 8.

Structures

The most common structure found in picinc areas is the shelter. These vary from simple "lean-to" types to large "recreation" types, designed to accommodate large picnic groups. Many shelters have fireplaces and public toilets built in as a part of construction, whether log, stone or some other type. In any event, maintenance should be based on the following principles:

1. Heavy use, requiring constant checking and policing. Trash and garbage must be removed promptly.

2. Painting, whether by a lead base paint or by a creosote base stain, should be done as often as required to keep the structure in good condition and good appearance. Log construction especially should be treated with a wood preservative annually.

3. Repairs to other wood sections should be done periodically. Broken or split members should be replaced as soon as the damage occurs. Parts which have rotted should be removed and replaced.

4. Masonry construction requires checking for cracks and broken stones.

These should be repaired as they occur and not left until they become a major problem.

5. Shelters with fireplaces need to be checked constantly. A clogged or faulty flue may cause serious damage or complete loss.

6. Public toilets in shelters should be maintained in the same condition as described above.

7. Shelters wired for lights need to be checked periodically. Faulty wiring or vandalism may cause serious damage or complete loss. Light bulbs should be replaced as soon as they burn out. Fixtures should be of a type to discourage vandalism as much as possible.

8. Tables and benches should be maintained as outlined earlier in this chapter.

9. Roofs, especially wood shingle roofs, need to be checked quite frequently. Repairs should be made as needed to prevent an accumulation of repairs leading to a major replacement. Winter accumulations of leaves should be cleaned off roofs to prevent rotting of shingles. Pine needles left on wood shingles are especially injurious.

Trails

Maintenance of trails depends a great deal on their use. Even when not in use, trails need to be maintained in order to repair damage from heavy rainfall and frost damage, and to remove fallen trees and branches.

Constant horse travel tears up the surface, destroys the crown, impairs the drainage and causes the surfacing material to disappear into the soil base. This requires regrading and resurfacing. In areas where trees and shrubs grow fast, overhanging or projecting branches must be trimmed annually to protect the equestrian.

Drainage ditches and culverts need to be repaired and cleaned out annually for efficient operation. Wherever erosion has started to cut the drainage ditches deeper than necessary, check dams should be constructed to control the flow of water.

ILLUSTRATION CREDITS

Asplundh Chipper Co.
Fig. 4.18

California Department of Public Works
Fig. 7.16–7.25

Emhart Manufacturing Co.
Fig. 4.27

Finn Equipment Co.
Fig. 4.26

Ford Motor Co.
Fig. 4.7, 4.8, 4.19, 4.28, 4.29

Good Roads Machinery Corp.
Fig. 8.8, 8.9

Hoffco Inc.
Fig. 4.15, 4.16

Hudson, H. D., Manufacturing Co.
Fig. 4.4, 4.6

Bean, John; Division, Food Machinery
and Chemicals Corp.
Fig. 4.5

Maintenance, Inc.
Fig. 8.10

Myers, F. E.
Fig. 4.1–4.3

Royer Foundry and Machinery Co.
Fig. 4.14, 4.15

Seedburo Equipment Co.
Fig. 6.1, 6.2, 6.5–6.7, 6.10–6.18, 6.20–
6.23, 6.25–6.27, 6.30–6.40

Tennessee Valley Authority
Fig. 1.1–1.4, 4.13

Toro Manufacturing Co.
Fig. 4.9–4.12

United States Department of Agriculture
Fig. 2.1–2.13, 5.1–5.27, 6.3, 6.4, 6.8,
6.9, 6.19, 6.24, 6.28–6.29

West Point Products Corp.
Fig. 4.17

Willys Motors
Fig. 423

GLOSSARY

annual: A plant that completes its life cycle in one year, germinating from seed, producing seed, and dying in the same growing season. *See also* winter annual.

awn: One of the slender bristles found at the ends of the lemmas or scales of some grasses.

axil: The angle between a branch or leaf and its stem.

basal treatment: An application to the stems of plants at and just above the ground line.

berm: A shoulder or flat area separating two steep slopes.

biennial: A plant that completes its life cycle in two years. The first year it produces leaves and stores food; the second year it blossoms and produces fruits and seeds.

bract: A leaf giving rise to a flower at its axil.

broad-leaved plants: Plants with wider leaves than the grasslike plants.

brush control: Control of woody plants.

bulb: A subterranean bud with a short, thick stem, rootlets, and overlapping leaves.

butt: The larger end of a log.

callus: The tissue that forms over any wound on the surface of a stem.

cambium: The tissue that gives rise to new growth in the stems and roots of shrubs and trees.

cant hook: A wooden lever with an adjustable iron hook, for use with logs.

carpel: A modified leaf, which by the folding together and union of its edges forms a closed receptacle for the ovules.

carrier: The liquid or solid material added to a chemical or formulation to facilitate preparation, storage, shipment, or use in the field. *See also* diluent.

chamfer: To level the edges of timber columns of beams.

chert: An impure, flintlike rock.

compatible: An adjective describing two compounds or products that can be mixed without affecting each other's performance.

concentrate: A condensed formulation usually diluted with water or oil before use. Also, in a product name, the strongest commercially available formulation of the active ingredient.

concentration: The amount of active material in a given weight of a mixture or volume of a solution. Recommendations and specifications for concentration of agricultural chemicals are frequently given on the basis of pounds per unit volume of mixture or solution.

contact herbicide: A weedkiller that acts primarily by contact with plant tissue rather than as a result of translocation, affecting only that portion of a plant with which it is in direct contact. Young seedlings are killed, but perennials may recover from the uninjured parts below ground.

corm: A bulblike stem, with scale leaves, which bears buds at the summit.

course: A horizontal layer.

creosote: An oily liquid used as an antiseptic and deodorizer.

crown: The top of a tree, including living branches and foliage.

culm: The jointed stem of a grass.

deciduous: Shedding leaves at the end of a growing period.

decumbent: Adjective describing stems or shoots lying on the ground, but with vertical tips.

defoliant: A material that causes the leaves to fall from plants; for example, a spray used to remove leaves from cotton plants just before harvest.

diluent: Any liquid or solid material serving to dilute or carry an active ingredient or formulation.

disk: To cultivate with a disk harrow or disk cultivator.

dormant spray: A chemical applied in winter or very early spring before treated plants have started active growth.

emulsifying agent: A material that helps to suspend globules of one liquid in another, as oil in water.

emulsion: A mixture in which one liquid is suspended in minute globules in another liquid, as milk or an oily preparation in water.

fibrous root system: A system composed of profusely branched roots with many lateral rootlets, and often with no main or taproot development.

fumigant: A chemical used in the form of a volatile liquid or gas to kill insects, nematodes, fungi, bacteria, seeds, roots, rhizomes, or entire plants; usually employed within an enclosure or in the soil.

gall: A swelling of a plant tissue caused by parasite attacks.

germination: The start of vegetative growth; usually from a seed.

girdle: A circle made by removing the bark around the trunk; usually fatal to the tree.

glabrous: Smooth and hairless.

glume: A bract; especially one at the base of a grass spikelet.

grout: Thin mortar used for filling in the joints of masonry, brickwork, or brick or stone pavements.

heartwood: The hard center wood of a tree trunk.

herbaceous plant: A plant that remains soft or succulent and does not develop a woody tissue.

herbicide: A chemical for killing weeds.

lemma: The lower bract enclosing a grass flower.

miscible: Capable of being mixed. Usually refers to liquids.

neutral soil: A solid neither acid nor alkaline, with a pH of 7.0.

nonselective herbicides: Chemicals or formulations which destroy or prevent plant life in general without regard to species.

noxious weed: A weed arbitrarily defined by law as undesirable, troublesome, or difficult to control.

oils: References are usually to aromatic or paraffnic oils used in formulating products as diluents or carriers for herbicides, or for direct use. *See* Aromatics.

palmate: Having lobes placed about a common center.

panicle: Any pyramidal loosely branched flower cluster.

peavy: A lever ending in a sharp spike, similar to a cant hook.

perennial: A plant that continues to live from year to year. In many, in cold climates the tops die but the roots and rhizomes persist.

pesticide: Any substance or mixture of substances intended for controlling insects, rodents, fungi, weeds, and other forms of plant or animal life that are considered to be pests.

petiole: A stem supporting a leaf blade.

pinnate: Having parts arranged along the two sides of an axis.

pith: The spongy tissue within a stem.

post-emergence treatment: Treatment made after plants emerge above the soil surface.

pre-emergence treatment: Treatment made after a crop is planted but before it emerges. Contact pre-emergency treatment is made after weed emergence, but before crop emergence. Residual pre-emergence treatment kills the weeds as the seeds germinate or as they emerge, either before or after crop emergence. Application is made before crop emergence.

pubescent: Hairy. Pubescence affects ease of wetting of foliage and also retention of spray on foliage.

raceme: A flower cluster.

rate or *dosage:* These terms are synonymous. "Rate" is the preferred term, and usually refers to the amout of active ingredient material applied to a unit area (such as one acre) regardless of percentage of chemical in the carrier.

residual: Having a continued killing effect over a period of time.

resistant: Tolerant. Resistance of weeds determines the rates of weed killer application required for control.

rhizome: Underground rootlike stem that sends out roots and leafy shoots.

rootstock: A rhizome.

runner: A decumbent branch that forms a new plant by rooting at the joints or end.

sapwood: The younger wood just beneath the bark.

shoulder: Either edge of a road, exclusive of pavement.

slag: The nonmetallic residue of smelted ore.

spall: A chip or fragment.

spray drift: The movement of airborne spray particles from the intended contract area to other areas.

spud: A sharp, narrow spade.

spudding: Digging, removing, or otherwise treating with a spud.

square blading: Blading at right angles.

stamen: The organ of a flower that bears the fertilizing cell.

stem: The part of a plant above ground that supports leaves, flowers, or fruit.

stolon: A runner or rootstock, or a piece of either, used to propagate a grass.

style: A prolongation of the ovary that supports the stigma, where pollen grains are received.

sump: A pit or depression serving as a drain or receptacle for fluids to be further disposed of.

suspension: A liquid or gas in which very fine solid particles are dispersed, but not dissolved.

template: A pattern.

tolerance: In connection with pesticides, the amount of a pesticide chemical allowed by law to be present in or on a food product sold for human consumption.

tolerant: Capable of withstanding effects. For example, grass is tolerant of 2, 4-D to the extent that this herbicide can be used selectively to control broadleaved weeds without killing the grass.

toxic: Poisonous; injurious to animals or plants through contact or systemic action.

tuber: A short, fleshy, usually underground stem or shoot bearing minute scale leaves with buds or "eyes" in the axils.

volatility injury: Injury from herbicide vapors.

wattle: A framework made of flexible rods.

weed eradication: The elimination from an area of all live plants, plant parts, and seeds of a weed infestation.

winter annual: A plant that starts from seed germination in the fall, lives over winter, and completes its growth, including seed production, the following season. *See also* Annual.

woody plants: Plants that develop woody tissue.

INDEX

Beetles (cont.)
  May, 54, 55
  Oriental, 55
  red cedar bark, 229
  rose leaf, 230
Begonias; size grades, 150
Bentgrasses, 16, 18, 64
Bermuda grass, 20–24, 64, 326, 328
Biennials; description, 287
Bindweed; field, 302, 326
Birch borer, bronze, 210
Birches, 275
Bittersweet; American, 244
Bituminous road mix, 397–400
Bituminous seal coat, 411–413
Bituminous surfaces; construction of,
    401–405, 414–419
  maintenance of, 363, 413
Black alder, 252
Black-banded leaf roller, 209
Black medic; control, 61
Black spot, 209
Black vine weevil, 209
Black walnut curculio, 210
Bladder gall mite, 210
Bladder maple gall, 210
Blight, 210
  needle and twig, 226
Bluegrass leafspot; 53
Bluegrasses, 18–20, 64
Blue pine borer, 210
Bordeaux mixture, 192
Borers; ash 207–208
  Apple tree, 217
  blue pine, 210
  bronze birch, 210
  brown wood, 211
  callous, 212
  cottonwood, 213
  dogwood, 214
  elm, 215
  lilac, 223
  linden, 224
  locust, 224
  maple leaf stem, 225
  mottled willow, 225
  pine, 210
  poplar, 228
  ribbed pine, 229
Borrow areas, 380
  rehabilitation of, 58–59
Bowline; how to tie, 112
Box-elder bug, 210
Boxwood, 244
  pruning method, 83
Boxwood leaf miner, 210
Boxwood psyllid, 210
Bracken fern; control, 298

Brenthian, northern, 226
Bridal wreath, 263
Broad-leaved evergreens; planting in
    limestone regions, 89
  standards for, 138–139
Broad-necked prionus, 210
Bronze birch borer, 210
Brown patch; in grass, 52
Brown-tail moth, 211
Brown wood borer, 211
Brush; control with chemicals, 297,
    319–326
Brush chippers, 175
Brush dams, 337–339
Brush or wire check dams, 337
Brush paving, 340–341
Brush removal; rules for, 121–122
Buckeye; Ohio, 274
Buckhorn; control, 61, 298
Buckthorn, 258–259
  pruning method, 84
Buck or maia moth, 211
Bud gall, 211
Bulbs; size grades for, 147–151
Bull's-eye spot, 211
Burning bush, 248
Butterfly weed; control, 298
Butternut curculio, 211

C

Cabbage looper, 211
Caladium; size grades for, 150
Calcium chlorate; for weed control, 290
Calcium chloride; for dust control, 373
California oak moth, 211
Callous borer, 212
Canada bluegrass, 20, 64
Canker, 212, 216
Canker worm, 217
Cannas; size grades for, 151
Carbon bisulfide; as insecticide, 194–
    195
Carpenter worm, 213
Carpet grass, 25–26, 64
Carrot, wild; control, 318
Case bearer, 213, 215–216, 221
Catchfly, night-flowering; control, 309
Caterpillars, 213
  Antered maple, 207
  Datana, 214
  Eastern tent, 215
  forrest tent, 218
  mourning cloak, 226
  Oriental moth, 227
  red-humped, 229
Cecropia moth, 213
Cedars, 268
Centipede grass, 26–27, 64
Check dams, 337–340

Red-headed pine sawfly, 229
Red-humped caterpillar, 229
Red spider, 229
Redbud tree, 245
  pruning method, 85
Redtop, 16, 65
Reforestation methods, 96–100
Repellent washes; use against insects, 194
Rhododendron, 259
  pruning method, 85
Rhododendron clear wing, 229
Ribbed bud-gall, 229
Ribbed pine borer, 229
Road maintenance, 363–369, 376
Rope; use for climbing, 111, 112
Root pruning, 94
Rose beetles, 218
Roses, 261–262
  insects and diseases, 230
  pruning methods, 85
  standards, 142–144
Rotenone; use of, 193
Ryegrass, Italian, 30, 59, 65
  perennial, 31, 65
S
Saddle-backed caterpillar, 231
Safety rope; use of, 115
Sanitation in picnic areas, 483
San Jose scale, 231
Satin moth, 232
Sawdust; as soil conditioner, 12, 15
Sawflies, 206, 216, 219, 229, 232
Saws; power, 173
Sawyer, 232
Scale insects; dogwood, 214
  English walnut, 216
  European elm, 216
  gloomy, 219
  golden oak, 219
  holly, 219
  Kermes, 221
  lecanium, 223
  obscure, 227
  Oleander, 227
  oyster shell, 227
  peony, 228
  San Jose, 231
  Scotch pine, 232
  Scurfy, 232
Seal coat; hot bituminous, 411–413
Seashore; plants for, 105
Seeding; hydro method, 43–44, 182, 349
Seedling trees and shrubs; specifications, 146
Selective cutting; woodland, 107–108
Shadblow; pruning method, 85
Shadbush; downy, 240

Shade; effect on grass, 46
  plant materials for, 106
Sheep sorrel; control, 61, 315
Sheepsfoot roller, 352–353
Shepherd's purse; control, 314
Shoulders, highway; erosion control on, 354
  maintenance of, 374
  repair of, 368
Shredders; soil, 170
Shrubs; master list of, 152–158
  pruning of, 82
  standards for deciduous, 129–134
  time required to plant, 98
  transplanting from native stands, 93
Sitka spruce gall, 233
Size grades for bulbs, corms, and tubers, 146–151
Slag; specifications for crushed, 425–426
Slag chips; specifications, 432
Slippery surfaces; repair of, 367–368
Slopes; control with annual grasses, 351
  erosion control, 345–354
  maintenance, 356
  repair of eroded, 362
  stabilization methods, 356–361
Slugs; rose, 230
Snakeroot; control, 317
Snow on the mountain; control, 315
Snowball; pruning method, 86
Snowberry, 264
Sod-cutters, 179
Sod webworm; control, 54, 56, 231
Sodium compounds; for weed control, 290–291
Soft scale, 233
Soil; acidity control, 78
  fertilization of, 14
  preparation of, 11–12, 67
  tests for, 13
Soil erosion: see Erosion
Soil-saving dams, 330
Soil shredders, 170
Sorrel, field; control, 302
Sorrel tree, 280
Sourgum, 279
Soybeans, 38
Sphinx caterpillars, 233
Spicebush, 243
Spider; red, 229
Spider mites, 233
Spiny elm caterpillar, 233
Spiny oak worm, 233
Spirea, 263, 264
  pruning method, 86
Spittle bug, 233
Spotted hemlock borer, 233